Best wishes to you, John McCarter
from
Tom Roberts Jr.

THE STORY OF THE

DEKALB "AG"

FROM COUNTY CO-OP
TO LEADER IN
AGRICULTURAL RESEARCH
1912-1998

THOMAS H. ROBERTS, JR.

First Printing December, 1999
Printed in the United States by Carlith Printing, Inc.
Carpentersville, Illinois 60110

Library of Congress Catalog Card Number: 99-96276

Credits:

Editor: **Thomas H. Collins**

Index By: **Sandy Schroeder**

Cover Photographer: **J. Womack Photography**

Thomas H. Roberts, Sr.

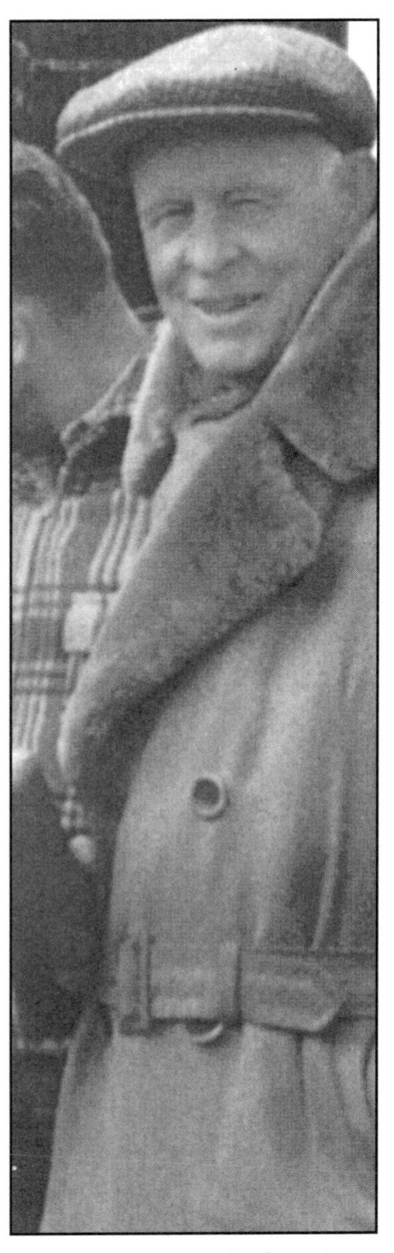

This book is dedicated to my father, the man most responsible for DeKalb's growth and success

1923: He led DeKalb into the hybrid seedcorn business by initiating a hybrid research program.

1924-1935: He steadily increased the DeKalb Ag's year-end equity from $88,000 to $220,000 during an eleven year depression.

1935: He produced the first hybrid seedcorn adapted to the northern corn belt.

1936: He produced hybrids that were in such strong demand that DeKalb was paid by farmer customers before his contract seed growers had to be paid, thus maximizing hybrid seed production by DeKalb without needing to produce hybrids through franchised growers.

1941: He reduced war-time tax payments by leading DeKalb into exploration for oil and gas. He also initiated a DeKalb poultry research program and started a profit sharing plan for employees.

1946: He significantly increased hybrid research and expanded seed processing facilities substantially.

1955: He led DeKalb into hybrid grain sorghum production.

1956: He started DeKalb's international seed production and sales.

1961: Realizing that inbred lines had improved sufficiently during the first twenty-five years of breeding and selection to justify their use as parents of pure single-cross hybrids, Tom became a leading advocate of single crosses. He priced them high because their pure unbred parents were not high yielding, but the superior performance of their single-cross program justified higher prices. By 1999, most farmers planted single-cross hybrid seedcorn.

The Development of this Books' Title

I had planned on naming the book *The Story of DeKalb* based on the company's original name, DeKalb Agricultural Association, Inc.. This name was quickly shortened by our employees, who called it the "DeKalb Ag."

The contents of this book serve as a testament to those hard working men and women that helped to make DeKalb "Ag" a world leader in hybrid corn. Accordingly, it is a pleasure to honor them by naming their book, *The Story of the DeKalb "Ag"*.

From Your Author,

Thomas H. Roberts, Jr.

Thomas H. Roberts, Jr.

Thank You,

Tom Collins

For your patience and intelligence, which combined with your good sense and computer expertise, made this book possible.

Acknowledgments

My original intent in writing this book was to tell the story of DeKalb so that my children and the generations to come would know their family history. As the project unfolded, many DeKalb employees, past and current, expressed an interest in reading the story too, and I heard similar expressions of interest from outside the immediate DeKalb "family." Since DeKalb has been directly involved with many of the significant events in the evolution of U.S. agriculture, I hope this story will shed light on that broader history along the way.

As I probed into the story of the company, interviewing people who had been a part of its history, reading Richard Crabb's book *The Hybrid Corn Makers*, and leafing through Leo Olson's unpublished history of DeKalb, my respect for the company's founders grew. I came to realize that my father, Tom Roberts, was truly a great man who fully deserved the respect and affection his colleagues had for him. He was an honorable man who built a great company and is, therefore, a model for those of us who followed him. I want others to know what he achieved and how he did it, as I believe him to be the personification of the best of capitalism. Conveying that message is the most important reason I wrote this book.

I appreciate the help of many good friends, most of whom had worked with me at DeKalb, in putting my thoughts together here. They include: Ramon Agrasar, Jerry Armstrong, Sherret Chase, Tom Collins, Leo Damkroger, Linda Ferguson, Ralph Gunn, Cliff Heglin, Harold Heinold, Dick Holland, Ralph Klopfenstine, Charlie Krull, John Leteta, Nate McGuire, Fabio Nider, Scott Sindalar, Hank Slade, Tom Swaney, Art Tiddens. Forrest Troyer, and Basil Tsotsis.

The story of DeKalb reflects the challenges that have faced many farmers and shaped life itself in rural America since the early 1900s. I have taken great care to be accurate about names, dates, and events. Of course, as with any story that is told by one storyteller, this one is shaped by my own memories and interpretations.

The opinions expressed within are those of Thomas H. Roberts, Jr.'s and are not necessarily the opinions of the Roberts Family, Dekalb Genetics Corporation or any agent thereof. All sources stated as Thomas H. Roberts, Jr. or Roberts Family Archives are contained in the personal files of Thomas H. Roberts Sr. and or Jr. or are from the personal knowledge of Thomas H. Roberts, Jr.. Every effort has been made to confirm the figures stated within as accurate. Figures stated within are for comparison purposes only and not in all instances verifiable.

Thomas H. Roberts, Jr.

Table Of Contents

Preface

This book is the story of DeKalb Genetics, its growth, its products and its people. It emphasizes these fundamentals:

- Hybridization of Seedcorn, Sorghum and Poultry - all of which were successful
- Hybridization of Cotton and Wheat - which failed
- Exploration for Oil & Gas
- Acquisitions & Divestitures

Each story is told, mostly in ten year sequences, with some exceptions when it was best told in only one chapter.

Throughout this book, I cite the sources of the information I present as accurately as possible. In previously published documents, the DeKalb Company has not publicly reported unit sales for each of the products sold, in order to keep this information from competitors. Records were kept, however, and were used by managers for analyzing and recognizing district, regional, and total annual sales management and performance.

My father, Thomas H. Roberts, Sr., kept his own records from 1935 through 1945, when responsibility for keeping annual unit sales records was given to Elmer Williams, seed distribution manager, who was assisted by Ruth Peterson, Rus Rasmusen's secretary. From 1968 through 1981, Elmer Monson, marketing manager, kept these records, and Leo Damkroger assumed the record-keeping responsibility from 1981 through early 1996, when he retired. He was assisted by Jerry Armstrong, a key man in the accounting and finance departments, and Nate McGuire, seed production manager.

The records I used came from these people. I have included in this book seed sales information through 1992, the year when I retired as chairman of the board. The disclosure of this information, which surely has historic merit, could not possibly affect current company operations.

The Story of the

DEKALB "AG"

From County Co-op to Leader in Agricultural Research 1912-1998

Thomas H. Roberts, Jr.

Part One

1912-1920

Chapter 1

The Origin of the DeKalb "Ag" 1912–1917

The DeKalb company's roots trace back to a cold winter day, January 20th, 1912, when a group of DeKalb County farmers formed the DeKalb County Soil Improvement Association, the first such organization to become a "Farm Bureau" in the U.S.. The Association's leaders believed they needed the full time services of an expert in farming who would not only help them with their soils problems, but also help them to buy quality seed. They chose Dr. Bill Eckhardt, a soils professor from the University of Illinois at Urbana. He was a well known and respected scientist and turned out to have entrepreneurial leanings as well.

SOURCE: Al Golden

Dr. Bill Eckhardt

Eckhardt was a top-notch soil expert, and his was the kind of expertise DeKalb County farmers needed. He became manager of the Association on June 1, 1912, at the handsome annual salary of $4,000, a much more attractive sum than the $1,800 he had earned at the University of Illinois ($4,000 in 1912 dollars, after adjustment for inflation, was worth $58,750 in 1990 dollars).

In 1914 the Smith-Lever Act authorized federal funding, with state matching funds, for Farm Advisers (County Agents) of up to $4,000

SOURCE: Al Golden

DeKalb County Soil Improvement Association Founders
Left to Right: John Blair, C.D. Schoonmaker, George Hyde, W.G. Eckhardt, Farm Advisor, G.W. Gurler, Aaron Plapp, F.B. Townsend, H.H. Parke, E.E. Hipple, George A. Fox, W.F. Leifheit and Orton Bell

per year. These public funds were made available to compensate Eckhardt, beginning in 1915.

DeKalb County land had been farmed heavily for sixty to seventy years, and soil surveys showed them to be deficient in essential nutrients. In addition, Eckhardt's soil tests showed most DeKalb County soils to be acidic. To remedy this, he arranged to apply limestone to the soil, a treatment that tremendously enhanced both the initial stands and the longevity of legume seedlings. Perennial legumes like alfalfa and red clover often lasted several more years than they would have without the limestone in highly acidic soils.

SOURCE: Corporate Records, Dekalb Genetics

Eckhardt's Limestone

Having won farmers' confidence with his soil testing, Eckhardt told them that their crops would show even greater improvement with better-quality seed. Drawing on the advice of his agronomist friends at the University of Illinois, he recommended plant varieties best adapted to DeKalb County, and he also searched personally in seed-producing areas for high-quality seeds. For several years his purchases were paid out of bank credit lines guaranteed by the Association's board, but in 1917, when Eckhardt realized that the Smith-Lever Act prohibited business activity by County Agents, he recommended the formation of a corporation to perform the business activities of the Association.

The "DeKalb Ag" is Formed

His board authorized the formation of an Illinois corporation with $50,000 in capital to supply products and services to DeKalb County farmers. Committees were formed to raise the money, and the DeKalb Agricultural Association, Inc., was licensed at Springfield on June 21, 1917.

Fifty years later, Charlie Gunn, a seed expert Eckhardt had hired in 1917, proudly showed his fellow DeKalb directors the issue of the Illinois State Journal announcing formation of the company. Gunn had worked part time for Eckhardt for several years, but came aboard full time on November 30, 1917, as Emergency Demonstration Agent, with a salary of $200 per month. Gunn's title stemmed from a damaging early-September freeze that had swept the corn belt. It had been so destructive that few farmers had seed-corn to plant in 1918, and was extremely serious because it threatened the food supply of our nation, our troops, and our wartime allies in Europe.

At a statewide meeting of Farm Bureaus, Eckhardt was asked to lead an effort to obtain suitable seedcorn for farmers throughout the state. The state provided its full support, and after the DeKalb County Soil Improvement Association agreed to loan him to the Illinois State Council of Defense in Chicago, he procured more than 100,000 bushels of two-year-old, early-maturing seedcorn that had not been ruined by the freeze. His seed was distributed to Illinois, Indiana, and Iowa farmers. Bill had done his nation a great service.

Charlie Gunn: A Key Man

The 1918 choice of Charlie Gunn to be his seed specialist was one of Bill Eckhardt's most important decisions. Gunn was dedicated and knowledgeable as well as absolutely loyal, hard-working, and trustworthy. As a child, I liked him very much because he smiled at me a lot. (I thought he winked too, but my dad said Charlie's wink was a twitch. It probably was, but I still like to think he was winking at me.)

Charlie was raised on a farm near McNabb, Illinois. In 1906 at the age of twenty-one, he left home to work as a carpenter, accepting a job building barns for a contractor who paid him thirty-five cents an hour. One of his customers was W. G. Griffith, a respected farmer who was also a breeder of open-pollinated corn. Griffith liked what he saw in Charlie Gunn and put him to work sorting ears of corn to be used for seed the next spring. His job with Griffith brought him to the attention of Bill Eckhardt, who was then in charge of the Illinois state experimental field near Magnolia. Eckhardt hired him to build barns at several experimental farms in northern Illinois in the summer of 1909.

Charlie's friendship with Bill Eckhardt would be a long and fruitful one, but Charlie was intrigued by the potential of irrigation in eastern Colorado and took a job (according to records provided by his son Ralph) managing a 640-acre ranch sixty miles north of Greeley, Colorado, where he made a valiant effort to pump irrigate from a twenty-eight-foot well that was twelve feet in diameter—an imaginative project very similar in concept to the pipe and center-pivot systems now so common in the area. When the well failed to provide enough water, Gunn turned his efforts to dry land farming, which was much more successful. He imported sudan grass, white blossom sweet clover, black winter emmer, and proso millet, none of which had been grown before in Weld County, Colorado. Some of these crops flourished there, so he wisely switched his operation from farming to ranching and built up a herd of cattle that thrived on his good hay.

Life was hard on Colorado dry land farms in those days. Winters were particularly harsh, and summers brought their own peculiar challenges, such as keeping children away from rattlesnakes. Charlie wrote in his journal: "One day when Clara was perhaps eighteen months old, we saw her standing in front of our - house looking down upon a coiled rattlesnake. After killing the snake with a hoe, I tacked it up on the hitching post and its tail touched the ground."

Charlie's life changed dramatically in the spring of 1917 on a trip to Illinois. Bill Eckhardt, who was speaking at a central Illinois Farm Bureau picnic, asked him to return to Illinois to manage the seed department of the DeKalb Ag. It didn't take Gunn long to accept. That was a great day for DeKalb.

SOURCE: Corporate Records, Dekalb Genetics

Charlie Gunn ready to drive his Model T Ford to Idaho to buy alfalfa seed.

Gunn was assigned responsibility for purchasing the best seed available and for breeding improved seedcorn varieties for DeKalb County. He started selections of the "Western Plowman" variety of open-pollinated corn by selecting the ears from the best plants in his field and using the grain from those ears for seed the next year. He emphasized selecting for early maturity because DeKalb was on the northern edge of the corn belt. He paid appropriate attention to yield, disease resistance, strong stalks, and "easy" husking, but progress from this kind of breeding was slow because he was selecting only from the mother plant, without knowing the nature of the father plant. Nevertheless, Charlie was justifiably proud of the improvements he made in the selection of a fast-maturing Gunn's Western Plowman variety that was well adapted to DeKalb County.

He also arranged to procure the best varieties of other crops recommended by University of Illinois agronomists. For example, every year from 1918 to 1928 he traveled to Idaho to personally select "winter-hardy, Idaho-grown" alfalfa, red clover, and alsike seed from the best seed producers. He usually made the trip in a new Ford Model T, which allowed him to drive out to the fields where the crops were "going to seed," to inspect them firsthand. The trip took an average of thirteen days, averaging 130 miles per day. He usually purchased six to eight carloads of seed, sold his car for more than he had paid for it in Illinois, and returned home on the train.

Tom Roberts Sr., Joins DeKalb

After he was "mustered out" of the army in 1918, Tom Roberts, Sr., returned to operate his farm in order to qualify to be an Assistant Farm Adviser. Although he was strong and worked hard, he recognized that Bill Rolfe, a German immigrant he had hired could work circles around him. Tom decided to leave the farm in Rolfe's hands and become the Assistant Farm Adviser to Bill Eckhardt, working for both the DeKalb County Soil Improvement Association and its business branch, the DeKalb County Agricultural Association. His annual salary was $4,000. He reported for work in June of 1919.

Soon after Tom was hired, directors of the DeKalb County Agricultural Association, Inc. (DeKalb) decided they needed more capital to support its growing businesses and gave Tom the job of raising an extra $50,000. He was limited to soliciting funds from members of the DeKalb County Soil Improvement Association, and his sales pitch was simple: if farmers invested in the company, they would be assured of a good source of quality seed, and the managers would do their best to operate it profitably and pay modest dividends, depending upon the need of the firm for retention of funds in the capital accounts of its growing business.

High-Priced Alfalfa Seed

On his 1919 trip to Idaho, Charlie Gunn encountered a problem that proved pivotal to the company. Idaho's alfalfa seed crop was very small that year, and the price he had to pay for seed would require him to price the seed in DeKalb County at seventy-five cents per pound, considerably higher than the thirty-five cents per pound DeKalb County farmers were accustomed to paying. Realizing that farmers would balk at paying the higher price, he recommended to Eckhardt that farmers who had ordered alfalfa seed be advised that the price would probably be seventy-five cents per pound.

Eckhardt agreed and obtained orders based on a high price expectation. However, he didn't tell his customers (probably because he didn't know) that red clover seed would be available at unusually low prices because there had been a big crop of red clover seed the prior year. Consequently, when loyal DeKalb Agricultural Association members came in to pick up their high-priced alfalfa seed, many chose to go home with the much cheaper (and almost as acceptable agronomically) red clover seed instead, leaving the company with a large carryover supply of alfalfa seed.

The next year Idaho produced a normal crop of alfalfa seed, so the company had to write down the price of its carryover alfalfa seed from seventy-five cents to thirty-five cents, creating an inventory loss of almost $50,000. This was nearly exactly the amount of new capital Tom Roberts had raised for the DeKalb Ag a few months earlier. Loss of half of the company's equity in one year was a traumatic experience for everyone concerned with DeKalb's future, especially the company's board members, Bill Eckhardt, Charlie Gunn, and Tom Roberts.

Eckhardt Resigns and Tom Roberts Takes Over

Bill Eckhardt's many meaningful contributions to the Farm Bureau movement in Illinois had earned him the high regard of the Illinois Agricultural Association (the State Farm Bureau), which offered him an attractive position in the spring of 1920. He accepted and resigned his position on July 1, 1920 as DeKalb's County Farm Adviser. Tom Roberts was his successor.

Tom hit the ground running as the new DeKalb County Farm Adviser. Farmers were under tremendous economic pressure in 1920, and it was his job to assist them. This was how he went about it in his first year:

- He was appointed secretary-treasurer of the new Federal Farm Loan Bank, making $215,000 in low-interest loans to distressed farmers.
- He attended ten Farmer Institutes with a total attendance of 450. Farmer Institute meetings were usually called by the county Farm Adviser to confer with experts—University of Illinois professors, livestock and grain marketers, and the like.
- He bought and distributed 131 carloads of Idaho apples and potatoes to DeKalb County farmers.
- He set up a flour mill to custom-mill flour for farmers, a project organized to circumvent the perceived excess profitability of large milling companies.

- He kept the seed business going.
- He bought and sold much needed limestone and rock phosphate.
- He organized "Wallace Day," bringing Secretary of Agriculture Henry C. Wallace to DeKalb on August 31, 1921.
- He visited 300 farms.

Always vigorous on behalf of DeKalb County farmers, Tom was fast accepted by both his board and the farmers of the county. Some of his achievements during his term as Farm Adviser were:

- Hosting the Farm Bureau De-Centennial Celebration on June 30, 1922.
- Inviting U.S. Agriculture Secretary Wallace to discuss potential of hybrid corn with Gunn and Tom.
- Helping found the Pure Milk Association to market milk.
- Helping found the Chicago Producers Association to market livestock.
- Working to keep farm electrical rates low.
- Developing a farm record keeping system.
- Campaigning successfully for a county veterinarian to test cows for tuberculosis.
- Campaigning successfully to keep farm telephone rates low.
- Arguing successfully for more equitable city-farm tax rates.

Tom Roberts and Charlie Gunn fully appreciated the risk of buying and selling seeds that farmers could purchase from anyone else in the seed industry. Unfortunately, nearly all crops grown anywhere in the world at that time were self-pollinated and would reproduce themselves. This meant that scientists who improved seeds could not benefit financially from the improvements they had created because farmers could easily reproduce the seeds themselves and pay no royalty. Recognizing this problem, federal and state governments set up Experiment Stations to employ scientists to improve crops at government expense. To the seed industry, self-pollination meant all competitors could offer the same products, but the products would sell only at very low profit margins because all seed companies were selling the same thing. Such low margins would not allow for the kind of year-to-year inventory losses DeKalb had experienced in alfalfa.

SOURCE: Corporate Records, Dekalb Genetics

Dekalb's employees in the late 20's. FROM LEFT TO RIGHT: Ted Johnson, Dorothy Bartlett, WW Coultas, Orton Bell, C.L. Gunn, Edna Nelson, Tom Roberts, Inez Nelson, Bill Johnson.

SOURCE: Corporate Records, Dekalb Genetics

FROM LEFT TO RIGHT: Unknown, Unknown, Dorothy Bartlett, Edna Nelson, Unknown, Inez Kivaloma, Catherine Pesut, Lillian Carr.

Part Two

1920-1936

Chapter 2

The Hybrid Corn Opportunity

1920-1936

The "finger-burning" experience of a $50,000 write-down of alfalfa seed had a profound influence on both Charlie Gunn and Tom Roberts and was a vital factor in stimulating their interest in a new corn-breeding concept that Secretary of Agriculture Henry C. Wallace endorsed when he visited DeKalb in the summer of 1923. Wallace had learned of the possibility of hybrid corn from several of his Experiment Station directors, who were intrigued by the performance of hybrids developed by crossing inbreds. However, most of them had decided not to fund hybrid corn research with public money because they thought that parent crop failures from inbred seeds would cause hybrid seed to cost so much that it would not be accepted by farmers.

SOURCE: Pioneer HiBred

U.S. Secretary of Agriculture Henry C. Wallace in 1923

Wallace disagreed. He was convinced that hybrid seed production costs would be substantially reduced by the "four-way-cross" system that had been proposed in 1919 by Dr. Donald Jones at the Connecticut Experiment Station, and that four-way crosses would be accepted enthusiastically by farmers. Jones had shown that four-way-cross hybrids would cost much less than single crosses because the final four-way-cross product could be produced in volume using high-cost, highly productive single crosses as seed parents for the final high-volume production of four-way-cross seed that would be sold to farmers.

Convinced that hybrid corn would be at least 20 percent more productive than open-pollinated seed, and dismayed by the foot-dragging at Experiment Stations, Secretary Wallace had decided to encourage seed firms to initiate research aimed at developing, producing, and selling hybrid seedcorn. His son, Henry A. Wallace, agreed with his father and organized his own company (which he called Pioneer) to develop hybrid seedcorn.

Secretary Wallace's hybrid corn concept made a lot of sense to Tom Roberts and Charlie Gunn, who visited with him after his speech at a DeKalb County Soil Improvement Association picnic. While waiting for the train that would take him home to Des Moines, Secretary Wallace admired some "show ears" of Gunn's Western Plowman but told Charlie that he had some seed from small nubbins back in Washington that he was sure would out-yield seed from Charlie's open-pollinated variety by at least 20 percent. They listened to Wallace's ideas with great interest because Charlie had seen a small strip demonstration of hybrids versus non-hybrids that impressed him favorably. Both Tom and Charlie were very determined to bring the best possible seeds to DeKalb County farmers.

HYBRID CORNS' ILLINOIS ORIGIN

The observation of hybrid vigor in corn was an off-shoot of research being conducted in the late 1890s by Edward Murray East, a graduate student in chemistry at the University of Illinois. He was working under the direction of Cyril G. Hopkins, a soils specialist, whose research was supported by Station Director Eugene Davenport, a livestock specialist. Their goal was to increase the quality and quantity of protein content in corn grain to make it a more nutritive livestock feed.

Nutritionists knew that animals grew most efficiently when their rations contained about 16 percent balanced protein. The protein content of grains was typically not more than 10 percent, so most animal rations were a mixture of grain with expensive protein supplements such as meat scraps (High protein soybean oil meal is now used to fill the "protein gap" in animal feed). Hopkins had done sufficient analytic work with corn to know that strains differed considerably in their protein content, so there was a lot of enthusiasm among his colleagues for his experiment to develop a new kind of corn with better feed value. His protein selection efforts began in 1896, and his first public report was made in 1899. His work attracted intense interest among agronomists, nutritionists, and research-minded farmers.

By 1900 it was clear that more help was needed to do the chemical analyzes of the protein content of Hopkins' selections. The man chosen to do that work was Edward Murray East. Richard Crabb reports in his book *The Hybrid Corn Makers* (Rutgers University Press, 1948):

> The moment at which the young chemist decided to go to work on the Hopkins corn breeding project proved to be one of those historic turning points not only for him personally, but for the cause of plant breeding, America over. Today (in 1948) there is hardly a plant breeding scientist in the country who is not either a student of East or of one of East's students or associates. East's association with the Illinois corn breeding program was to prepare him to be a dominant force among the small band of men who were to make possible hybrid corn in our time. (P. 20)

Crabb reports that shortly after East became first assistant in plant breeding in 1904, H. H. Love, who in a career at Cornell was later to become another of the country's great names in plant breeding, joined the Hopkins staff. East showed Love the results of the chemical analysis he had run for three years and pointed out, in the case of high-protein lines, two things that seemed to him of major importance and that Hopkins had steadfastly refused to recognize. One was that all of the high-protein lines were descended from a single one of the 163 selected by Hopkins at the beginning of the project. The other was that the yield of these high-protein strains of corn had dropped constantly as the percentage of protein increased.

Love became the first to agree with East that Hopkins' corn breeding project was doomed to fail unless some means could be found to prevent decreasing yields in the high-protein lines. Together East and Love outlined an experiment for the purpose of studying the effects of inbreeding or close breeding, an experiment they hoped would point to some new method that would preserve the advantages of the high-protein grain and at the same time avoid the curse of low yield.

Crabb reports that Hopkins, whose fame as a soils scientist was growing, approved of East's proposal, so in the spring of 1905, East laid out the first plot designed to study corn inbreeding. (Apparently he had already done some inbreeding because he had some partially developed inbreds in his plot.) Unfortunately, Hopkins' successes in soil research were diminishing his interest in breeding for high-protein content in corn. Whatever his reasoning, in the summer of 1905, when he visited East's corn plot, he saw how runty the inbred lines were and ordered that the work be discontinued. Fortunately, he did not demand that the plot be destroyed on the spot, so it was duly harvested that fall, and the inbred seed was placed in storage.

Subsequently, East was offered an attractive job in corn breeding at the Connecticut Experiment Station, where he continued the work he had begun at Illinois. A fast start was possible with the seed of the partially inbred lines that East's office partner at Illinois (H. H. Love) sent to him in Connecticut.

Crabb tells us that East reported to Connecticut farmers that "in an experiment at the Illinois Experiment Station, by detasseling alternate rows in a breeding plot [these were almost certainly rows of partial inbreds], a cross was forced upon the detasseled rows . . . and it was found that the crossed rows yielded in the second and third years an average of about ten bushels per acre more" (p. 40).

In my opinion, these comments by Edward Murray East shortly after he arrived in Connecticut in 1906 make it clear that he was the first to observe hybrid vigor in corn. East continued to develop inbred lines and to cross them to make and study hybrids, as did others who were impressed by his reports of the vigor hybrids showed in his test plots. *Nevertheless, weak inbred seed parents made hybrid seed too costly for farmers until 1919, when Donald Jones showed that four-way-cross hybrids could be made virtually as productive as single crosses, and at costs so low that hybrid seed could be a very good buy for farmers.* I believe, therefore, that East and Jones are the two scientists who should be given the most credit for making the great hybrid corn revolution of the late 1930s possible. Ultimately, their data showed that hybrid seed would produce yield increases of 20 percent or more, but that protein content percentages would not increase along with yields. Nevertheless, the value of yield increases for hybrids would be highly significant.

Henry C. Wallace, Republican Secretary of Agriculture in the early 1920s, also deserves credit for understanding that four-way crosses would make hybrid seedcorn an attractive economic proposition for farmers, and for his successful crusade to convince private seedmen to do the developmental research necessary to develop it. He fought a courageous battle in the face of an almost unanimous conviction by professional agronomists that hybrid seed would cost too much to be accepted by farmers.

Table 2-1
How Inbreds Are Made
Seven Generations of Selfing Required for Purity
(Selfing is pollinating the female ear of a plant with pollen from the same plant's tassel.)

Cross ordinary corn plants to themselves.	1st generation Normal yields.
S-1 generation Select best plants, self.	2nd generation Selfs less vigorous, 50% inbred. Weak, undesirable traits begin to show up.
S-2 generation Select best plants, self again.	3rd generation 75% inbred. Less vigor. Weak plants show up. Select good plants, self.
S-3 generation Select best plants, self again.	4th generation 87 1/2% inbred. Less vigor, more uniform. Select and self best plants.
S-4 generation Select best plants, self again.	5th generation 93 3/4% inbred. Select and self best plants.
S-5 generation Select best plants, self again.	6th generation 96 7/8% inbred. Select and self.
S-6 generation Select best plant, self again.	7th generation 98 5/16% inbred. Select and self.
S-7 generation Select best plants, self.	8th generation 99 7/32% inbred.

SOURCE: Thomas H. Roberts, Jr.
Note: After seven years of selfing and selecting, the inbreds are essentially pure and can be multiplied in isolated fields.

Table 2-2
How Single-Cross Hybrids Are Made

Inbred A x Inbred B	All inbreds are weak, low-yielding plants.
Single-Cross A x B	Vigorous, highly productive, seed expensive because inbred parents are low yielding.

SOURCE: Thomas H. Roberts, Jr.

Table 2-3
How Four-Way Crosses Are Made

Inbred A x Inbred B	Inbred C x Inbred D	Inbreds weak
Single-Cross Hybrid AB x Single-Cross Hybrid CD		Single crosses vigorous, high yielding
Four-Way Hybrid ABCD		

SOURCE: Thomas H. Roberts, Jr.

Four-way-cross seed is less expensive than single-cross seed because its single-cross parents are more productive, more reliable seed producers. Moreover, four-way crosses were nearly as productive as single crosses in farmers' fields for the first twenty-five years of the hybrid seedcorn "revolution." During that twenty-five-year period, inbreds were improved steadily, and by 1960 we judged them to be sufficiently reliable seed producers to permit single crosses to be produced on a large scale. Because single crosses are the purest kind of hybrids, the best single crosses have better yield potential than the best four-way crosses, but four-way crosses were the only practical way to exploit hybrid vigor until breeders had selected more disease-resistant inbred lines about twenty-five years after four-way crosses were introduced in 1936.

THEY GO FOR IT!

In the early 1920s, when Tom Roberts and Charlie Gunn met Secretary Wallace, Wallace explained the difficulties he was having in persuading his Experiment Station agronomists to develop hybrids. Tom and Charlie realized that if they were to conduct research to develop hybrids, and if farmers found the seed of four-way-cross hybrids to be sufficiently productive to justify paying more for the hybrid seed, then the research that would take twelve years to perform would be well worth their time. They agreed with Wallace that hybrid vigor might become a prominent force in improving yield in corn. They figured farmers would buy hybrids enthusiastically if they could get three to four dollars back from each "extra" dollar they paid for the seed—a return that would be possible if hybrid seedcorn would yield 20 percent more than non-hybrid seed.

Further, because farmers could not buy DeKalb hybrids from anyone except DeKalb, the price fluctuations that had characterized the commodity seed business in the case of alfalfa would no longer be a problem. DeKalb would be able to control its own prices and farmers would have no choice but to pay full price if they liked DeKalb's hybrids. Here was the opportunity Tom and Charlie had been looking for—one on which they would bet their careers. Paradoxically, their interest in hybrids had been spurred by a $50,000 inventory loss on alfalfa seed, which was a self-reproducing product—a "commodity."

They agreed with Wallace that four-way crosses could be produced and sold for as little as $15 per bushel and be a profitable proposition for most farmers, even though they would have to buy new hybrid seed each year. One bushel of seed would plant five acres and hybrids would produce a 20 percent increase in yield per acre, or about 50 extra bushels. These 50 extra bushels valued at $1 per bushel grain price would be worth $50, compared with only $15 extra in seed cost.

TWELVE YEARS OF PREPARATION: 1924–1937

Having decided to bet their careers on hybrid corn, Tom Roberts and Charlie Gunn planned their activities carefully. They realized their biggest risk would be the expenditure of their personal time developing and testing hybrids to determine if this "wild idea" would really work out. They knew it would take seven generations of inbreeding and selection to develop pure inbred lines, and after that, they would have to cross inbred lines to make single crosses and then cross the single crosses to make four-way-cross hybrids and test them.

Getting Started

They anticipated very challenging financing problems during the ten to twelve-year period it would take to develop hybrids, because the DeKalb County Agricultural Association did not have any surplus cash to fund research. Gunn took on the task of developing hybrid corn in his "spare time," and Tom made land available to him on a farm between DeKalb and Waterman that was owned jointly by Tom and his brother, my uncle Ralph Roberts.

Gunn's first hybrid corn research plot was planted in May 1925. He planted forty varieties of the best open-pollinated corn he could find and started inbreeding, culling out weak plants, and further inbreeding the strong. Gunn's "Western Plowman" became the parent of one of DeKalb's best inbreds.

He worked at first in very small plots similar to garden plots, but soon his plots expanded, until in 1930 he was operating on ten acres of land. I am not sure how the rent for these acres was paid, but I assume it was paid by the company and was low enough that, indirectly, Tom was financing part of the rental payments on his land. He performed his management duties at very low cost to the company because he was also being paid a full salary by the federal government for his services as DeKalb County's Farm Adviser.

Gunn felt frustrated in the late 1920s and wrote in his pedigree book, "Not enough inbreds yet to make a quadruple cross." Dr. Jim Holbert of the USDA research station on Funk's farm near Bloomington, Illinois, suggested he try several Experiment Station inbreds in combination with Gunn's best, to see whether Holbert's later-maturing Experiment Station lines in combination with Gunn's early lines would make four-way-cross hybrids that would mature early enough for northern Illinois. Gunn made these crosses and field-tested hundreds of single-cross and three-way and four-way hybrids in 1932 and 1933. The tests showed some of the hybrids would work well in northern Illinois, so Tom asked Holbert, "If you and Gunn have that much confidence in these figures, why not produce the hybrids?" (Crabb, The Hybrid Corn Makers, p. 219).

High Risk, Many Doubters

Their decision to begin a breeding program to develop hybrid seedcorn had been high risk and potentially controversial in the mid-1920s, for two reasons. First, most agronomists were convinced the program would never produce hybrids at prices farmers could afford to pay; second, the DeKalb Agricultural Association was small, thinly financed, and, arguably, incapable of carrying the costs of research before hybrids could be offered for sale. Several of DeKalb's farmer shareholders were eager for the company to pay dividends, thereby establishing a value for its stock, which they wanted to sell to meet mortgage payments on their farms. To silence the skeptics, Roberts and Gunn decided to keep their work secret until they could be confident that the project would be successful. As Crabb put it:

> By the middle of the 1928 growing season, Gunn and Roberts were convinced that their program was going to yield results, and they decided that the time had come to break the secrecy that had been maintained for more than four years. During late summer and fall, they took the members of the board of directors of the DeKalb Agricultural Association to see the inbreeding plot and to explain its objectives. With but one exception, the board heartily concurred with what had been done. One member of the board, however, was critical of the way the matter had been handled. He resigned. (P. 217)

According to Tom, the dissenting director was a prominent,

respected farmer who wanted the company to show a profit and create value for his stock. When he was overruled by his fellow directors, he sought advice from a professor of agronomy at the University of Illinois who told him that although the idea of inbreeding and hybridizing was intriguing, he believed it would never be a commercial success. On returning to DeKalb, the farmer told Tom that he believed the company should either shut down its hybrid breeding program or buy him out. The company did not have funds to repurchase stock, so Tom bought it back with his own money, paying the same amount per share that had been paid for his "founder's" stock in 1917. Thereafter, Tom always advised shareholders against selling their shares, but for those who insisted, either he or the company repurchased their shares at cost.

Years later, Harold Noren, who had become a key man with DeKalb, told me a similar story that confirms the stubborn doubts about hybrid corn that persisted even through 1936. That year Noren was a farm boy from central Illinois attending the University of Illinois. Somehow, he obtained two bushels of Funk's hybrid seed and planted it on his dad's farm. Noren said, "We had an extensive drought on our home farm that year and I couldn't believe the difference between our hybrid corn and our open pollinated." He returned to the U. of I. seeking more information from Dr. W. L. Burlison, who told him to forget hybrid corn—that it would never be practical.

However, Dr. Burlison later realized that his earlier doubts about the significance of hybrid corn had been wrong, and to his great credit, he admitted it. Richard Crabb, author of The Hybrid Corn Makers, told me that Dean Burlison became one of the most enthusiastic supporters of corn hybridization, and that he also believed strongly that the production of hybrid seed should remain in the hands of private enterprise. I conclude that he was a man of real character and integrity.

In the meantime, the "DeKalb Ag" had to stay in business, operating as profitably as possible. Accordingly, Tom was always on the lookout for other businesses that might generate some profit that could be put into hybrid corn research. One opportunity presented itself in the early 1930s during the depths of the Depression, when a farmer named Albert Morehouse lost his farm. Tom knew Morehouse and thought he had good potential as a salesman, so he set up a new business—oil and gas for delivery to DeKalb County farmers—and put Morehouse in charge of it. The oil and gas business quickly became profitable and ultimately branched out as far as Humboldt, Iowa, where Tom and Morehouse formed another distribution company to provide oil and gas to Humboldt County farmers.

Tom dedicated himself to performing the duties of Farm Adviser and to overseeing the business activities of the DeKalb Agricultural Association between 1921 and 1932. The figures in Table 2-4 show that his efforts were successful. Although the company struggled through the 1920s and early 1930s, it held on to its principles, waiting for hybrid corn with increasing optimism as their test plots began to show exciting results.

TOM ROBERTS, SR.: A MAN WITH MANY HATS

In the early 1930s, when several Illinois Farm Bureau executives asked Tom to join them in the management of the Country Life Insurance Company, he was both flattered and tempted, knowing that insurance was one of the state Farm Bureau's most profitable businesses. However, Tom realized he could not stay in DeKalb County if he joined Country Life, and would have to give up his dream of managing the DeKalb Ag's hybrid seedcorn business. He declined their offer and made some immediate career decisions. Believing he had accomplished all he could as Farm Adviser, he looked for work that would permit him to continue managing DeKalb's hybrid corn program in his spare time.

SOURCE: Corporate Records, DeKalb Genetics

Careful Hand Harvesting of Precious Seed in Mid 1930s

The Sycamore Preserve Works and the Federal Land Bank

In 1932 John Leslie asked Tom to manage a canning factory and offered a salary with incentive bonuses. Leslie was the chief executive officer of a large Chicago company, Signode Steel Strapping, and the sole owner of the Sycamore Preserve Works, a canning factory in Sycamore. Leslie was willing for Tom to continue as part-time manager of the seed company as well as to keep his job as county farm loan administrator. Tom accepted.

The stock market crash that triggered the Depression in 1929 had a profound influence on everybody, including my father, Tom Roberts, Sr. Many farmers were faced with bankruptcy because they had mortgaged their farms at high interest rates, and there was no way they could meet their mortgage payments when the price of their main crop—corn—dropped as low as five cents per bushel in the early 1930s. At that price, it was more economical to burn corn in a stove than it was to sell it on the market.

To help farmers survive, the federal government increased its funding of the Federal Land Bank, allowing it to offer farmers lower-interest mortgages. Tom Roberts administered the Federal Land Bank loan program in DeKalb County for several years in addition to his duties as county Farm Adviser. He wanted to stay on the Land Bank job because he was one of the few county farm loan administrators financially independent enough to not fear for his job as he joined other farm leaders in their never-ending battle to keep control of the Federal Land Bank system in the hands of locally elected farm leaders. Tom had backed and voted for the Democrat, Franklin D. Roosevelt, in 1932 (I can remember tacking up election posters in rock-ribbed Republican Sycamore), but he steadfastly resisted the new administration's tendency to concentrate administrative power in the hands of Washington-based "bureaucrats."

Switching jobs, however, did not relieve the tremendous pressure on Tom of doing three jobs at once. In fact, the job of managing the cannery was considerably more stressful than being DeKalb County Farm Adviser. When all of these stresses began to wear on Tom and he became ill, a doctor in Chicago told him that he had two ulcers and likely wouldn't live longer than six more months if he didn't slow down. The opinion of a second doctor was not as alarming, though he did prescribe an extremely strict diet and less work—or at least a vacation. A few weeks after receiving these diagnoses he developed appendicitis and had his appendix removed, but the problems with ulcers remained.

He took a fishing vacation with my mother and me at Butternut-Franklin Lake in Wisconsin and simultaneously undertook a strict ulcer diet, which involved taking "powders" of antacid every half hour, drinking a half pint of milk every two hours, and avoiding all fried foods and fatty meat. He felt better, but frequently in the evenings his stomach would burn and he had to remove the food from it by pumping it out. This was a rather common treatment for ulcers at that time (so common, in fact, that men at Kishwaukee Country Club in DeKalb who had ulcers once had a contest to see who could pump out his stomach the fastest).

Tom's stomach pumping became a nightly project, which he could perform easily, and in fact he pumped out his stomach every night for seventeen years. His strict diet lasted that long, too. The stomach pain caused Tom to become a hypochondriac, fearing constantly that the discomfort in his stomach might be cancer. However, worrying about his health didn't prevent him from successfully working at three jobs simultaneously. I am convinced that my good health at age seventy-one stems from having grown up on my dad's ulcer diet.

Problems at the Cannery

In the middle of the Depression, all Tom could pay the workers at the Sycamore Preserve Works was 37 cents an hour ($3.12 in 1990 dollars). In 1934 they threatened to strike, and all of the employees came at night to our home chanting and demanding higher wages. Out on the front steps, Tom simply told them that the company was in the middle of harvesting peas, that its financial condition was very poor, and that he could not pay them more. If they did not go back to work, the peas would not be canned, the factory would go broke, and there would be no jobs at all. They returned to work with considerable grumbling, but it was rather clear that they understood Tom was telling them the truth.

At about that time, in 1935 when I was eleven years old, I got my first job—as a water boy in the pea harvesting operation at the Esmond, Illinois, farm my mother owned. Workers cut the peas with a farm mower, which made windrows of them and then fork-pitched the pea vines from windrows onto wagons (a very strenuous job), The wagons then transported the vines to the "pea viner" machines, where the peas were separated from the vines.

About half of the forty-man crew at the viner station consisted of college boys trying to earn a little money in the summertime, and the other half consisted of migrant workers, most of whom were hired off of West Madison Street in Chicago, where many of the unemployed at that time accumulated. All hands were paid 37 cents an hour, with nothing extra for overtime.

When I went to work at the viner station, I asked the boss what time he wanted me to get there in the morning, how long he wanted me to stay in the afternoon, and what my pay would be. The boss was a gruff man, a former Methodist missionary in South America who had come to be the tenant farmer on the 636-acre Esmond farm. He told me I would be making twenty-five cents an hour, and that he wanted me to work seven days a week from 8 a.m. until 5 p.m. Also, he indicated that if I wanted to get to work earlier and stay later, I could do so as long as I made sure to be there from 8 to 5.

I got to work by riding on the trucks that transported the peas from the vining station to the canning factory and then returned to get more peas. When I found out that the first truck going out from the factory to the Esmond farm left at 6 a.m. and went right by our house, I arranged with the truck driver to be picked up on the highway outside our house at 6:05. I arrived at work at 6:30 a.m. and stayed until the last truck left at about 7:30 p.m.

The wage of twenty-five cents an hour looked pretty good to me, so I calculated carefully what my first paycheck would be. When it arrived at the end of two weeks, it was only about one-quarter of what I had been promised. When I asked about it, Mr. Cunliffe-Owen, the crotchety company bookkeeper, told me I was being paid a dollar a day. Dismayed, and knowing that the other water boys were paid two dollars a day, I said that Paul Kline had promised me twenty-five cents an hour. Mr. Cunliffe-Owen replied, "a dollar a day is all your dad said to pay you. Your dad didn't want to play any favorites." Of course, I expressed my displeasure to my dad, but my arguments got me nowhere. Looking backwards in 1999, sixty-four years later, I realize that his "unfair" compensation was purposefully done to reach me to stand on my own feet.

The next day at work when I griped about the injustice, one of the smart college boys on the viner crew drew up a petition and got everybody at the viner station to sign it, saying that they would go on strike immediately if their water boy were not paid the same amount as other water boys. I presented the petition to my father at the dinner table. His face was a study in mixed emotions. He seemed to want to laugh, but at the same time felt he must strongly admonish me, his son, for being a strike instigator. He tried to carry off a lecture, but he did not punish me—neither did he give me any wage increase. The men at the farm laughed when they learned of Tom's reaction, and of course, they wouldn't go on strike. All of this taught me that I would have to look out for myself.

The men I carried water to in the field preferred Coca Cola, and often wanted Hershey bars, cigarettes, and chewing tobacco, so I bought these items from a friendly wholesaler and sold them to the Esmond workers on the side. This turned out to be considerably more profitable than the job would have been had I been making 25 cents an hour. In fact, I earned a little extra bonus from Mr. Maiser, the man who lived across the street from our house, was so impressed with my entrepreneurial activities in the pea fields that he rewarded me with several baseballs and bats and a very nice mitt that his son had outgrown.

Later that summer I attended Camp Edwards, a YMCA boys' camp near Elgin, and came home with some slogans my dad loved, had framed, and featured in his office. They were: "**TO ESCAPE CRITICISM: DO NOTHING, SAY NOTHING, BE NOTHING**." and "**YOU ARE EXPECTED TO MAKE GOOD, NOT TO MAKE EXCUSES**." These were the credos he put before all of his employees—not just his son.

That summer Tom made his decision to seize the opportunity he saw in hybrid corn. He resigned from the cannery and began to fulfill his destiny. **During the period of economic depression from 1924 to 1935, shareholder equity climbed steadily, increasing from $88,097 to $220,570—no small accomplishment for a young County Agent who was working two jobs simultaneously.**

Thrift—A Vital Virtue for Tom

Tom had a remarkable record of business success. At a time

when many businesses were failing, his business grew steadily. As I look at his company's fine growth record for the twelve years before the introduction of hybrid seedcorn in 1936, I realize that his success during those tough times was due significantly to a combination of imagination, thrift, and determination. Imagination led him to the decision to bet his career on hybrid seedcorn, but thrift and determination were the key to his success between 1924 and 1936. He knew low prices for farm products were making life so tough for farmers that they had to pinch every penny they earned, so he had to offer them both quality and low prices. He hired good people who needed jobs badly and paid them minimum wages.

He saved pennies, identifying opportunities to serve farmers' needs for services like delivery of gasoline directly to those who were gradually mechanizing. Thrift in the management of his seed and farm supply business was absolutely necessary to the offering of quality products at low prices. It was the only way to survive in business. He knew that and somehow managed to scrimp and save and turn it into the profitable, growing business it became.

Financial Results - Part Two

EQUITY GROWTH, 1924 THROUGH 1935

Here is the record of book-value growth that the DeKalb County Agricultural Association, Inc., achieved between 1924 and 1935. Tom served full time as DeKalb County Farm Adviser until 1932, and as part-time DeKalb Ag manager, adviser to the hybrid corn breeding program, Federal Farm Loan administrator, and canning factory manager. All in all, these figures, which were achieved during the Great Depression, reflect work well done by many people, but especially by Tom Roberts.

Table 2-4
DeKalb Agricultural Association, Inc.,
Shareholder Equity: 1924–1935

Year	Equity (as reported)	Equity (in 1990 $)
1924	$88,017	$695,400
1925	$80,446	$619,400
1926	$80,789	$613,500
1927	$92,141	$692,700
1928	$90,911	$694,600
1929	$107,935	$650,600
1930	$141,097	$1,103,800
1931	$167,495	$1,440,500
1932	$176,076	$1,679,800
1933	$186,765	$1,679,800
1934	$216,671	$2,117,800
1935	$220,570	$2,104,200

SOURCE: Personal Records, Thomas H. Roberts, Sr.

Part Three

1936-1950

Chapter 3

Hybrid Corn Takes Off
1936-1950

Charlie Gunn's 1933 field test data convinced Tom Roberts that hybrid seedcorn would increase farmers' yields and make corn growing so much more profitable for them that demand for hybrid seed would grow very fast. He believed that this exciting new product would make farmers a lot of money. The data in Table 3-1, taken from an impartial University of Illinois Corn Performance Test Bulletin for 1936, show why Tom was excited.

Table 3-1
Value of Hybrid Seedcorn and
Open-Pollinated Seedcorn, per Acre, 1936
(assumes market value of corn grain @ 90 cents/bushel)

Open-Pollinated Seed		*DeKalb Hybrid Seed*	
45.4 bu./a.	$40.86	57.6 bu./a.	$51.84
Less cost of open-pollinated seed/acre*	.50	Less cost of DeKalb seed/ acre*	$ 2.44
Value/acre	$40.36	Value/acre	$49.40

SOURCE: T. H. Roberts, Jr.
* Open-pollinated seed priced @ $2.50, hybrids @ $12.20/bu.

One bushel of seed would plant five acres. Therefore, to the buyer, one bushel of hybrid seed was worth $45.20 (5 x $9.04), and he payed only $12.20 for his bushel of seed!

Needless to say, these and other test results were important selling information and were used widely to convince farmers that they should plant DeKalb hybrids. Furthermore, by 1936 Tom had produced enough hybrid seedcorn to be convinced he could make a good profit selling his hybrid seed at $12.20 per bushel for the medium flat kernels farmers preferred. Table 3-2 shows DeKalb's actual hybrid seed costs and earnings in 1936.

These figures spelled opportunity to Tom. It seemed clear to him that farmers would reap extra profits of $9 per acre from hybrid seed, even when the market price of corn grain was as low as 90 cents per bushel. Demand for hybrid seedcorn was going to be tremendous.

SOURCE: DeKalb Genetics

A farmer, Ward McCallister, comparing hybrid vs non hybrid, A Happy Customer.

Table 3-2
The Economics of DeKalb Hybrid Seed, 1936

	Total	Per Bushel
Payments to Farmer Growers	$21,000	$1.75
Sales & Advertising	4,200	.35
Detasseling	7,800	.65
Drying, Sizing, Bagging	27,000	2.25
Distribution	3,000	.25
Administration & Overhead	12,000	1.00
Foundation (Parent Stock)	10,200	.85
Research	12,500	1.25
Total Costs	**97,700**	**8.35**
Wholesale (Dealer) Price		10.35
Net Pre-Tax Profit		**2.00**
Retail Price		12.20

SOURCE: Leo Olson, "Genetics to Genius."

It was clear that DeKalb could realize a pre-tax profit of $2 per bushel by selling four-way-cross hybrid seed for $12.20 per bushel. Acreage planted to corn annually in the United States had fluctuated between 80 million and 100 million acres. Taking 90 million acres as the "average" U.S. market for seedcorn, Tom calculated that each 1 percent of market penetration by DeKalb would require 180,000 bushels of hybrid seed, which at a profit of $2 per bushel would produce $360,000.

DeKalb's competitors Funk, Pfister, and Pioneer had been developing hybrids adapted to the central corn belt, where the growing season was longer, and were in approximately the same development stage that DeKalb was a bit farther north. So far, however, none of them had begun aggressive expansion. All aimed to sell "proprietary" hybrids which, by definition, could be purchased only from the company that developed them.

GOVERNMENT EXPERIMENT STATIONS

In the meantime, the government Experiment Stations had awakened and could be expected to offer parent seeds of their own hybrids to licensed seed producers within the next two or three years. Tom thought the probability of release of Experiment Station parent lines would create both opportunity and problems for DeKalb. "Station" inbred lines, when released to DeKalb, would allow the company to expand its marketing efforts into the central corn belt with full-season ("later") hybrids best adapted there. However, the public release of Experiment Station parent lines could be expected to spawn hundreds of small local growers producing hybrids certified by state Experiment Stations and recommended by county agents. DeKalb would need to hire corn breeders to stay ahead of its competitors, particularly in the central corn belt.

Given the probability that competition would increase in the near future, Tom realized that DeKalb must grow as fast as possible, building for the future by being the first company to provide hybrid seedcorn to as many farmers as possible. He knew his hybrids would perform superbly (20 to 30 percent better than non-hybrids) and figured that DeKalb had an opportunity to win legions of enthusiastic customers whose first hybrid seed had come from DeKalb. Perhaps, too, some of these enthusiasts would become dealers, selling DeKalb hybrids to their neighbors—thereby cementing DeKalb's position in their neighborhoods for years to come.

AMBITIOUS GOALS FOR DEKALB

Convinced that DeKalb's lead time in the northern corn belt provided a unique opportunity, Tom set the following goals for the company:

- To produce all the DeKalb hybrid seed possible. If he eventually overproduced, he could carry over and sell his surplus seed the following year.

- To finance his growth opportunity without diluting shareholder equity, and without sharing any profits with outsiders. To achieve this goal, he would need to build seed processing plants and find a way to pay for them as well as to pay contract farmer-growers and detasselers for their seed production efforts.
- To offer the first hybrid seedcorn to as many farmers as possible. The more farmers who bought their first hybrids from DeKalb the better, because they would likely be repeat customers.
- To overcome any financial limitations that might prevent DeKalb from becoming the first hybrid seedcorn to be planted in as many farming communities as possible.
- To develop a sales organization based on farmer-dealers selling to their neighbors.
- To employ able, hard-working people capable of growing on their jobs as the company grew.
- To expand research as soon as possible into stations serving the central and southern corn belts.
- To quickly develop a strong quality-control program.
- To develop a compensation program that would allow all employees to benefit personally from the company's growth.

Financing Challenges

Achieving maximum hybrid production in 1935 posed no big financial problem, because DeKalb's parent seed supply was small and limited hybrid production goals to only 14,000 bushels of seed. Tom's experience in the canning business had taught him how to obtain warehouse-receipt financing as a last resort. This type of financing would be both expensive and hard to administer but could be used, if necessary, to finance the construction of seed processing plants in 1935 and 1936, postponing the need to obtain a credit line from Chicago bankers, who had to be convinced the hybrid seedcorn business was "for real."

Should DeKalb Maximize Short-Term Growth by Franchising?

Franchising associate growers must have been a tempting solution to financing Tom's plans for rapid growth. It would have involved finding well-to-do farmers or seed companies to produce the hybrid seed and sell it in specific "territories," paying the parent company a royalty of $1 per bushel of seed sold, or about half of the profit expected from each bushel of seed. Funk and Pfister had built their businesses around franchised "associate growers," limiting their own function to hybrid breeding. Pioneer had one big franchise grower, Bob Garst, who lived in western Iowa at Coon Rapids and served western Iowa, Missouri, Nebraska, Colorado, Oklahoma and Kansas. Tempting though franchising was, Tom didn't like the idea because it involved "cutting up the profit pie" with franchised growers.

Tom needed to demonstrate to banks not only that he had a great product but also that he was a capable and imaginative manager. In short, he needed to be an entrepreneur—one who had a great product and could figure out ways to finance growth that would be sound and would justify banks' backing him with the credit lines needed to support optimum growth.

To win respect and support from his bankers, Tom conceived the following system:

- DeKalb would require down payments of $1 per bushel from customers placing orders as early as August for delivery the following spring ($1 per bushel was 10 to 12 percent of the price of a bushel of hybrid seed). Demand was so great that farmers would pay the deposit. Income from deposits would be more than sufficient to pay off detasseling loans, as well as to pay for some "start-up" seed processing plant construction.
- Most important, Tom developed a grower contract that agreed to pay growers a 25 percent premium over the Chicago cash corn market for the hybrid seed the grower delivered to DeKalb's seed processing plants at harvest time. The contract gave the grower opportunity to select his payment date based on the Chicago cash corn price on any day the grower chose between November 1 and May 1 of the following year.

This grower contract was a unique feature that Tom thought would lead his growers to delay payment demands until spring because (1) Chicago cash corn prices were generally low at harvest time and higher in the following spring months, and (2) the contract growers' need for cash was generally low at harvest time because most growers were harvesting and selling other crops in sufficient quantity to meet their winter cash needs. Their peak need for cash would be at planting time the following spring.

Get Dollars from Customers before Paying Growers

Tom planned not only to delay payments to growers but also to expedite drying and processing seed for delivery to dealers in January, followed by organized delivery campaigns in February and March. His aim was to collect the full $12.20 price per bushel for the finished product before his contract growers would ask him to pay for his "raw material"—seed that would cost DeKalb somewhere between $3 and $5 per bushel of finished seed in grower payments. The success of his plan depended on a combination of the following:

- extremely strong demand from customers willing to pay full retail price in January, February, or early March because they wanted to be sure of receiving the hybrid seed they had ordered, and
- delayed payment to farmer-growers who could expect to benefit from high grain prices in the spring.

Tom's plan involved considerable risk, because severe economic depression could cause contract growers to demand payment for their seed soon after they delivered it to DeKalb at harvest time.

Accordingly, Tom needed a bank credit "back-up" line large enough to finance fall purchase and processing of DeKalb's seed "raw material" until income from the sale of "finished goods" had been received the following spring. After being rebuffed by several bankers, Tom found a Chicago banker with both farming background and imagination. That man was Guy Reed of the Harris Bank in Chicago, who agreed to extend the credit line Tom needed to produce 75,000 bushels of seed in 1936 for delivery in the spring of 1937. Reed appreciated the growth potential of hybrid corn and also realized that his bank would benefit from DeKalb's willingness to keep its seasonal surplus on deposit at its lending institution without asking for interest. DeKalb's account could be expected to hold surplus funds from May through August or September.

At a critical moment in the mid 1930s, Tom found himself in a cash bind. He had a payroll to meet and didn't want to reveal to his bankers how desperately short of cash he was, because he was negotiating with them for long-term commitments at minimum interest rates. He feared the rates might go up if they realized how badly he needed short-term funds, so he asked Harold Viking Engh, a very successful friend, for a short-term loan. Harold had faith in him and made the loan. When his peak need passed, and deposit money started coming in from dealers, Tom repaid the loan, asking Engh, "Would you rather I pay you in DeKalb stock or cash?" Engh chose cash. Years later, Harold Engh's son told me that story in a friendly, though slightly rueful way!

Building a Capital Account

When his business started booming in the late 1930s, Tom's experience sweating out payrolls told him that the boom would not last forever, so he decided to build an equity base that would carry the company through any future "rainy days." His goal was to become as free of dependence on bank debt as possible.

To do this, he resolved to delay paying dividends as long as he could. Nevertheless, he paid his first small dividend in 1938. It amounted to only 5 percent of earnings, but that single first dividend was larger than the initial shareholders' 1917 investment in the company!

Imaginative, entrepreneurial financing arrangements achieved by Tom Roberts were unique in his industry and were major contributors to DeKalb's success.

Sharing Profits with Employees

Tom made another key move in 1938 that assured DeKalb of the support, affection, and respect of its employees. He established an employee profit-sharing plan, which set aside 15 percent of its annual pre-tax profits to be divided equally among all employees. Employees welcomed the plan enthusiastically when it was presented in the fall of 1941, and over the years it was an important contributor to both their "team spirit" and their financial well-being.

Annual profit-sharing meetings were very similar to shareholder meetings. The primary difference was that each employee received a report showing the value of his or her portion of the plan. The personalized reports presented annually told an exciting story to each employee, partly because DeKalb's profits grew rapidly, but also because the value of investments made in DeKalb and IBM common stock by the profit-sharing management committee grew very rapidly.

Table 3-3 tells the story of the retirement security and wealth enhancement of every DeKalb profit-sharing member (all were eligible to join after completing their first full year of employment, and virtually all "signed up"). After 1942 each member contributed $150 annually.

Table 3-3
DeKalb's Profit Sharing Benefits:
Cumulative Value per Employee Member ($), 1941–1980

Year	Member	DeKalb	Other	Value
1941	100	359	0	459
1951	1,735	6,734	1,210	9,679
1961	3,917	17,220	4,041	25,178
1971	7,931	132,701	30,773	171,405
1980	5,675	357,189	0	372,864

SOURCE: A single full-term member's account record from Wilbur Straun
Notes: The "Member" column includes cumulative annual $150 dues from each member plus income and current value of investment. The "DeKalb" column shows cumulative annual contributions to the fund by DeKalb plus income and value of investments. The "Other" column shows funds relinquished by departing employees. In perspective, $342,864 in 1980 was the equivalent of $512,095 in 1990 dollars.

Tom Invests in IBM

The profit-sharing committee's decision to invest heavily in IBM was influenced by the good experience Tom and the company had had with IBM's machines, which became available to small businesses in the early 1930s. In 1936, when orders for DeKalb hybrid seed began to roll in fast, Tom came into the company office on a Saturday afternoon and found Edna Nelson, his bookkeeper, sitting at a desk working on an overwhelming number of orders, most of which were accompanied by cash deposits.

Tom's auditors suggested that he install an IBM punch-card system. So impressed was he with its accuracy and speed that he vowed to invest most of his personal funds in IBM, after giving first priority to the purchase of DeKalb stock. He pursued this policy for the rest of his life, and when he died, his IBM holdings exceeded the book value of his DeKalb stock, which was, in fact, its market value.

His success with IBM stock caused him to recommend that profit-sharing funds be invested in IBM as much as prudence would allow. The soundness of that advice is reflected in Table 3-3.

Hospitalization

Shortly after the profit-sharing plan was announced, a hospitalization plan was put into place for all full-time DeKalb employees. This employee-administered plan was originally financed equally by employees and by DeKalb, but later (around 1970), DeKalb began paying 80 percent and employees 20 percent. The employees understood and supported the concept of employee financial participation as being fair and as a means of ensuring that the benefits of the plan would not be abused.

Wilbur Strawn was the company's credit manager and administrator of both the hospitalization and the profit-sharing plan. He helped organize and capably administered them, relieving Tom of the administrative detail so essential to their success.

Chapter 4

A Farmer-Dealer Sales Force 1936-1950

Tom's experience as farm adviser and manager of the DeKalb Agricultural Association left him with high regard for the leading farmers who were elected to be directors of their county Farm Bureaus or chosen to be advisers to AAA county programs. He knew they had the respect of their neighbors, he anticipated they would be the most willing to try out hybrid seed, and he felt sure they would become enthusiastic about it once they had proved its merit on their own farms. What better candidate to sell DeKalb seed to his neighbors?

THE CONCEPT

A farmer-dealer could do these things:

- Enthusiastically sell DeKalb seed to his neighbors on the basis of his personal experience.
- Plant test plots to demonstrate DeKalb's hybrids to his neighbors.
- Make sales calls in the free time he has between the end of cultivation in early July and harvest in October.
- Take delivery of his seed from January through March.
- Warehouse the seed in his barn.
- Ask his customers to come to him to pick up their seed. "Come get it early, supply is short."
- Make every sale a cash sale—or take the credit risk himself if he chose to extend credit to a neighbor-customer.

For performing all of these sales functions, the DeKalb farmer-dealer in the late 1930s received a 15 percent discount on a $12.20 per bushel retail price; the price varied with the "grade" or size of kernels purchased. Many corn belt farmers planted at least 100 acres of corn, which required about twenty bushels of seed costing the farmer-customer $2.50 per acre, or $250.00 to plant 100 acres. The dealer's 15 percent discount (commission) would amount to approximately $37.50 per 100-acre customer sold. Selling hybrid seed would clearly be good business for an enthusiastic farmer-dealer.

From DeKalb's point of view, marketing hybrid seed through farmer-dealers made sense because:

- Dealers selected would be respected farm leaders, enthusiastic about DeKalb's product.
- Farmer-dealers would sell DeKalb exclusively.
- A farmer-dealer would have to *solicit* orders because he had no store or elevator where he could wait for customers to come to him.
- Dealers would be knowledgeable corn growers, familiar with handling corn-growing problems, and therefore capable of dealing with most of the problems their customers might encounter.

For all of these reasons, Tom was convinced DeKalb should sell through farmer-dealers in territories of two to four townships. A typical thirty-township county would have eight to twelve DeKalb dealers, so the company's sales organization would have to organize to administer an active, aggressive selling organization.

District managers would be needed to:

- Hire and train dealers.
- Administer sales incentive programs for dealers.
- Recognize dealer achievements.
- Replace the poor performers.
- Organize field days and promotions.
- Be in touch with dealers at least once every two weeks during the sales season, mostly at dealer sales meetings, where hybrid performance, selling techniques, and individual dealer successes would be recognized.
- See that dealers erected DeKalb signs on their customers' fields.
- Be sure that every prospect was asked to buy.

The size of a sales district would need defining and evaluation. Many of DeKalb's first districts had 100 dealers per district, but over time (about twenty years) sales districts became smaller and the number of dealers per district was reduced to about fifty. Districts in fringe areas on the edge of the corn belt still frequently have as many as 100 dealers.

Richard Crabb's account of the role played by farmer-dealers is telling:

> In the job of acquainting a million farmers in the heart of the United States with the advantages of the new corn, these farmer salesmen collectively made a momentous contribution. Without them, all the fine efforts of the experiment station extension workers, the farm bureaus, the vocational agriculture and 4-H club demonstrations, and work done by other agricultural educational agencies might have taken a generation or more getting the complete acceptance that has been achieved

for hybrid corn.

How did this small army of farmer-salesmen become interested, able, and willing to accomplish their difficult task? The experience of Dan Hayes, an east central Nebraska farmer, is more or less typical. Hayes had a little farm and a big mortgage near the small town of Silver Creek, a hundred miles due west of Omaha in a country where people still living can remember having seen the last herds of buffalo roaming in the 1880s.

In the spring of 1934, a man came to Dan Hayes' farm one evening about milking time and told him he should plant some hybrid corn. Hayes' acquaintance with hybrid corn was limited to having seen it mentioned several times in the Nebraska Farmer, but his visitor told him that the new corn would yield twenty to twenty-five per cent more than his open-pollinated corn and would stand drought much better. The result was that although Hayes didn't have enough ready cash to his name at the moment to pay the ten dollars for a bushel of the seed, he took it.

Considering the state of the Hayes family finances, he didn't tell his wife about it, and Mrs. Hayes didn't know about the transaction until she found the bushel of seed resting on the back porch. Then Dan explained the deal, and his wife went to the sack to have a look at seed corn that could cost ten dollars a bushel when the best open-pollinated seed could be had for a trifle more than the market price of corn. She opened the sack and looked inside.

"You don't call that stuff seed corn," she explained as she beheld the small kernels her husband had bought. The price on small kernels was less than on regular flat kernels generally used.

Dan Hayes, a little embarrassed about it all and fearing that perhaps he had been swindled, planted this hybrid corn back from the road where it wouldn't be in common view of the neighbors. About the same time he learned that his neighbor, Henry Galus, had bought a bushel of another hybrid. The two Silver Creek farmers visited back and forth about their new hybrid corn frequently as the season advanced. Dan Hayes thought his hybrid corn looked a little better than his open-pollinated, but Mrs. Hayes was by no means sure that it looked enough better to justify having spent ten dollars a bushel for the seed. Henry Galus was better pleased with his, or at least he said so.

Then on the Sunday afternoon before Labor Day, Dan suggested to his wife that they go over and visit the Galus family. Dan's general idea was to be neighborly, but his specific objective was to have a chance to go out to Henry Galus' cornfield and see if his new hybrid was actually as much better as he said it was.

"When I got to the corn field, I didn't have to be told where Henry had planted his new hybrid corn," recalls Dan Hayes. "You could see it a half-mile away. There it stood green and in good shape while the open-pollinated corn right next to it was going to make only half a crop on account of the drought. That sold me on hybrid corn. My own hybrid corn did a lot better than I thought it would. It repaid me for the extra cost of the seed and then some.

"That fall as soon as the heavy work was over, I told my wife that I could sell that new hybrid corn and earn some badly-needed money during the winter. I inquired of Henry Galus where his hybrid seed had been produced. He told me that it came from the Robinson Seed Company at Waterloo, Nebraska. So about a week later I went to Waterloo, met Ted Robinson and Bob Herrington, and told them I wanted a chance to sell their new hybrid seed corn in the Silver Creek community. Bob Herrington was a little reluctant to let me do it until he found out that I had actually observed the performance of one of their hybrids on Henry Galus' farm, because he said that he didn't want anyone selling their seed until he had personal experience with hybrid corn and was convinced of its superiority.

"I went home and began working. I would get up before five o'clock in the morning, do the chores, eat breakfast, and be on the road to sell hybrid seed corn by daylight. Naturally it was slow work because most of my neighbors hadn't any more than heard of hybrid corn and some of them hadn't heard of it at all. I worked from dawn to dark every day I could spare that winter and spring until planting time, and I sold 434 bushels of the new hybrid seed corn—most of it in 1 and 2 bushel orders to farmers who were—like me the year before—just trying it.

"I got along all right, but it wasn't as easy as it sounds," recalls Hayes. "This was especially true as I got farther away from home and wasn't so well acquainted. I sometimes asked a farmer whom I knew and who was better acquainted in his particular neighborhood than I to ride with me.

"On the particular day I have in mind, my good friend Harold Lundeen had been riding with me all day, and we hadn't sold a bushel of corn. Toward evening and chore time, Harold pointed out the home of a prominent farmer. I told him, "We'll stop and see him and make just this one more call, and if I can't sell him some hybrid seed corn, we'll give him some corn." After talking a few minutes to the man, I saw that we could not sell him, so I said to him, "Mister, I've got two seed samples of this new hybrid corn in my car. I'm going to give you these and I want you to plant them and let us know how they come out."

"No thanks," the man replied, "I don't think I want to take a chance on anything like that."

"I'm sure he never would have taken them either, but his Missus had heard us talking, and she came to the door and said to her husband, 'Why, I think you're foolish. These men are spending their time trying to sell you something that sounds like it might be a good thing, and you won't take it on, so they're offering to give it to you. I think we should try it.' With that the man took the samples, and from that day to this he has been a devoted hybrid-corn customer of mine."

One of the circumstances which made this sampling approach so effective during the mid-thirties was the outstanding performance of the new hybrid corn during the severe droughts that swept across practically all of the corn belt in 1934 and 1936 and on a more regional scale during other years. Farmers who had either bought or had been given the little four or eight-pound samples of seed voluntarily wrote thousands of testimonial letters to the producers, letters that read like this: "My hybrid corn didn't make much corn this year, only fifteen or twenty bushels to the acre, but it was a big improvement over my open-pollinated corn which wasn't worth picking. I'm not going to plant anything but hybrid corn next season."

The next year Hayes was able to sell more than 750 bushels. (Pp. 281–86)

DEKALB 404A

DeKalb's first real "winner," DeKalb 404A, was introduced in big volume in 1939. This hybrid put the name DeKalb on farms all across the north central corn belt and catapulted the company to the top of the hybrid corn industry. During the twenty-seven years it remained in DeKalb's product line it sold more than 6 million bushels. It caught on quickly and peaked between 1944 and 1947. It was easy to husk, had high-quality grain, matured quickly, and produced well on almost any soil.

DeKalb 404A was the winner the company needed. It made friends for DeKalb and made the task of building an effective sales force easier. In 1940, Rus Rasmusen received this poem from an anonymous but ecstatic customer:

As I set upon my doorstep
and gaze about my farm
I see a great improvement
In its beauty and its charm
The student and the scientist
Have turned to corn at last
And tangled rows and aching backs
Must soon be of the past
Where those ragged, tangled corn fields
Met my vision years before

Now I see the stately beauty
of that field of 404
There's a lot of satisfaction
Knowing that the yield is more
When combined with all the beauty
of that field of 404
It stands in trim and stately rows
In any kind of weather
A monument to such as Gunn;
We sing their praise together.

Lots of farmers shared our poet's enthusiasm for 404A in its first ten years, as Table 4-1 shows.

Table 4-1
404a—DeKalb's First Big Winner, 1938–1947

Year	Sales in Bushels
1938	31,746
1939	157,633
1940	210,503
1941	211,489
1942	309,504
1943	324,948
1944	489,023
1945	577,921
1946	492,148
1947	508,238

SOURCE: Personal records, T H Roberts, Jr.

CHOOSING LEADERS

Tom Roberts knew he would need good men to build a good organization. The man he chose in 1936 to be sales manager had been his successor as Farm Adviser, Rus Rasmusen. A farmer's son, he was a "bronze tablet" honor student at the University of Illinois. Knowledgeable, perceptive, and an exemplary leader as well as a hard-driving competitor, Rus was the perfect choice for sales manager. He, in turn, had to select and train the best of the hundreds of eager young men applying for jobs in this exciting new industry.

Rus tended to choose experienced County Agents and teachers of vocational agriculture (voc-ag) to build his sales organization. He studied the sales potential in each corn growing area, concentrating his best men where corn was "king." Support forces in advertising and sales promotion were organized. Sales districts were defined, district managers hired, sales campaigns organized. This sales force would make its new company a leader for years to come. The head start DeKalb had in the northern one-third of the corn belt made it the region's dominant force. Rasmusen's best men were promoted into DeKalb's leading districts and regions.

Some of the many fine men who worked these areas in the 1930s and 1940s were:

Harold Noren. An outstanding Illinois graduate, Harold joined DeKalb in 1946 after leaving the service, excelling in every job DeKalb gave him. From a district in Pontiac, Illinois, he went on to a higher-volume district in Minnesota, to poultry sales management, to sorghum sales management, to corn sales manager, and finally he became vice president for seed operations. In the early 1960s he insisted on DeKalb's moving into single crosses heavily—a move that doubled the company's sales and market penetration.

Sid Rasmusen. One of the first men Rus hired was his brother, Sid. As western regional sales manager, Sid was responsible for hybrid seedcorn sales west of the Mississippi River. He was sensitive, analytical, determined, and a great judge of people. He chose his own district managers, set goals for them, and insisted that his region be well covered by good farmer-dealers. Unfortunately, he died suddenly of a heart attack in the early 1950s.

Harold Nolin. Harold was Sid Rasmusen's best district manager in Iowa. He was promoted and transferred to DeKalb in the 1940s to become eastern regional sales manager. Before joining DeKalb in 1937, Harold had been a voc-ag teacher in eastern Iowa. He was a witty, dedicated man who retired as vice president in the mid-1980s.

Albert Morehouse. An outstanding district manager at Humboldt in north-central Iowa, Albert was a charismatic, persuasive leader. He achieved a market penetration in excess of 50 percent in his district. He was promoted in 1955 to regional manager for Iowa, Minnesota, and Missouri.

Ken Scott. Scott was a successful district manager at Spencer, Iowa, just west of Morehouse's district. He was a hard-driving, "sell seed or else" type of manager, a fact borne out by his sales record. A tough competitor, not always loved by his dealers, he was promoted to regional manager for the last fifteen years of his career with DeKalb.

John Rosenberg. John was a very effective district sales manager in DeKalb's home district after he joined the company in 1945. An able, persuasive, and analytic leader of his dealers, John kept his market penetration over or near 50 percent by reducing the territory size to levels that permitted dealers to be in closer touch with customers when the competition got tougher in the 1950s. Rosenberg was promoted to southeast regional sales manager in the late 1950s.

Leo Olson. Olson was the first and only DeKalb advertising and sales promotion manager from 1936 through his retirement in 1976. In his role as advertising manager he originated slogans such as this one: “DeKalb Quality Hybrids Will Be Your Mortgage Lifter.” This slogan was significant for DeKalb, because its use and the artwork on the first widely printed DeKalb ad was the beginning of the evolution of DeKalb’s distinctive “winged ear” logo.

SOURCE: Leo Olson, Corporate Records

The idea of attracting farmers to hybrid corn by reminding them that hybrids could be their mortgage lifters reflected Tom Roberts’ awareness of the heavy debt most farmers carried. The original format of the DeKalb ad had scrolled mortgages, instead of an ear of corn, being carried away by wings. Leo Olson had the idea of substituting the ear of corn for the mortgages but retained the slogan “DeKalb Quality Hybrids Will Be Your Mortgage Lifter.” The ad was timely and attracted a lot of farmer attention. The winged-ear DeKalb logo is still in use today, far outliving the original ad. In his capacity as sales promotion manager, Olson worked with the regional sales managers to develop dealer incentives, sales campaigns, and dealer education, as well as corn picking contests, and fair displays.

Bob North. A born salesman, Bob moved from a dealership in the Midwest to York, Pennsylvania, to build a DeKalb sales organization on the East Coast.

There were many more good salespeople, but these were the men I remember most. Their efforts were largely responsible for putting DeKalb into the number-one position it enjoyed in the industry. From 1936 through 1972, “more farmers planted DeKalb than any other hybrid” (a phrase the company later used freely in its advertising), in large part because of the fine marketing organization Rus Rasmusen organized and administered. Table 4-2 shows his sales record from 1935 to 1950.

Table 4-2
DeKalb Hybrid Corn Sales Record, 1935–1950

Year	Sales (000 bushels)	Acres Planted (000s)	Market Share (percent)
1935	365	95,975	.00015
1936	12,000	100,957	.06
1937	70,000	97,170	.35
1938	239,013	94,475	1.26
1939	318,781	91,632	1.74
1940	557,545	88,692	3.12
1941	608,479	86,835	3.47
1942	1,020,240	88,811	5.79
1943	1,308,262	94,346	6.91
1944	1,629,905	94,472	8.51
1945	1,685,984	89,261	9.39
1946	1,705,379	88,898	9.51
1947	2,151,357	85,038	12.60
1948	2,416,335	86,527	13.90
1949	2,090,276	86,731	12.00
1950	1,800,536	82,859	10.90

SOURCE: Ruth Peterson, assistant to Rus Rasmusen, Seed Sales Manager.

Chapter 5

Developing Hybrid Seed Production 1936-1950

Tom Roberts' determination to move tested hybrids into the largest possible production, his belief in the soundness of selling through farmer-dealers, and his imaginative plan for financing DeKalb's growth were key factors in DeKalb's emergence as an industry leader during the late 1930s.

The sales people and strategies discussed in Chapter 4 were vital to the success of DeKalb, but equally important were those who were responsible for the production of the seed offered for sale. Before hybrid seed was offered to farmers, most of them had simply saved the seed of their best ears and planted it. There was, therefore, no seed company that could serve as a model for DeKalb, which sought to increase its seed production from zero in 1934 to 1 million bushels per year by 1940. The men who made this possible were therefore every bit as important to DeKalb as its new sales force.

SOURCE: T. H. Roberts, Jr.

Farmer and Son collecting ears to shell for next season's planting

With the introduction of hybrids, enormous changes took place in the handling of the seed. When farmers had selected their own seed, they had simply hung the ears up to dry. When hybrid seeds were introduced, drying and seed processing plants replaced farmer selection of seed.

Ben Harrison, who left the Sycamore Preserve Works with Tom to join DeKalb in 1935, faced tremendous challenges as he planned construction of the company's first large seed processing plant at Waterman, Illinois, in the fall of 1935. That plant was scheduled to produce 90,000 bushels of finished seed in the fall of 1936 for delivery to dealers in the spring of 1937. Next, he would plan and build two processing plants that would each need to be ready by the fall of 1937 to process 100,000 bushels of finished seed for delivery to dealers in the spring of 1938. These plants were to be located at Monmouth, Illinois, and Humboldt, Iowa.

PLANNING SEEDCORN DRYING AND PROCESSING FACILITIES

Ben Harrison and Hugh McCorkle, his young construction foreman, ordered enough fixed-position driers for their new plant to dry down their entire crop in six weeks. Harvest would begin when the seed reached physiological maturity, so the first load for each drying bin would have a moisture content of about 35 percent, to be dried to a 12 percent level, at which it could be safely handled and processed. It would be dried slowly to ensure good germination, conveyed out of the drying bins, and a new batch would replace it. After drying, the seed would be shelled and cleaned of chaff, graded into sizes that would fit farmers' planter plates, treated with chemicals to control insects, bagged, and identified by lot numbers that would facilitate quality control and identify problem lots for discard if germination tests showed them to be below DeKalb's standards.

Harrison calculated that each drying bin could handle two, maybe three, or more batches of seed before a hard freeze reduced the germination of grain still in the field so much that it would be unusable as seed. He couldn't be confident of his calculation, however, because no one had undertaken the drying of such large quantities of seedcorn before. Accordingly, he was much interested when he learned of the portable driers available from the Campbell Heating Company of Des Moines, Iowa. He and Hugh McCorkle figured they could hook up Campbell's portable driers to emergency drying bins made of snow fences to meet emergency harvesting needs made necessary by an approaching freeze.

Portable Driers Purchased to Protect against Early Freeze

Harrison and McCorkle decided the Campbell portable driers were what they needed in case of either harvesting delays caused by rainy weather or long-term predictions of early heavy freezes. They purchased more portable driers than they really expected to need and added surge bins between the emergency driers and their processing equipment.

Campbell had emerged as the leader in seedcorn drier design and remains so today. The simple portable driers gave seed producers the flexibility they needed when their large drier bins were full of drying seed and a freeze was forecast.

Much improvisation was necessary as Harrison and McCorkle raced to design and construct the processing plants needed to process the volume of seed Tom wanted. Driers, shellers, cleaners, and sizers were arranged so the dried seed would flow steadily into the baggers, in twenty-four-hour shifts. Germination testing procedures were established to be sure that each bag of newly processed seed would germinate satisfactorily. Statistics used were used to develop sampling procedures, as tests were run constantly to check on seed lots that might have been nipped by frost.

SOURCE: DeKalb Genetics

To beat the first freeze, portable driers expedited harvest.

Process Quickly for Quick Payment

The seed grading, processing, and bagging work was done fast in the winter of 1936–37 because Tom Roberts and Rus Rasmusen wanted seed deliveries to dealers to begin in January and to be completed by mid-March. The company's ability to grow fast by selling the finished product before paying for the raw material required:

- the seed to be in dealers' warehouses in January for February delivery campaigns;
- cash sales by dealers to customers and quick remittance to DeKalb; and

- the contract growers' willingness to wait for high spring corn prices before demanding payment for the seed they had delivered at harvest time. Tom figured they would wait for higher spring grain prices to ask for the money due to them.

SOURCE: DeKalb Genetics

Newly finished Waterman, Il. seed drying and processing plant ready to dry and process seed in time for the first big harvest.

An Anxious Spring

In the spring of 1937, Tom's ulcers must have been strained to the limit by anxiety about his early delivery concept. Only if cash came in from dealers during February and March would the company be able to finance its expansion from its own cash flow, rather than have to expand its business by sharing profits with franchised seed growers, as other hybrid corn seed producers were doing. As a last resort, he could fall back on his line of credit, but its full use would not only reduce profits; it might also limit future expansion. The spring of 1937 tested Tom's entrepreneurial idea.

By mid-March, it was clear that Tom's drive to collect cash early was a total success. Only a few of his contract growers had asked for payment by then, and more than enough cash had come in from dealers to pay the contract growers without drawing down DeKalb's credit line materially. In its first big expansion, DeKalb had proved it could self-finance its own growth. No more would Tom have to worry about the adequacy of his credit lines. He could be highly confident his bankers would back him if growers demanded early payment. He had demonstrated that, in a normal year, he could collect for his finished product before he had to pay for his raw material.

As Dick Crabb reported in *The Hybrid Corn Makers:*

> Roberts' DeKalb organization was now on its way to establishing unmatched leadership in the job of giving northern corn belt farmers the benefits of this new kind of corn. The hybrids developed during this period by Gunn were proving so much better than open-pollinated corn that demand was without precedent before or since. No corn like it had ever been seen on the farms of those great corn growing regions of northern Iowa, upper Illinois and Indiana. Gunn's hybrids outyielded the old corn on farm after farm by twenty-five to thirty-five percent, came up better in the spring, withstood drought better in the summer, and stood up better in the fall. A revolution in corn growing was unfolding on thousands of farms because of the work done by a few men living in DeKalb. (P. 224)

SOURCE: DeKalb Genetics

Graders in DeKalb seed processing plant. The seed must fit them exactly for precision planting.

When he learned years later how Tom had financed DeKalb's growth by receiving cash from his finished product before having to pay for his raw material, Crabb described his feat as "a marvelous example of entrepreneurial genius."

Explosive Growth

Assured in mid-March of 1937 that he could finance production expansion by delivering early and being paid before he had to pay his contract growers, Tom gave the go-ahead to contract with farmer-growers to plant enough acres to produce 250,000 bushels of finished seed to deliver to farmer-dealers in the spring of 1938.

Construction of new plants would be a hectic process for the first eight years, as DeKalb's sales shot upward. Construction of a plant had to begin fifteen months before it would be scheduled to begin processing. Table 5-1 shows DeKalb's plant-expansion schedule between 1935 and 1950.

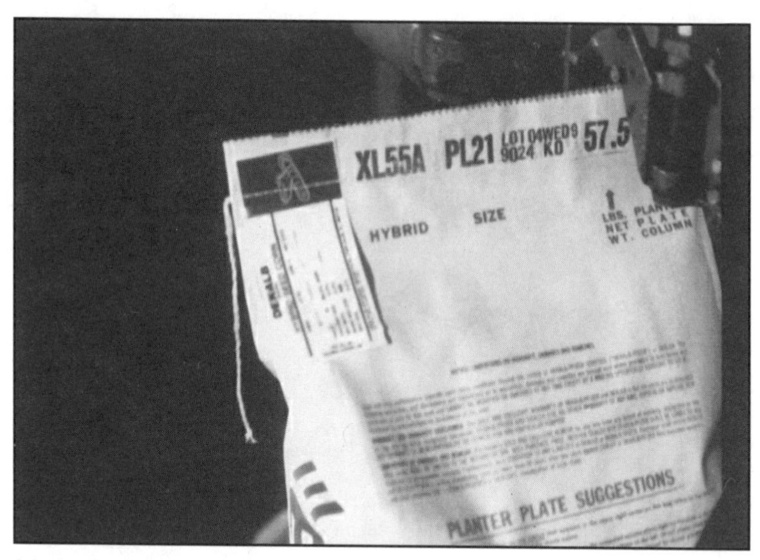

SOURCE: DeKalb Genetics

The finished product—quality seed, well identified as to source, germination, and seed size.

The race for hybrid corn leadership in the corn belt was on. DeKalb increased its hybrid production from 90,000 bushels in 1936 to 265,000 bushels in 1937, to 352,000 in 1938, and to 655,000 in 1939. In the fall of 1942, Tom telephoned me at the University of Illinois to say that the company expected to sell more than 1 million bushels of DeKalb hybrids for planting in the spring of 1943. By 1947 Tom could, and did, claim proudly in DeKalb advertising and on seed bags: "**More Farmers Plant DeKalb Than Any Other Hybrid**." Table 5-2 shows the number of bushels produced, by year, between 1935 and 1950.

Table 5-1
Seed Processing Plant Expansion, 1935–1950

Year Begun	Locations
1935	Waterman and Esmond, Illinois
1936	Humboldt, Iowa, and Monmouth, Illinois
1937	Tuscola, Illinois, and LaFayette, Indiana
1938	Storm Lake and Grinnell, Iowa
1939	Warren, Illinois, and Jackson, Minnesota
1940	Deshler and Johnstown, Ohio; Shenandoah, Iowa; Chatham, Ontario
1941	Fremont, Nebraska, and Oelwein, Iowa
1943	Marshall, Missouri
1944	Warehouses at North Platte, Nebraska; Sioux Falls, South Dakota; York, Pennsylvania
1947	Redwood Falls, Minnesota; Mt. Carmel, Illinois
1948	Crawfordsville, Indiana
1950	Warehouses at Adrian, Michigan, and Topeka Kansas

SOURCE: DeKalb Production Department records.

Table 5-2
DeKalb Seedcorn Production, 1935–1950

Year	Bushels
1935	11,900
1936	74,848
1937	265,570
1938	352,236
1939	655,936
1940	676,088
1941	753,107
1942	1,051,260
1943	1,348,460
1944	1,655,137
1945	2,139,297
1946	1,885,320
1947	2,503,308
1948	1,991,962
1949	2,473,674
1950	2,357,085

SOURCE: DeKalb Seed Production records.

DeKalb's rapid growth was exhilarating for everyone involved. Many farmer-dealers were able to pay off their mortgages with commissions earned from selling DeKalb seed. Farmers' yields increased by at least 20 percent, and the nation benefited tremendously from an enormous increase in its food production capacity. Dick Crabb calculated that hybrid corn contributed at least "three Iowas" to the nation's much-needed food production during and after World War II.

The Other Side of the Story

But success didn't come without problems, even heartaches. Sometime in the late 1930s, for example, farmers in parts of northwest Iowa opened their bags of DeKalb seed to find an inch or two of kernel-sized pieces of cob had "floated" to the top. The problem should have been detected in sampling, but all Tom could do was to call the complaining farmers together, tell them it should not have happened, assure them DeKalb would tighten its quality control, and then make every effort to improve the quality of its product. He also replaced the faulty seed at no charge. The farmers respected his frankness, and most remained DeKalb customers.

There were accidents in vehicles carrying teenage detasselers, difficult romances between office girls and German and Italian POW detasselers, key men who became alcoholics, and mistakes in planting seed fields. These are human problems not unique to DeKalb, but they happened and had to be dealt with. Success didn't come easy, or by accident. It was the product of hybrid vigor and a lot of hard work.

Key Seed Producers

The production men whose energy, intelligence, and hard work made DeKalb's growth possible included:

Ben Harrison, working with construction manager Hugh McCorkle, built fifteen DeKalb seed processing plants, hired and trained their operators, and produced a fine product. Harrison's work was, of necessity, innovative, because no seedcorn processing plants of DeKalb's size had ever been built. Unfortunately, he died in 1947 at the peak of his career.

Jim Forster, who succeeded Ben Harrison in 1947, effectively managed production for more than twenty-five years. Truly a DeKalb pioneer, Forster started as a laborer and performed his tasks so well that he moved rapidly up the ladder to become plant manager at Oelwein, Iowa. Sensitive, dedicated, socially aware, and conscientious, Jim performed superbly from 1945 through 1967, when he resigned to operate a John Deere dealership. He later became president of the DeKalb Bank.

Harold Wright, a vocational-agriculture teacher hired as a district manager so consistently pointed out seed quality problems that surfaced in his district that he was brought in to DeKalb to be in charge of quality control. He greatly improved DeKalb's quality control procedures, coordinating his central seed laboratory with smaller labs at each plant and supervising field inspection and isolation. Harold became an expert on chemical seed treatment and persuaded the company's sales group to market Heptachlor, an effective insecticide. It was sold by dealers for planter box application for many years.

Elmer Williams, distribution manager, who oversaw shifts of seed inventory from plant to plant throughout his career, became an informal assistant to Rus Rasmusen and Harold Noren, spending hours touring DeKalb test plots, where he evaluated experimental hybrids. Elmer's field notes, as well as his knowledge of the product line's strengths and weaknesses, were extremely valuable when the time came to decide on individual hybrid production goals.

Paul Vance, whose Storm Lake, Iowa, plant was always a DeKalb leader, was a great manager of people, insisting on top quality and volume. In slow seasons, his men never played cards in Paul's warehouses—they were painting, sweeping, polishing, and making their plant the best in the world. Paul was put in charge of all DeKalb seed production in 1967, after Jim Forster took early retirement.

Hugh McCorkle's contributions to plant construction and design are especially noteworthy. Starting with DeKalb in 1935, he was in charge of and personally managed all construction. After serving as a pilot-instructor in the Navy air force during World War II, he returned to DeKalb, and DeKalb bought a single-engine Navion, its first airplane, to permit McCorkle to manage three plant construction jobs simultaneously. He later piloted DeKalb's Aero Commanders, recording more flying hours in the Commanders than any other pilot in the world.

The War Years

In keeping with the spirit of the nation, Tom Roberts did not seek deferment from military service for his employees. Those who produced DeKalb seed during the war years were either older men or women, many of whom worked at tasks never performed before by women. German and Italian POWs and Jamaicans were as detasselers and production personnel. Claude Wilson, district manager, corn-husking champion, and resident poet, penned these words about those days:

> To make this seed, you all must know,
> We detassel every female row.
> This monstrous task evokes a moan,
> With 50,000 acres grown.
> It's one job you can't delay,
> It must be done every day.
> From everywhere we get recruits,
> Some Mexicans with their "zoot suits."

Jamaicans, Theologians, too,
Each plant put out a ladies crew.
Boy Scouts and teachers by the score,
'Til fifteen thousand, less or more,
Were pulling tassels with great speed,
So we could have the finest seed.
And they really got the job done well,
They had lots of fun and worked like ____ .
So DeKalb Ag again came through,
With the perfect job, as they always do.
So now we'll have some first-class seed,
With which to fill our nation's need.

The Postwar Years: 1946–1949

After the war, DeKalb welcomed back all of its veterans, built more seed plants, expanded its research, and increased sales efforts in "fringe" areas like Pennsylvania, New York, and the eastern seaboard states. Sales pushed upward and reached 2 million bushels by 1949, led by 404A.

Another Tom Roberts Prepares for a DeKalb Career

I returned home from the Pacific and reconsidered an earlier decision not to join the company. By 1946, DeKalb's hybrid poultry research program, which had begun in 1942, expected to market a limited number of DeKalb Chics in 1949. The prospect of joining the company during the growth years of a new DeKalb product appealed to me, so I enrolled in Iowa State College to study agriculture. I had accumulated four semesters of college credit in the University of Illinois Commerce School and four quarters of math and physics at the University of Chicago (my first year in the army). The credit and good grades qualified me to be a special student at Iowa State, taking courses that would prepare me for a job with DeKalb.

I graduated first in June of 1949 and went to work for Ray C. Nelson, who was responsible for the growth and development of the DeKalb hybrid chicken business, in addition to being assistant general manager of the company. He had rejoined the company in 1944 after fourteen successful years with the Federal Land Bank of St. Louis. My job for the next three years was to contract and manage relations with the hatcheries I signed up to hatch and sell DeKalb Chics.

Another little-known DeKalb diversification had begun in 1948, when research began at Lubbock, Texas, aimed at developing DeKalb hybrid sorghum. I knew little about it in 1949, but it would become very important to both me and DeKalb.

Competitors Grow Stronger

Steadily increasing hybrid corn sales between 1946 and 1949

masked developing problems in our seed business. In the north-central corn belt, our sales were leveling out as competitive pressures increased, but total hybrid seed sales continued upward in Pennsylvania, New York, Kentucky, Tennessee, Missouri, and Oklahoma.

In the fall of 1947 and again on November 11, 1949, severe storms in Iowa caused extensive ear dropping in 404A, which had been bred for easy hand-picking (by 1949, nearly all corn was picked with machinery), and 404A lost its largest market. Many loyal customers stayed with it on fewer acres, and it continued to be popular in eastern markets, but its sales volume had been cut in half three years after the first big storm in 1947. The record of 404A is set forth in Table 5-3. Dr. Forrest Troyer of Pioneer, in a publication, described 404A as "the all-time largest selling four-way hybrid."

Table 5-3
The Rise and Fall of 404A, 1938–1956

Year	Bushels Sold
1938	31,746
1939	157,633
1940	210,503
1941	211,489
1942	309,504
1943	324,948
1944	489,023
1945	577,921
1946	492,148
1947	508,238
1948	340,539
1949	339,085
1950	214,839
1951	206,823
1952	159,938
1953	177,659
1954	120,243
1955	145,007
1956	58,225

SOURCE: DeKalb corporate records.

Furthermore, competitive corn breeders were making progress developing high-yielding hybrids because farmers could plant more seeds per acre without fear of many plants "going barren" (not producing any ears), as was typical of most hybrids planted in the late 1930s and early 1940s. The new hybrids that resisted going barren were called high-population hybrids. DeKalb would face serious product performance problems from competitors' "high-pop" hybrids in the 1950s.

Chapter 6

Building Corn Research 1936-1950

To understand Tom Roberts' management of the evolution of DeKalb's corn research, it is important to understand the environment in which he and Charlie Gunn were working.

Between 1915 and 1935, the men developing inbred lines and crossing them to make hybrids were few in number, were generally considered to be impractical dreamers, and were operating under severe budgetary constraints. Some worked at the federal and state Experiment Stations, which were usually located near land-grant colleges. Others, like Charlie Gunn, Lester Pfister, Ben Moews, and Henry A. Wallace worked on hybrid corn development in small private plots either self-financed or as part of a seed-company effort to improve its products.

Initially, none of these men had a clear vision of how hybrid seedcorn would be produced if and when their research was successful; they all realized that inbred lines were quite weak and low yielding and would need tender loving care by careful seedsmen to produce any seed at all. The broad understanding was that leading farmers in each community would be asked to produce hybrid seed and sell it locally to their neighbors. This seemed a logical expectation, given that most farmers at the time were either saving their own seedcorn or buying it from a trusted friend.

SPEEDING PROGRESS BY EXCHANGING INBRED LINES

Nearly every breeder was frustrated by his inability to develop more than one or two good inbred lines. Many realized that the quickest way to develop good hybrids would be to swap inbred lines with other breeders. Charlie Gunn did this with Jim Holbert of the USDA, Ralph St. John of Purdue, and several other private breeders.

By 1930, state and federal breeders had organized programs to exchange inbred lines in order to accelerate the development of good hybrids. However, Dr. Forrest Troyer tells us that in the 1940s, many state corn breeding programs delayed release of their inbred lines for five to six years to support state certification programs. This favored small seed growers, as the major companies did not believe state certification was useful - - indeed, they thought it unfair. To "level the playing field," DeKalb, Funk and Pioneer exchanged some inbreds in the 1950s to counter the favoritism they felt the "public" (tax supported) breeding stations had granted to smaller "State Certified" seed growers.

Over the long haul, companies like DeKalb, Pioneer, Funk, and Pfister were better able to maintain the competitiveness of their product lines because they could fill in gaps in the mix of hybrids they offered by producing non-proprietary "station hybrids" until they could develop better hybrids from their own research. They were therefore assured of being able to market hybrids at least as good as their competitors'.

Release of public inbreds also created opportunities for smaller companies that did no research of their own to produce good-quality station hybrids at lower cost than could companies like DeKalb or Pioneer, which carried on expensive research programs. Private foundation seed companies were organized to multiply and cross station inbreds to provide parent seed for the smaller companies. By and large, farmers came to be served well by an ethical industry striving to produce the best product at the lowest possible cost.

In the industry's early years, nearly every hybrid DeKalb produced utilized some station inbred lines in combination with DeKalb's own inbreds. Some of the outstanding station-released inbreds used extensively in hybrids were:

From Indiana (Purdue):	WF9, 3811
From Ohio:	OH43, OH7, OH51A
From Iowa:	B14, B37, B73, L317
From Missouri:	MO17, MO13
From Nebraska:	N6, N28
From Minnesota:	A632, A634, A635, A619
From Wisconsin:	W64A, W117
From Connecticut:	C103

SOURCE: DeKalb Genetics

Developing Conflict?

Clearly, cooperation between public and private breeders expedited hybrid improvement, but the explosive growth of the hybrid seedcorn industry was not anticipated by many of those who would be involved in it. There was potential for conflict between people managing public and private institutions.

Some state Experiment Station directors jealously guarded their own turf and supported seed certification laws that favored growers in their own states. Over time, however, state university administrators came to accept the idea that their job was to train competent plant breeders to serve the public regardless of whether they were employed by public or private institutions.

Nevertheless, as DeKalb, Pioneer, Funk, and Pfister emerged as leaders, many public research workers were concerned about the changes that would take place in their institutions as corporations became active in plant breeding, which had been an important (and essentially exclusive) function of universities and government-financed Experiment Stations before corn hybridization. It was, therefore, incumbent upon the emerging companies to behave responsibly and to cooperate with their public colleagues.

Charlie Gunn Focuses His Efforts

Charlie Gunn, a highly skilled corn breeder, was always scouting for early-maturing varieties—that is, for breeding material he could use to develop hybrids for areas north of DeKalb. He would cross earlier strains onto his own inbreds, backcross, and select for earliness, plant type, and yield during years when the partially developed lines were segregating. His efforts were extremely successful and permitted DeKalb in the late 1930s and early 1940s to extend its product lines into Wisconsin and Minnesota as far north as areas with only eighty-five- to ninety-day growing seasons.

Gunn also was intrigued by prolific tropical varieties that produced several small ears per plant; his own hybrids seldom produced more than one ear per plant. His interest in these prolific types stemmed from his realization that his best hybrids, which had been selected for planting densities of 16,000 seeds per acre, sometimes failed to produce ears (went barren) when stressed by dry weather or when crowded in fields where farmers planted upward of 18,000 seeds per acre in hopes of achieving higher yields. Gunn's efforts to develop inbreds and hybrids that would resist "going barren" were, however, only slowly successful.

Ralph St. John Joins the Team

In 1937, Charlie Gunn told Tom that he wanted to focus his efforts on the northern corn belt and suggested hiring another breeder to develop hybrids for the central and southern corn belt areas. The first man they contacted was Dr. Jim Holbert, director of the USDA's central corn belt breeding program. Although Holbert could not accept because of his commitment to the USDA, he recommended Dr. Ralph St. John of Purdue University. Tom made a good offer to the man we came to know as "Saint," and he accepted.

When St. John joined DeKalb in 1937, he recommended that DeKalb get started in the central corn belt by producing hybrids made with Experiment Station lines. He believed a DeKalb presence in this great corn-growing area was essential to build a base for sales of the better hybrids he would soon be developing.

Tom and Rus Rasmusen agreed with St. John's proposal. They realized that farmers whose first experience with hybrid corn was with DeKalb would likely be steady repeat customers for the future. The concept was a good one and the hybrids "Saint" recommended were excellent. However, by 1939, when DeKalb seed was available in volume in the central corn belt, competitors like Funk, Pioneer, and Pfister already had sold hybrid seed to many of the region's farmers. Accordingly, DeKalb's sales progress was much slower in the central and southern areas than it was in the north, where DeKalb hybrids were the first hybrids many farmers had planted. Similarly, competitors who arrived in the northern corn belt after DeKalb found their sales penetration was slow.

St. John was not only a great corn breeder; he was also charming and full of good cheer and good jokes. He was also an intense, conscientious, and hard-working man who, like Tom Roberts, had ulcers as a consequence of many long days and nights of hard work.

Saint Gets His Goat

Around 1940 a farmer-dealer in the best corn-growing area of Tennessee held a "field day" featuring good DeKalb hybrids, a great goat barbecue, and Ralph St. John, who was a talented speaker. Field days gave DeKalb the chance to show off its best hybrids to farmers and dealers in a festive yet focused atmosphere. The barbecued goat was a bit too strong for Saint's northern colleagues, though, who ate it only sparingly. But Saint took a bite, extolled its flavor to the dealer who had prepared it, told him how sorry he was that he couldn't eat more because of his ulcer and how much he envied his colleagues from the north, all the while piling their plates higher and higher with the goat meat. Not wanting to offend their host, they were forced to eat far more barbecue than they wanted.

To get back at Saint, Harold Nolin, the regional sales manager, drove out into the Tennessee farm country early the next morning, bought the biggest, meanest, and smelliest billy goat he could find, and had it shipped COD to St. John's Champaign office, knowing the goat would get there before Saint returned and confident his secretary would pay for it. The joke worked perfectly, and that goat was on hand for Champaign, Illinois, field days for many years.

Saint developed central and southern corn belt hybrids that would help DeKalb through tough times that were coming in the 1950s. Unfortunately, he died of a heart attack in 1946. His broad knowledge of both the corn plant and the genetics of hybridization were sorely missed by DeKalb, as competition grew much more intense in the postwar years.

Saint's assistant carried on his corn breeding program, but in my opinion he lacked the technical background to fill Saint's shoes. Dr. Dick Johnson of Iowa State was hired to take over the key central corn belt corn breeding nursery in 1965. I believe our failure to replace Saint earlier was a significant mistake.

THE CHALLENGE OF HIGH-POPULATION HYBRIDS

Competitors pushed hard with the "high-population" concept, arguing that to maximize yields farmers needed to fertilize more heavily and to plant their hybrids at the higher rates per acre for which they had been selected. They offered high-population hybrids before DeKalb's were available, especially in the northern corn belt, and DeKalb's sales, heavily dependent upon "low-population" hybrids like DeKalb 404A, peaked at 2,416,000 bushels (14 percent of the total market) in 1949, and declined steadily for the next nine years.

Table 6-1 shows the yield advantages available from planting corn at high seed rates on good soils. It clearly shows why farmers were interested in hybrids that would take thick planting without going barren.

Other problems with 404A were its susceptibility to the European corn borer and its small shank attaching the ear to the plant. Charlie had selected for the small shank because it made hand-picking easier, but it became a weakness when machine corn pickers came into wide use; too often, ears with small shanks fell on the ground when the mechanical picker hit the plant.

Problems were ahead in the 1950s, but research expansion and some bold decisions built a base for recovery in the 1960s.

Figure 6-1
State average grain corn yields over average plant density for Iowa and Minnesota 1964 through 1974.

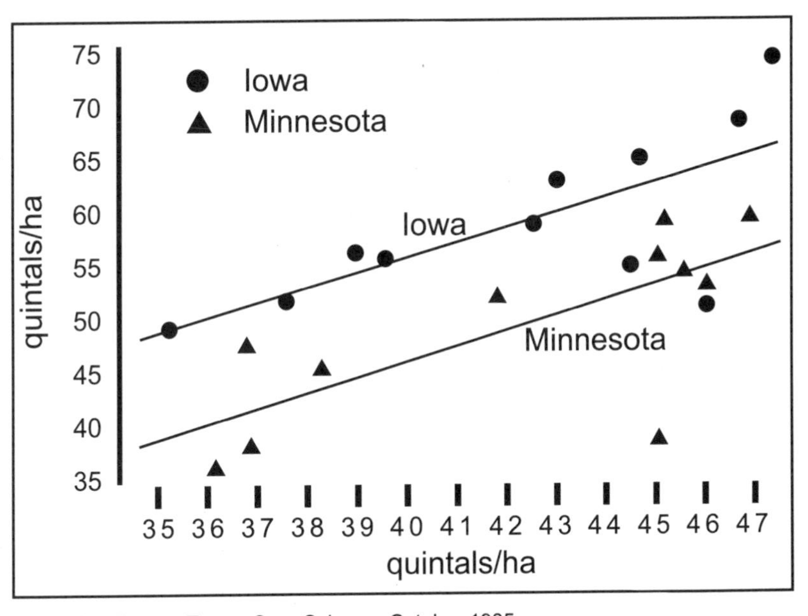

SOURCE: Forrest Troyer Crop Science, October 1985

Chapter 7

Oil Exploration and Tax Savings Attract DeKalb 1936-1950

In the preceding chapters, I have identified Tom Roberts, Sr.'s, most important contributions to DeKalb's success as:

- the farmer-dealer concept;
- the farmer-grower contract;
- the profit-sharing plan; and
- the courage to undertake large quantities of hybrid seed production in the key early days of hybrid corn, making "DeKalb" the first hybrid seed many customers had planted.

Tom made another highly significant contribution to DeKalb's future when he decided, in 1942, to take the company into the business of exploring for oil and gas. One might reasonably think that his oil venture was a reckless diversion from his success in hybrid seed, but it really was a sound, reasoned decision based on the fact that, from 1942 through 1946, a wartime excess-profits tax drained off all corporations' profits in excess of their average earnings between 1936 and 1939. Because DeKalb had grown rapidly during this base period, it faced taxation at a 95 percent rate for the duration of the war.

Tom was appalled by the seeming injustice of such a tremendous tax burden, partly because DeKalb was in no way a war industry, and partly because in 1942 it was still borrowing heavily to finance its growing business. A 95 percent tax rate would compel DeKalb to remain in debt for the duration of the war. Not only did he dislike paying interest, he was also determined to strengthen the company's balance sheet against the possibility of tough economic times after the war.

OIL EXPLORATION TAX BENEFITS

To protect the company's earnings, Tom Roberts, Sr., was attracted by the possibility of qualifying for the significant tax shelters available to companies exploring for oil and gas in the United States. The capital costs (called intangible drilling expenses) of drilling oil wells could be taken as a business expense in the year they were incurred, thereby reducing earnings and taxes.

Tom had invested a small part of his personal funds as well as some company funds in syndicates of investors drilling for oil in southern Illinois during the late 1930s. The wells with which he had experience were low-cost, shallow prospects that were thought to have potential for fast payout. Quite often, though, when his syndicate struck oil, competitors would drill very close to the well (there were no drilling restrictions in Illinois) and quickly draw down the production of his syndicate's wells. He commented wryly, "In Illinois, I got half of my money out of my oil investment in the first six months, and spent ten years recovering the rest of it."

Tom realized that DeKalb could benefit from oil exploration in several ways:

- The capital invested in drilling for oil (intangible drilling expenses, which were a large percent of the cost of successful wells, plus 100% of the cost of dry wells) could be "expensed" annually against the profits of the seedcorn business, which otherwise would have been heavily (and unfairly) taxed under the rules of wartime excess profit taxes. Hence, the seedcorn company could avoid heavy taxation during wartime and continue to grow by being financed by a combination of cash from its oil wells, cash from its own profits, and cash loaned by banks.
- By exploring for oil in Texas, which allowed only one well on each forty acres, he could be assured that successful wells would have long, productive lives. Profits from the wells would therefore be realized well into the postwar era, when taxes would likely be lower.
- The Texas Railroad Commission, which regulated the amount of oil that could flow from each active well, tended to limit overproduction, thereby assuring successful oil finders that their oil would be sold at a "fair" price, avoiding the precipitous price declines that in the past had followed the discovery of new oil fields.

In 1942, DeKalb hired Paul Pugh, a respected geologist, and E. A. McClure, a production and drilling superintendent to run the new office in Lubbock, which at that time was the center of new oil discovery in Texas. Pugh's assignment was to purchase properties on the edge of proven productive fields, where the wells might not be sufficiently productive to pay for themselves in three years or less, as most of the major companies required. Properties were, therefore, available to people who would be willing to accept four to five year payouts. By drilling this kind of farm-out, DeKalb could avoid the 95 percent tax assessment.

Managing Exploration to Avoid a 95 Percent Tax Rate

DeKalb's objective was to develop a "library" of property leases that could be drilled on short notice. Then, nine months into the seed company's fiscal year, when profits for the year could be reasonably forecast, Tom would instruct his Lubbock office to drill up enough of its leases to accumulate sufficient intangible drilling costs to offset nearly all of the profits that the company would otherwise have reported, and which would have been taxed at high rates. I found Table 7-1 in Tom's records. My best guess is that it was prepared by DeKalb's accounting department at Tom's request for presentation to his board after the war to demonstrate how much the oil business had saved DeKalb in taxes between 1939 and 1945, and to justify his decision to stay in the oil business after the war.

Table 7-1
DeKalb's Intangible Drilling Costs and Tax Savings, 1939–1945

Year	Tax Rate	Spending on Intangibles ($)	Tax Savings ($)
1939	19%	129,032	24,516
1940	19%	11,863	2,254
1941	55%	160,767	88,422
1942	75%	256,416	192,312
1943	95%	426,266	404,953
1944	95%	437,453	415,580
1945	95%	544,411	262,750
Totals in 1945 $		1,966,208	1,390,787
Totals in 1990 $		16,771,754	11,867,580

SOURCE: DeKalb's Ben Mattik, 1990 line DeKalb Genetics

For as long as the exorbitant tax rates were in effect, Tom minimized drilling until DeKalb was about nine months into its fiscal year, when he had a pretty good idea what his seed profits (and taxes) would be. He then instructed Paul Pugh to incur enough intangible drilling costs to substantially reduce the company's taxable income for the year. Consequently, a flurry of drilling activity would occur during the last three months of each wartime fiscal year, and the company's tax obligation to the federal government would be substantially reduced.

Some of the first farm-outs taken by the company were on the undefined edges of the developing Wasson and Slaughter fields in the Texas panhandle. They were highly productive for many years, not only because they flowed high-quality oil but also because they were suited to "water flooding," a process of pumping water into the lower sections of the field, forcing the oil to rise and be concentrated in areas where it could be pumped for many years of highly profitable "secondary" production. These wells were so good, in fact, that as late as 1985, forty years after they were drilled, they were still producing 25 percent of DeKalb's oil business profits. Tom Roberts had himself another winner.

SOURCE: T.H. Roberts,Jr.

DeKalb's first oil well in Texas

OIL RESERVES: A HEDGE AGAINST A RAINY DAY

When the war was over, and tax rates on profits were reduced to a more normal 50 percent rate, Tom and his directors had to decide what to do about their oil business. Should they continue to explore for oil and gas as they had done so effectively during the war? Or should they sell the business and focus on the company's primary corporate strategy, which was to be a major factor in the hybrid seed-corn business?

This question was rather easily answered in 1946 when they determined that the cash flow from DeKalb's seed business would be sufficiently large to provide all the funds for seed facility expansion and research expenses that would be necessary to compete effectively in DeKalb's first love—its seed business. At the same time, because the oil business had become a sound and prosperous "independent" operation, producing enough income to finance its own growth, Tom made the important decision to let DeKalb's oil business grow from its own cash flow.

Tom Roberts, Sr., thought of DeKalb's oil business as a hedge against a rainy day in the seed business. That thought was fully justified in the 1970s and 1980s, when the company's hybrid corn business was struggling competitively and at the same time found it necessary to battle some natural disasters such as the southern corn leaf blight epidemic of 1970. During that period, the price of oil increased from $3 per barrel to as high as $35 per barrel, permitting DeKalb's earnings to grow at rates attractive to stock market investors, especially during the 1970s. It was expensive to maintain a year-round staff whose work did not effectively begin until the last three months of the fiscal year; the tax benefits of oil exploration made drove up the cost of promising leases; and the oil boom in west Texas slowed down, as the best "plays" were drilled up.

With farm-outs and attractive oil plays increasingly hard to come by in Texas, DeKalb started to look for plays in neighboring states. But DeKalb's Lubbock personnel were not inclined to spend a lot of time away from home, and because the out-of-state plays required more careful geological and economic study than those in Texas, their forays were disappointing. Even in Texas, they missed out on a long-term, highly profitable play in the Sprayberry zone, a blanket of sand that covered a large area in their Texas "playpen."

We "missed" in the Sprayberry because it was widely considered not to have long-term potential. Our geologists believed this too, and missed the boat because the first wells drilled were not spectacular successes. But others who were in the field stayed with the play, gradually expanding it as the oil production rates remained higher than most had expected. By the time it became clear that the Sprayberry was a good field, others had leased it fully, and it was too late for DeKalb to find good leases.

Financial Results - Part Three

OPERATING RESULTS, 1935 THROUGH 1949

Table 7-2
DeKalb Stockholder Equity Increases, 1935–1949

Year	Reported Equity ($000)	Multiplier	In 1990 $
1935	220	x 11.3	2,800
1936	260	x 11.0	2,860
1937	518	x 10.7	5,542
1938	920	x 10.3	9,476
1939	1,479	x 10.0	14,735
1940	1,945	x 9.7	18,866
1941	2,432	x 9.2	26,434
1942	3,330	x 8.6	27,172
1943	4,166	x 8.4	34,994
1944	5,084	x 8.3	42,197
1945	6,072	x 8.1	48,183
1946	6,627	x 6.6	43,738
1947	8,853	x 5.7	50,462
1948	11,104	x 5.4	60,156
1949	14,104	x 5.4	76,162

SOURCE: Records of Thomas H. Roberts, Sr., adjusted to 1990 dollars.

Part Four

1951-1960

Chapter 8

DeKalb Management Deals with a Tough Decade 1950-1959

Acknowledging that DeKalb's hybrid corn product line had lost some of its superiority on its own turf, the northern and north central corn belt, was difficult for everyone, including Tom Roberts, Sr. After fourteen years of exciting growth, expansion, and success, DeKalb's hybrid corn product line began declining competitively in the late 1940s, and the trend continued into the 1950s.

Farmers who had become dealers in the late 1930s with evangelical enthusiasm stemming from having seen DeKalb's superiority to open-pollinated seed on their own farms didn't see the early signs of diminishing DeKalb superiority. After all, they were accustomed to dealing with customers who experienced yield disappointments that stemmed from factors other than seed quality. The problems were legion: poor fertilizing practice, insect damage, low rainfall, untimely storms, early frost, etc., etc.

Rus Rasmusen and his marketing people trained their dealers in the art of coping with the many agronomic problems that could limit yields. District managers held dealer meetings every two to three weeks between the August sales kickoff and spring delivery campaigns, so the dealers became corn experts, but the heart of their sales success was their absolute enthusiasm for their product. They liked the 15 percent per bushel discount they earned, they liked being recognized for sales achievements, they wanted to keep their dealerships and knew they would lose them if they didn't go hard for orders. But, most of all, they believed in DeKalb hybrid corn. Theirs was a proud sales organization.

Even DeKalb's corn breeders did not believe that competing products were as good. They made test comparisons, but these were often not really accurate, because entire plots often showed no significant differences between hybrids. Furthermore, comparative tests were often used to show hybrids off to dealers and customers, and the planting rates and the cultural practices hybrids they used too often tended to skew results in direction of relatively low planting rates (that is, 16,000 plants per acre or lower).

Our researchers believed their products were the best. They were also proud and believed that farmers who planted seed at rates exceeding 16,000 plants per acre were asking for trouble. They were right about the hybrids they had selected for optimum performance at 16,000 plants per acre, but they needed hybrids that would perform better at higher planting rates. A bit belatedly, in the early 1950s DeKalb's corn breeders put a lot of emphasis on selecting parent lines and hybrids that would perform well when planted more densely. Their success was remarkable (see Chapter 11 for details).

The management people were believers, too. They had to admit that 404A dropped its ears too often in Iowa, but they believed DeKalb hybrids 406, 407, 410, and 459 (replacements for 404A) would be winners, and sometimes they were right. Tom and Rasmusen responded to the bad news by putting pressure on their sales force. They encouraged district managers to limit dealer territories to the two townships closest to each dealer. They believed (correctly, I think) that dealers in larger territories were often too far away from some customers to even know they were having problems until after the customer switched to competitive hybrids. More district managers were appointed, and advertising was intensified.

Their moves to strengthen sales in problem areas were often effective. So was the intensification of selling effort in fringe areas like New York, Pennsylvania, and New Jersey in the East and Colorado, Kansas, and Oklahoma in the West. Moreover, customers didn't turn their backs on the company. Nationwide sales dropped off slowly after peaking in 1948, but in key 404A districts in Iowa and Minnesota, where DeKalb's market share at 404A's peak popularity had risen above 50 percent, DeKalb's share fell back to between 30 percent and 40 percent. DeKalb was still the leader in these districts in the early 1950s, but it was not riding as high as it had been before 404A ran into its ear-dropping problem in Iowa and Minnesota in 1947 and 1949.

There was a feeling in the industry during the mid-1950s that product performance was leveling off because many four-way crosses looked and performed alike. Smaller companies using low-cost Experiment Station inbreds offered hybrid seed at prices 10 to 20 percent lower than the "majors," and farmers couldn't see much performance difference, so low-cost locally produced hybrid seed was pushing into the major companies' market share. Fred Lehman, Pioneer's president, expressed his concern when I introduced myself to him at a seed trade association meeting in the early 1950s. He welcomed me into the hybrid seedcorn business but predicted I wouldn't have as much fun as he and my father had because hybrids were beginning to look and perform too much alike. I hoped he was wrong.

Our 1957 and 1958 sales conventions were filled with long faces; sales were at the lowest levels in ten years. Sales after 1957 were influenced by the acquisition of the Cornhusker Hybrid Seed Company of eastern Nebraska, a feisty competitor whose hybrids had been giving our Nebraska sales organization a very tough time.

Table 8-1
DeKalb Seedcorn Sales in Bushels, 1945–1960

Year	404A	Total U.S. Sales
1945	577,921	1,685,984
1946	492,148	1,705,379
1947	508,238	2,151,357
1948	340,539	2,416,355
1949	339,085	2,090,276
1950	214,839	1,800,536
1951	206,823	1,873,669
1952	159,938	1,807,571
1953	177,659	2,031,208
1954	120,243	1,832,617
1955	102,655	1,854,243
1956`	58,225	1,821,368
1957	42,309	1,740,960
1958		1,703,630
1959		2,030,256
1960		1,988,466

SOURCE: Ruth Peterson's records via files of Harold Noren and THR, Jr.

THE TURNAROUND BEGINS

Good fortune turned DeKalb's way in 1956, when Harlan Coy and Amos Gramlich, proprietors of Cornhusker Hybrids, approached DeKalb about buying their company. Virgil Welch, their corn breeder (an old Pfister hand), would be willing to join DeKalb, too. Coy and Gramlich wanted to sell because they were both in their sixties and didn't want to borrow $300,000 to build a new seed plant to meet demand for their leading hybrids, all of which were three-way crosses: 3X1, 3X2, and 3X3.

Table 8-2 shows how three-way crosses differ from the more traditional four-way-cross hybrids. Three-way crosses are more uniform than four-way crosses because the male parent is a pure inbred line. The female (seed) parent is a single cross, which yields well. Therefore, most of the extra cost of producing a three-way hybrid is the low yield of the male (inbred) parent.

Cornhusker's price was right, at $560,000, and DeKalb had unused plant capacity in Nebraska, so we snapped up the opportunity. Our sales organization was delighted, and sales increased immediately. By 1959, DeKalb's "3X" had reached sales of over 500,000 bushels and were pushing eastward across Iowa into Illinois. The wind was back in our sails! Table 8-3 shows the boost

Cornhusker hybrids gave DeKalb.

Table 8-2
How Three and Four Way Crosses Differ

Four-Way Crosses		Three-Way Crosses	
Line a x Line b	Line c x Line d	Line a x Line b	Line c
ab x cd		ab x c	
Four-Way Cross abcd		Three-Way Cross abc	

SOURCE: Thomas H. Roberts, Jr.

Table 8-3
Bridging The Gap:
DeKalb's Sales of Cornhusker 3X Hybrids, 1957–1964
(in bushels)

Year	3X2	3X2	3X3	3X4	Total	% of Sales
1957	95,677	70,985	2,698		169,360	9.8
1958	86,817	115,905	113,106	4,817	320,645	18.8
1959	197,370	163,185	90,011	21,168	471,734	23.2
1960	276,062	147,770	65,225	33,181	522,238	26.1
1961	179,345	118,342	57,036	18,265	372,988	23.1
1962	149,447	73,995	45,877		269,319	17.6
1963	129,643	52,931	44,429		227,003	12.9
1964	68,576	21,946	30,319		120,841	5.5
Total	1,365,43	765,057	448,701	77,431	2,474,12	

SOURCE: Corporate sales records in files of THR, Jr.

However, Cornhusker hybrids, with their beautiful dark green color, drought tolerance, and big ears, weren't perfect. They were susceptible to both stalk rot and leaf blight when planted in humid areas east of Des Moines, Iowa, and they did not perform well at the higher planting rates that were growing in popularity in the central corn belt. In Illinois, they fell apart so badly that DeKalb's reputation was tarnished.

Fortunately, however, the weak sales performance of Cornhusker's hybrids after 1960 was mitigated by the introduction of a tougher series of three-way crosses bred by Hank Slade (discussed in Chapters 16 and 17). Ominously, the company that most benefited from DeKalb's problems in the 1950s was Pioneer. It had penetrated the northern corn belt, where DeKalb was still king, but it sat on a wobbly throne. Perhaps most significant of all DeKalb moves in the 1950s were Tom's efforts to expand and reinvigorate his corn research organization.

I Prepare for Greater Responsibility, 1952–1955

Competitive pressures rose in the two years I spent as a DeKalb district sales manager in the western half of Wisconsin in 1952 and 1953. I took that job not only because it was challenging, but also because my performance was measurable, sales campaign to sales campaign and year to year against my peers and against goals I set for myself. I was competing, at last, in the sales arena, where achievement of goals was instantly measurable and published within the organization. On this job, I had the satisfaction of proving myself to myself, as well as to my bosses and my peers.

I inherited a good organization of 110 farmer-dealers, met with them in five different cities every two weeks during our sales campaigns, learned that some responded well to a pat on the back and that others needed a kick in the pants. Motivating dealers, recognizing those who performed well, detecting and replacing loafers, and generally learning the task of selling seedcorn were challenges I thoroughly enjoyed. I knew that if I did well I would be recognized for having done so. With a lot of hard work and a little luck, I managed to increase sales in my district from 37,000 to 43,000 bushels during the two years I was a district man.

With new-found confidence, and realizing that DeKalb's main office was short on trained business people, I applied for and was accepted into a special group forming at the Harvard Business School in February of 1954. Seventy-eight men from thirty companies, most in their late twenties and early thirties, were enrolled in a special sixteen-month program dedicated to their development from promising young specialists into managers who might someday lead their companies. I focused on expanding my abilities in the areas I thought DeKalb needed the most, primarily business planning for growth, financial management, management of scientists, and marketing.

Many of these my dad had carried on his own shoulders for the entire business life of DeKalb. As the company grew and began to encounter serious competitive challenge, and as he aged, the burdens on him became very heavy. I chose courses that would prepare me to help him.

Single Crosses: An Opportunity?

During the mid-1950s, Lester Pfister, whose nationwide company had broken up in squabbles with his licensed associate growers, had shrunk his organization back to serving his "home" territory in central Illinois. Always an innovator, Pfister knew from experience growing the single-cross seed parents of four-way crosses that single-cross hybrids were often superior to four-way crosses. Other breeders had noted this phenomenon, too, but most were concerned that inbreds were too weak to be widely grown in big fields producing single crosses in volume. On the other hand, Pfister believed that by the mid-1950s he had made enough improvement in his inbred lines to justify volume production of single-cross hybrids. He decided to find out if farmers would accept them at twice the price of standard four-way-cross hybrids.

Pfister's single crosses were not outstanding but were slowly growing in popularity in central Illinois when Harold Noren, the brightest star in DeKalb's sales force, first discussed the idea of commercial single-cross production with Rus Rasmusen. He, too, had become interested in single-cross hybrids, because he thought they might offer DeKalb a chance to jump back into industry leadership. He and Noren both knew that station inbred lines C103 crossed with a WF9 derivative made a beautiful, high-yielding single cross that would be attractive to farmers, so they entered it in DeKalb's research tests. It performed so well that Rus decided to produce it and sell it as DeKalb 805. One thousand bushels of the 805 single cross were produced in 1957 and test marketed in 1958.

DeKalb 805 had one serious defect, however. It did not perform well at seeding rates over 16,000 plants per acre. Rus knew that, and made sure dealers and customers knew it, too. He also knew that better, tougher, high-population single crosses were coming along in our research department right behind it. He reasoned that 805 could be a market-tester that would determine farmers' willingness to accept high-yielding single-cross hybrids selling for at least twice the price of four-way hybrids.

After two years of "trying out" 805, Rus knew that farmers would pay double for high-yielding single crosses, and that dealers would sell them enthusiastically. However, 805 was not a single cross to build a business on. DeKalb needed strong-standing single crosses that could take thick planting without going barren.

Thanks to the research-strengthening moves Tom had made in the 1950s, and to the successful marketing trial Rus Rasmusen and Harold Noren had with the single-cross 805, in 1960 DeKalb was at the threshold of significant growth, and the stage was set for a turnaround in our seed business.

Chapter 9

Progress in Corn Research 1950-1959

DeKalb's corn research organization grew larger and stronger in the decade from 1950 to 1960. New corn breeders were hired, trained, and assigned, in most cases to new research farms in weaker areas. Segregating lines were selected with greater emphasis on their ability to yield well in hybrids planted at high populations.

In the testing program, both the number of test locations and the populations each entry was exposed to were increased. Every corn breeder as well as all key corporate officers received the data as plots were harvested. Hybrids were advanced into commercial production only after discussion at hybrid advancement meetings, which were recognized as the most important meetings of the year.

A NEW USE FOR INBREDS

Perhaps the most significant new idea in corn breeding during the decade was that the quality and viability of the inbred lines was now so good that they might be used directly in commercial hybrids without fear of the devastating inbred line crop failures that had been experienced three or four decades earlier. A few breeders began to wonder if the diluting effect of using an outstanding inbred line as only 25 percent of a hybrid was necessary, given the highly viable inbred lines they were routinely producing. However, the great majority of breeders were still so sold on the economy and reliability of four-way crosses that they were reluctant to recommend the risky commercial production of either three-way crosses or single crosses (the most direct means of utilizing hybrid vigor).

A logical first step in the use of inbred lines directly as parents of commercial hybrids was to use them as the male parents of three-way hybrids, because inbreds could be relied upon to survive in seed production fields long enough to pollinate adjacent single-cross seed parents.

Fortunately for farmers, a few imaginative breeders decided to try using their best inbreds as 50 percent of the parentage of test hybrids. Among these bold breeders was Virgil Welch of the Cornhusker Hybrid Seed Co. Welch's three-way crosses were marketed in Nebraska in the late 1950s and gave the conventional four-way crosses lots of competition. They were priced only 20 percent higher than four-way-cross hybrids because the only extra cost of producing three-way crosses was the low yield of the inbred male parents, which constituted only 20 percent of each seed production field; and the superior yield of Virgil's "3X" hybrids certainly justified their price.

A RARE PATHOGEN DESTROYS STERILE FEMALE SEED PARENTS

Late in his career, Dr. Donald Jones, the man who had first proposed four-way-cross hybrids in 1917, became a leading advocate in the 1950s of a new method of producing hybrid seedcorn without detasseling. In this system, "female" seed parents with male-sterile pollen were developed and were pollinated by male parents carrying fertility-restoring genes, producing male-fertile hybrid seed. The system worked well, and reduced the cost of producing hybrid seed by approximately $1 per bushel for those seed producers who chose to use it. However, in the 1970s a pathogen evolved that destroyed plants carrying male-sterile cytoplasm and reduced the size of the nation's corn crop substantially. That was the end of the use of sterile cytoplasm to produce hybrid seedcorn.

SOURCE: DeKalb Genetics

Sherret Chase planting a nursery

DR. SHERRET CHASE JOINS DEKALB

In 1954 DeKalb hired Dr. Sherret Chase of Iowa State College. "Sherry" was a brilliant cytogeneticist who had developed a new and promising method of producing inbred lines.

To prepare himself for the challenge of becoming a practical corn breeder, "Sherry" studied published hybrid pedigrees, performance data, and corn genealogies, in an attempt to identify a pattern of heterosis (hybrid vigor). He found such a pattern, concurrently recognized by Bill Brown of Pioneer: inbreds out of the Lancaster Sure Crop variety often combined well with inbreds out of the Reid Yellow Dent variety.

Sherry was so impressed with this heterotic pattern that he planned to utilize it in his breeding work at DeKalb. Fortunately, a unique Iowa Stiff Stalk Synthetic population also behaved in the same manner as the Reid variety in hybrids, and other materials he had been working with fit the Lancaster slot. It is interesting to note that today this single heterotic pattern still dominates the successful hybrids of the American corn belt.

The traditional method of "selfing" for seven generations to develop inbred lines permitted identification of recessive genes as they came together during the inbreeding process and expressed themselves as traits that could be seen by the breeder, who would either select them for further breeding or discard them. Hence, inbreds that became pure after being selected for seven generations had a good chance to have merit, if the breeder was skilled. However, he still had to cross each inbred with other inbreds to see how good their hybrids would be. This method worked well, but Chase thought it took too long.

Doubled Haploids

In Chase's concept, the random occurrence of doubled haploids (which can be thought of as the pure progeny of virgin birth) from elite populations would produce inbreds in one generation, after which they could be crossed to see how good their hybrids would be, thereby saving valuable time. He could identify haploid seedlings by using marker genes that would show up as white (rather than red) root tips in germinators. These would then be grown into plants whose seed could be multiplied. Spontaneously doubled haploids were identified by either visual observations or by chromosome counts

Chase believed, however, that standard inbreeding would be the preferred method for relatively unselected material such as an open-pollinated variety, because in such material genotypic differences among segregates are extreme, and good segregates are infrequent. He pointed out that traditional breeders in the 1940s and 1950s were loaded up with similar, poorly evaluated materials that clogged their testing programs. He found that by starting with elite synthetics such as the Iowa Stiff Stalk Synthetic, and utilizing the monoploid (double haploid) method of inbred development, good inbreds could be frequently and rapidly developed.

Clearly, good inbreds could be developed either by selfing or by using the monoploid method. Chase regrets that he did not appoint a competent colleague to work exclusively on monoploids. Nevertheless, he produced some excellent inbreds and hybrids using the monoploid system of inbred development. DeKalb 640, a

1960 introduction to DeKalb's line-up, was a good example of such a hybrid. For several years, this hybrid constituted a high percentage of the hybrids DeKalb sold in Pennsylvania and eastern coastal areas, where its disease resistance and strong stalks made it outstanding.

Today, most corn breeders are "selfing" in the traditional way, to make new lines, preferring to select their inbreds slowly during selfing, and Chase himself used selfing when he felt it was more appropriate for the breeding material. He believed that the monoploid method should have been given a better shot by DeKalb, and I find his arguments persuasive.

Chase made lasting improvements in DeKalb's breeding programs, hiring new breeders, establishing new research locations across the corn belt, and tremendously improving our testing programs. He improved the accuracy of hybrid evaluation by testing hybrids at more locations, and by adopting better methods of statistical evaluation of data. He also established a winter breeding location in Florida to make possible two generations of inbreeding each year. He received the full support of management during his career with DeKalb, first as manager of monoploid research and later as manager of international corn research.

Problems Develop between Colleagues

Virgil Welch, at the age of sixty, became DeKalb's western corn belt breeder in 1956 when the company bought the Cornhusker Hybrid Seed Co. Welch was a proven corn breeder but had no advanced degree in plant breeding. Soon after we closed the deal with Cornhusker, he made it clear that he would insist on running his own breeding program independent of DeKalb, but he agreed to submit his experimental hybrids for testing in DeKalb's western corn belt testing program.

From the beginning, Welch was fearful of being dominated by DeKalb, and especially by Sherret Chase. Sales of Welch's three leading hybrids soared in Nebraska from the 125,000 bushel level Cornhusker had achieved to 522,238 bushels in 1960. Under Nebraska's weather conditions and cultural practices they were outstanding, but like all hybrids they had weaknesses. Susceptibility to Diplodia stalk rot and Helminthesporium leaf blight were weaknesses of Welch's 3X series of hybrids. These problems were not devastating in Nebraska because of its hot, dry climate, but they were sometimes devastating (to put it mildly) in the hot, humid climates of the central corn belt.

Fortunately, when Virgil's 3X hybrids began to decline in popularity, DeKalb was on the brink of releasing several outstanding disease-resistant, high-population, three-way and single crosses for sale. The Cornhusker purchase had been a timely and worthwhile investment since, without Cornhusker, DeKalb sales would probably have declined to less than 1,300,000 bushels in 1958 from the "high tide" of 2,416,335 bushels in 1948.

Tom Sr. Backs Away from an Important Decision

Friction between Virgil Welch and Sherret Chase continued. Their antagonism reached a critical point when Tom decided to appoint Chase director of all DeKalb corn research, and flew personally in the fall of 1960 to Fremont to advise Welch of his decision. Welch's response was to threaten to resign. Tom backed down, mostly because sales of Welch's 3X hybrid had reached a peak of 522,238 bushels that spring.

Upon his return to DeKalb, Tom announced that three corn breeders (Chase, Gunn, and Welch) would report to him directly, submitting their newest hybrids to a company-wide testing program to be supervised by Chase. At annual meetings breeders and sales executives would review testing performance data and decide which hybrids to advance.

To this day, I believe that Sherret Chase should have been given full authority over DeKalb's entire corn breeding program. Not doing so was, in my opinion, a major mistake.

The next step would be the production and marketing of pure single-cross hybrids. The bold, imaginative, and unconventional risk takers of the 1950s deserve credit for shaking the hybrid seedcorn industry out of its traditional, and excessive, conservatism.

GOOD BREEDING CASTS A LONG SHADOW

The breeding program originated by Chase was based on sound concepts. It was assisted and expanded by the efforts of Basil Tsotsis (beginning in 1958) and C. W. Crum (beginning in 1964} and continued under the designation "Program #5." Together, they and Chase produced the fine hybrids marketed by DeKalb in the late 1960s and early 1970s.

Chase's competence was also demonstrated by the success of a corn breeding program he set up with Fabio Nider in the late 1950s in Argentina, where DeKalb's seedcorn business grew steadily during and after the late 1960s into that nation's leading hybrid seedcorn business.

Dr. Basil Tsotsis, A Valuable Corn Breeder

Basil Tsotsis, a Fulbright scholar from Greece who had been studying at the University of Wisconsin, joined our corn research staff in 1958, reporting to Chase. He had been highly recommended by Dr. Norman Neal, a distinguished corn breeder at the University of Wisconsin, where Tsotsis had earned his Ph.D. He had computer experience that made him instantly valuable in the evaluation of research data. In fact, he was one of the first corn breeders in the country to develop a computer program to evaluate plots planted in a "lattice square" design. Further, his training in corn plant pathology reinforced DeKalb's techniques for inoculating segregating lines with diseases in order to identify resistant individual plants.

Basil Tsotsis, Sherret Chase, Virgil Welch, and Virgil's son Verne were added to our research effort in the 1950s, strengthening it substantially.

Chapter 10

Hybrid Sorghum: The Decade's Most Important New Product 1950-1959

When I finished Harvard Business School in June of 1955, I returned to DeKalb wondering what kind of a job would be open for me. My dad was looking around for something challenging but had nothing specific in mind. Fortunately for me, Dick Holland (our sorghum breeder) and his wife, Bobbie, showed up in DeKalb with their baby son, Alan. They checked into the Rice Hotel, and Dick let everyone know he was going to stay there until somebody listened. At the time, I knew Dick was our sorghum breeder, but I didn't know much about sorghum. For readers who do not know much about sorghum either, the next few pages describe its origin and uses.

THE ORIGIN OF SORGHUM

Sorghum is a member of a large family of grasses, the Gramineae, which includes wheat, corn, rye, barley, rice, and oats is a feed grain. There are several sorghum species, but by far the most important is Sorghum Bicolor (formerly called S. Vulgare). Both sudan grass and Johnson grass are considered to be subspecies and cross readily with grain sorghums.

Plant scientists believe that sorghum originated in Africa, probably in the upper Nile, where heavy seasonal rainfall is often followed by two or three months of extreme drought. This extraordinary climatic pattern is thought to be responsible for the ability of sorghum seedlings to survive under water for two or three weeks, and for the sorghum plant to remain dormant during long periods of drought until moisture becomes available and it can resume normal growth and grain production. This characteristic gives grain sorghum much better drought resistance than corn and makes it the leading feed-grain producer in the vast Great Plains of the United States, which stretch from south Texas to South Dakota.

Few plant families can compare with sorghum's variability: it ranges from very short to extremely tall with diverse colors of grain, different head and seed shapes and sizes, and widely ranging maturities. The leading classifications of sorghum in the United States are:

- Grain: Selected for shortness to permit combining, grain sorghum stalks are dry when ripe and have little sweetness in the stalk. Heights vary from two to five feet; they have large heads with a better ratio of seed to plant than other classes.

- Sorgo (sweet types): Used for silage, forage, and syrup. They are usually tall, ranging from five to ten feet in height, with sweet juices in the stalk. Sorgo was brought to the United States with the hope of starting a sugar industry.
- Broomcorn: The heads, with long, fibrous seed branches, are used to make brooms and stems for artificial flowers.
- Grass Types: Slender leaves and stalks and loose heads with small seeds characterize this type of sorghum. They usually have some sweetness of stalk and are used for pasture and hay. Sudan grass is the principal subspecies. Johnson grass (Sorghum halepense) is a primary noxious weed in the southern United States because its underground rhizomitous roots allow it to overwinter and come up year after year. Johnson grass pollen can fertilize grain sorghum, creating tall, obnoxious outcrosses in hybrid sorghum fields, but these crosses are sterile, do not produce seed, and their rhizomes (roots), though large, do not readily overwinter.

Sorghum made its first appearance in the southeastern United States through the slave trade and was called Guinea corn. All of the various forms of sorghum introduced were tall, ranging from eight to eleven feet in height. Plant breeders in the Great Plains states were attracted to sorghum because of its drought resistance, so they worked to identify dwarfing genes that would reduce the height of sorghum selected for grain production. Their goal was to shorten it to heights that would permit harvesting by combine harvesters. They found four recessive genes that were additive in their dwarfing effect. That is, each dwarfing gene, in its pure form, would shorten the sorghum plant by about 20 percent. When all four dwarfing genes are in the same plant, it usually does not grow more than three feet tall.

The first short, erect-headed grain sorghum able to be harvested by combine was developed by J. B. Sieglinger, working in the USDA program at Stillwater, Oklahoma. It was called "Beaver" and was released for farmer use in 1928. Table 10-1 lists some of the most important grain sorghum varieties.

All of the sorghum varieties were developed by government-supported Experiment Station workers, with the exception of Martin, which came from the work of a farmer in Texas by that name. Martin became one of the most widely used of any of the standard varieties and was still important when DeKalb released its first hybrids in 1956. This "first" for DeKalb was verified by Dr. Roy Quinby in his 1974 publication Sorghum Improvement and the Genetics of Growth. Table 10-2 shows the growth in acreage planted after the first combine grain sorghums were released. The information has been adapted from government reports:

Table 10-1
Sorghum Variety Releases

Variety	Release Date	Where Bred	Breeder
Beaver	1928	Oklahoma(USDA)	Sieglinger
Wheatland	1931	Oklahoma(USDA)	Sieglinger
Day	1934	Oklahoma(USDA)	Sieglinger
Plainsman	1937	Texas Exp. Sta.	
Milo 7078	1940	Texas Exp. Sta.	
C. Kafir 60	1941	Texas Exp. Sta.	
Martin	1941	Texas	W.P. Martin
Caprock	1941	Texas Exp. Sta.	
Westland	1942	Kansas Exp. Sta.	
Double Dwarf Yellow Sooner	1947	Texas Exp. Sta.	

SOURCE: R.F. Holland of DeKalb Genetics

Table 10-2
U.S. Sorghum Yield and Acreage History

Year	Acres	Yield per Acre
1928–1932 (avg.)	6,855,000	13.7 bu.
1940	6,374,000	13.5 bu.
1950	10,335,000	22.6 bu.
1960	15,592,000	39.8 bu.
1970	13,568,000	50.4 bu.
1994	9,000,000	73.0 bu.

SOURCE: R.F. Holland

The sharp yield increases in 1960 and 1970 were due mainly to the introduction of hybrids. Sorghum yields actually tripled in the forty years after hybrids were introduced—partly because hybrid vigor contributes about a 20 percent yield increase over non-hybrids, and partly because the lure of profits enabled private companies to spend more on sorghum research. Unfortunately for sorghum researchers, increased irrigation and more drought-resistant corn hybrids caused sorghum acreage to decline by about one-third between 1970 and 1994.

Other factors that contributed to yield increases include the steady improvement in farmer education, the quick dissemination of success stories by the media, and the better cultural practices that are possible with better equipment.

DICK HOLLAND'S RESEARCH OPENS THE DOOR TO HYBRIDIZATION

Sorghum has both female and male elements in each floret, resulting in its seeds being inbred under natural conditions. To utilize hybrid vigor on a large scale, a cytoplasmic male sterility-fertility restoration system similar to that being utilized to hybridize corn would be needed. One of the people experimenting with this system in the early 1950s was Dick Holland, who was studying under Professor Joe Stevens at Texas A & M.

SOURCE: Personal Records, T H Roberts, Jr.

Grain Sorghum in Test Plot

In his 1952 master's thesis, Dick identified the system that was needed: one that would produce hybrid sorghum by pollinating cytoplasmic male-sterile "female" parents with pollen from "male" parents carrying fertility-restoring genes. Dick's thesis was remarkable because it reported experiments he and Professor Stevens had set up to determine whether cytoplasmic male sterility occurred in some varieties and fertility restoration genes occurred in others. Hybrids produced on female parents with sterile cytoplasm did not require roguing in seed fields, so they would be much more uniform as well as less costly than hybrids made using the "genetic" system DeKalb had been developing since 1948. Dick's thesis proved that large-scale production of high-quality hybrid sorghum seed would be practical. He had opened the door for hybrid sorghum.

Dick's report was the talk of the scientific community and the seed trade. He convinced agronomists that hybrid sorghum could be produced by the superior cytosterile system and that it should not take more than three years to produce the first hybrids.

SOURCE: DeKalb Genetics

Dick Holland & Bob Christensen in Sorghum Plot

At the American Society of Agronomy meeting where Dick Holland presented his thesis, Tom, Sr., told Dick that DeKalb had some attractive sorghum breeding material in Lubbock and asked him if it could be converted from genetic sterility to cytoplasmic sterility. Dick said it could be done rather quickly and that he would be willing to undertake the job.

Dick proved to be a gentle, intelligent, hard-working person–perhaps the easiest man to get along with I have ever known. He was put in charge of DeKalb's Lubbock, Texas, sorghum research station. He asked Glenn Kuykendahl, who had been developing "genetic" sorghum hybrids for DeKalb, to serve as his assistant. Unfortunately, Glenn was disappointed that his genetic hybrid system was not going to be used, and he resigned. We regretted Glenn's decision to leave, because we respected him for having developed open-headed lines that performed well as hybrids utilizing genetic sterility and would be useful in hybrids made using cytoplasmic sterility. Dick went to work establishing cytoplasmic sterility in key varieties that were known to show good hybrid vigor in crosses. Of course, he also identified the strains that carried the restorer gene and would make good "male" lines.

SOURCE: DeKalb Genetics

Thomas H. Roberts, Jr. showing sorghum area

Dick's Message

By the spring of 1955, Dick Holland was certain that hybrid sorghum could be produced by DeKalb in large quantities using the parent seed he had recently planted at Lubbock. He had come to DeKalb to convince somebody to use that seed to produce hybrids in 1956. At the time, Tom Roberts, Sr., and Rus Rasmusen were focusing on the superior performance of our competitors' "high-population" corn hybrids. So I, fresh out of the Harvard Business School and looking for new opportunities, turned out to be the listener Dick needed.

His determination was contagious. Research tests with Kuykendahl's hybrids had been very promising, and Dick was confident that field tests he had planted in the spring of 1955 would turn out well. He was right. Table 10-3 displays some of our 1955 results.

Dick Holland was an east Texas farm boy who knew and understood farmers. He was convinced that sorghum growers would be eager to plant hybrid sorghum. He educated me not only in the fundamentals of sorghum culture, but also in the ABCs of producing hybrid sorghum seed. In 1955, more than 12 million acres of grain sorghum were grown annually in the United States. This amounted to one-sixth of U.S. corn acreage, but sorghum yields averaged only twenty bushels per acre, whereas corn yields were then averaging about forty-six bushels per acre. Dick reminded me, persistently, to remember that sorghum was grown in dry Great Plains areas where corn could not be grown without irrigation.

Table 10-3
1955 Hybrid Sorghum Yield Tests

Haxtun, Colorado

Variety	Yield (bus. per acre)
DeKalb Hybrid A*	78.7
DeKalb Hybrid B*	68.6
Early Hegari	51.0
Martin	51.0
D.D. Yellow Sooner	48.6
Norghum	40.2

SOURCE: R.F. Holland
* Produced utilizing genetic male sterility.

Littlefield, Texas

Variety	Yield (bus. per acre)
DeKalb Hybrid E*	62.7
DeKalb Hybrid F*	60.3
Martin	39.7
Combine Kafir 60	38.5
D.D. Yellow Sooner	34.6

SOURCE: R.F. Holland
* Produced using genetic male sterility.

Madrid, Nebraska

Variety	Yield (bus. per acre)
DeKalb Hybrid F*	62.4
DeKalb Hybrid G*	59.4
Reliance	35.2
Norghum	34.4
Redbine 66	33.6

SOURCE: R.F. Holland
* Produced using genetic male sterility.

DeKalb—One Step Ahead of the Competition

The parent seed multiplication fields Dick had planted a few days before visiting DeKalb in June 1955 would be sufficient to produce 225,000 bushels of hybrid sorghum seed in the summer of 1956, for sale to farmers in the spring of 1957. He was ahead of competitive seedsmen because he had multiplied his seed stocks the prior winter in Mexico, with help from the Rockefeller Foundation. Equally important, his hybrids would be noticeably different (more open-headed) from his competitors. He was quite sure that the 225,000 bushels of seed DeKalb could produce in 1956 would equal the total production of all the rest of the new hybrid sorghum seed industry combined. He was convinced, therefore, that DeKalb had a golden opportunity to win over lots of farmers whose first hybrid sorghum seed could be DeKalb, and that those happy customers would stay with DeKalb for years.

Dick showed me that sorghum was a kind of "dry land corn." It had an uncanny characteristic of "going dormant" when dry weather set in, just sitting there with leaves curled, waiting for rain to come along to bring it back to life. This was in contrast to corn, which keeps right on growing through severe dry spells, burning up and dying if the rains are too late. Accordingly, grain sorghum's drought resistance made it better suited than corn for planting in the vast dry plains stretching northward from Corpus Christi, Texas, into western Nebraska and South Dakota.

I was very much interested when Dick told me what DeKalb's position could be. Both of us realized this could be the opportunity of our lifetime! Dick argued that we should go ahead with the production of all 225,000 bushels of the seed that we could produce in 1956, despite the fact that our salespeople estimated they could sell only 100,000 bushels of DeKalb hybrid sorghum in 1957, its year of introduction. But Dick and I decided that we would "go for broke," producing all the hybrid sorghum seed we possibly could in 1956, figuring that if we couldn't sell it all, we could carry over the surplus and sell the second year seed in 1958.

The years 1955 and 1956 were very busy for Dick and me as we got ready to offer farmers 225,000 bags of the first hybrid sorghum seed—a quantity that turned out to be about equal to the total quantity of "station" hybrids developed by Texas A & M and released to our competitors. We knew that farmers were favorably impressed with the distinctive big, open-headed DeKalb hybrids they saw in our small plots in the summer of 1956.

New Facilities

We built a sorghum seed processing plant in 1956 in Lubbock, Texas to dry, clean, treat, and bag the 170,000 fifty-pound bags, or three-quarters of the 225,000 bags we expected to process in the fall for planting by farmers in the spring of 1957. (The additional 65,000 bags were produced at our western seedcorn plants.) The new plant at Lubbock was big, especially in light of our own sales organization's doubts that it would sell more than 100,000 bushels in hybrid sorghum's introductory year.

Pricing

Dick and I worked hard that summer estimating our costs. It appeared that we could price the seed at 16 cents per pound ($8.00 per 50-pound bag) and make about the same profit per 50-pound bag of seed that DeKalb was then making on its corn—a profit of $1.00 a bushel.

Our confidence grew as we observed the test plots of the genetic seed and sensed the enthusiasm of farmers for our hybrids. We began to believe that we could get 20 cents a pound ($10.00 per 50-pound bag) for our seed. At that price, we would realize triple the profit per bag DeKalb was earning from corn in 1956. This kind of profit would resemble the margins DeKalb had realized from hybrid corn back in the late 1930s.

We believed it would be important for DeKalb, as the industry leader, to set prices at a level that would raise the price expectations of our smaller competitors, who were accustomed to selling non-hybrid seed for 5 cents or less per pound. We thought it would be a mistake for DeKalb to start shaving prices early in the game because our competitors would likely respond with price concessions that would train customers to shop around for low-priced seed.

Our strategy of selling quality at a fair price worked well. Most of the small seed companies who were handling Texas A & M hybrids sold them for about 10 percent less than DeKalb's price. At that level, few of them cut prices very severely for many years because they enjoyed "reasonable" profits operating under the pricing leadership DeKalb provided.

Success!!

Dick had been right. Farmers were ready and willing to buy hybrid sorghum seed. By November of 1956 we were sold out. Our dream that most sorghum farmers would plant DeKalb hybrids and compare them with low-yielding varieties was actually coming to pass. As farmers sold themselves on hybrids in 1957, they sold themselves on DeKalb.

Profits realized from our first year's sales paid for all our research plus all the sales organizational costs we had incurred, as well as for half of the seed processing plant we had built in Lubbock. It was a grand success that cast a long shadow for years to come. Our product was very different and more attractive in appearance than our competitors', who were all selling tight-headed hybrids against DeKalb's attractive, high-yielding, open-headed hybrids.

Dissenters and First-Year Challenges

Nevertheless, there's always at least one dissenter. Bob Garst, an outspoken and well-known seedsman who had the Pioneer franchise for western Iowa and all of Nebraska, Kansas, and Texas, had produced only 30,000 bags of hybrid sorghum in 1956, his first year of production. When Bob told me that DeKalb was not charging enough for its seed and suggested that we could get more, I was surprised, because I knew we were making three times the margin that he was. I figured if he wanted to sell for a higher price next year, I could probably push DeKalb's price up as well. But I also knew he would have only about 15 percent as much sorghum seed as DeKalb to sell in 1957 and that he was obliged to amortize his costs of establishing his sorghum dealer organization over a sales base that was a small fraction of DeKalb's first-year sales volume.

Checking our Sorghum Seed Quality

Although we had taken orders for all of the seed we had harvested and were sold out by November of 1956, the product had not yet been delivered to dealers. Dick was aware that sudan grass pollen could blow into our seed fields and produce sorghum–sudan grass outcrosses that would be much taller than the grain sorghum we were producing and very unattractive in our customers' fields. Accordingly, we carefully divided the harvested seed into different lots in order to test each lot of seed in the winter of 1956–57 outside of Tampico, Mexico, before delivering it to our dealers.

The Tampico tests were ready for observation in late January of 1957. We saw that several lots of C44A, one of our most attractive hybrids, were unacceptable for sale to farmers because too many sudan grass–sorghum outcrosses showed up in our Tampico tests. The percentage of outcrosses was small, amounting to less than half of 1 percent, but sorghum seed is planted in the high plains at 10,000 seeds per acre or more, and 1 percent of 10,000 seeds would be 100 outcrosses per acre. We realized this number would be unacceptable to our farmer customers.

Consequently, we discarded 20,000 bags of C44A seed for which we had already received orders. Although we could not deliver in full on all orders, the farmers understood and appreciated our concern about quality. Most came right back the following year with large orders because they were pleased with the seed we had sold them.

Dick Holland - An Outstanding Man

Dissenters and outcrosses aside, the early years in sorghum were just as satisfactory to Dick Holland and me as the early years in corn had been to Charlie Gunn and my Dad. Dick Holland was a very real factor in our early success, not only because he bred a very good product, but also because he had a winning personality, attended a lot of sales meetings, showing slides, and selling our dealer organization as well as farmers on the merits of DeKalb sorghum. He listened to the farmers who had tried it, he responded respectfully, and his personality was one of a sincere, dedicated, modest scientist who really knew what he was talking about. Dick's early willingness to educate the DeKalb dealers in western Nebraska and western Kansas, as well as in Texas, was a key factor in making DeKalb's first year in hybrid sorghum a grand success.

In 1957 we hedged our seed production risk by planting a larger acreage in Marshall, Missouri, where Ed Uhland, a top-notch seed-corn plant manager, welcomed the challenge of pioneering in sorghum seed production. He soon found that the morning glory, a primary noxious weed, flourished in Missouri and produced a pesky seed that was the same size as sorghum seed, and therefore hard to separate out of the seed that contract growers delivered to his plant. Ed solved the problem in short order by installing spiral separators in his sorghum seed processing line. These spirals separated the slightly flat-sided morning glory seed from round sorghum seed, solving his morning glory problem.

In March of 1959, DeKalb built another sorghum seed production plant at Ulysses, in southwestern Kansas, an area where irrigation had recently been developed and where outcrosses from sudan grass and Johnson grass would not be as severe as at Lubbock. In fact, because the problem was so bad at Lubbock, it was not long before our sorghum production there was devoted entirely to forage hybrids. At Ulysses the problem was so minimal that we built our next plant at nearby Dumas, Texas, a few years later.

SOURCE: R.F. Holland

Herefords in Sudax

Sudax—A Great Idea from Dick Holland

There was a silver lining to the sudan grass outcross problem. When Dick and I were counting sudan grass outcrosses in January

1956 Mexican "grow-outs," we were both impressed with the vigor of the sorghum–sudan grass outcrosses. They were capable of growing more than two inches a day under good conditions. Dick suggested that we make some sorghum–sudan grass crosses on purpose, with a view to offering a fast-growing, palatable pasture grass to farmers. When Dick made up the crosses and found them to be superior to sudan grass, we decided to go ahead with production, calling the new product "Sudax."

Farmers liked Sudax, and sales grew rapidly. The potential for sales of Sudax hybrids was thought to be about one-third to one-half of the total hybrid grain sorghum market, but in 1965, seven years after we began offering Sudax, there was a corn surplus and the government asked farmers to cut back. Consequently, when a lot of farmers grew sudan grass–sorghum hybrids on their "set-aside" acreage, an unusual demand developed and Sudax sales peaked at 513,000 bags, a significant portion of the 815,000 bags of hybrid sorghum we were selling at that time. At $10 per bag, 513,000 bags yielded a gross income of $5,130,000! (The figure on Sudax production is from Leo Olson's "Genetics to Genius," p. 514.)

A NEW SALES ORGANIZATION

From the first wonderful day in June 1955 when Dick Holland convinced us that DeKalb sorghum was ready to move from research trials into production, we realized DeKalb would need to develop a new sales organization to sell it in the dry high plains area. In eastern Nebraska, Kansas, and Oklahoma we already had farmer-dealers selling seedcorn. For those previously marginal sales districts, the addition of hybrid sorghum to our product line gave dealers more sales opportunities and district managers an opportunity to upgrade the quality and intensity of dealer effort. Our existing sales force under Regional Sales Manager Vernon Johnson recognized its new opportunity and charged after it.

In the dryer western halves of those Great Plains states, however, we had few dealers and no district sales managers. It would have been easy for DeKalb, the company with at least half of the industry's first-year seed supply, to sign up "store" dealers to handle the seed. But we were wary of seed stores for the same reasons we had been wary of selling hybrid seedcorn through seed stores in the 1930s. We thought seed stores would not solicit orders. They might even stock cheap competitive hybrids in addition to DeKalb, to our disadvantage. We accepted store dealers only when a store totally dominated a trading area or when sorghum fields were too many miles apart for farmer-dealers to solicit.

Building Sorghum Sales

We needed district sales managers who could identify and sign up respected farmers to sell seed in their districts. We wanted our district managers to be "go-getters," preferably in their thirties, with ag-school educations and with some experience selling to farmers, and we wanted them to be selected by DeKalb regional sales managers. Harold Noren, an outstanding DeKalb district manager, was promoted in 1957 to regional sales manager for the Southwest, where he more than doubled his district manager force and girded for heavier competition.

Many of the new district managers hired in that second year of sorghum sales came from the ranks of successful dealers. For example, Bill Burrow, who later became a key man for DeKalb, had a great first-year record as a store dealer in Tulia, Texas, and became district manager for the north half of the Texas panhandle. He joined DeKalb in the summer of 1957, as did Gene Kerr, an aggressive young Nebraska graduate who took over in south Texas, where within 100 miles of Corpus Christi lay the most concentrated grain sorghum acreage in the country. Casey Casebolt and Frank Miller, both former County Agents, were key district managers in the Texas panhandle and western Kansas, respectively.

Advertising and Promotion

We began sorghum advertising in 1956 to support our first hybrid sorghum sales campaign. Farm papers and farm radio stations carried the DeKalb sorghum story, and we also used direct mail. At first, our mailing lists were short in the high plains, but this was soon remedied. DeKalb's catalog, Acres of Gold, included information on the sorghums in areas where they were adapted, and a separate southwestern edition was published beginning in 1957. Leo B. Olson, handled all of the advertising.

DeKalb spent only $70,000 on sorghum advertising the first year because we were sold out by mid-November, but second-year sales efforts were supported by a $190,000 advertising program. This amounted to 50 cents a bag, which had become a "standard" in our seedcorn business. One-minute farmer testimonials on television proved very effective in building the DeKalb image in Texas and Kansas, where the company was not well known.

Dealing with Shattering Sorghum and Vigorous Outcrosses

Harold Noren, our western sales manager, faced up quickly to a second year of discarding seed contaminated with outcrosses, and in June of 1957, which is sorghum harvest time in south Texas, he dealt with our first hybrid performance problems. The C44A we had sold in that area was high yielding and open-headed, but its grain would begin to shatter (fall on the ground) about two weeks after it was ready for harvest. Most farmers were accustomed to growing a non-hybrid variety called Martin, which could not match C44A in yield but would not shatter. Some dealers complained loudly, and both farmers and dealers had to learn that prompt harvesting of C44A was important to prevent shattering, but Harold handled the situation well, as he had throughout his fourteen years of selling DeKalb corn.

Johnson grass–sorghum outcrosses usually numbered two or three per acre, but when farmers saw that this outcross had vigorous rhizomes (underground spreading roots) that were bigger than Johnson grass roots they worried that the outcrosses would survive winters and become a serious weed problem. With help from Dick Holland, Harold reassured the dealers and customers that the outcrosses would not overwinter, and sales of seed for planting in 1958 increased to 329,797 bags from the 196,186 sold in 1957.

Harold was recalled to DeKalb in September 1958 to become poultry sales manager. Herb Carris, another outstanding Minnesota district manager, succeeded him as southwestern regional sales manager. With its great start, and with a solid product line, DeKalb has been the hybrid sorghum industry leader since the 1957 introductory year. Table 10-4 shows DeKalb's sorghum sales record through 1960.

Table 10-4
DeKalb's U.S. Sorghum Sales, 1957–1960

Year	Sales Volume (50-lb. bags)
1956–57	196,186
1957–58	329,797
1958–59	399,895
1959–60	446,687

SOURCE: T H Roberts, Jr. records of Sorghum sales.

PERSONAL FOOTNOTES

Aside from the excitement and personal satisfaction that come from being involved with a successful new business, I have had several renewing experiences in dealing with the hard-working, honest people who farm in our Great Plains.

"The Judge"—A Real Pioneer of the Old West

When I first visited the Texas high plains in the late 1940s, aware that I might be spending a lot of time there in my career with DeKalb, I visited with an old rancher friend of my dad's, Bill Eisenberg, who managed two ranches, one in Texas and another in New Mexico. To learn more about the high plains, he suggested that I talk with a local old-timer.

The old-timer looked like actor Gary Cooper would have if he had lasted eighty years. He told me he had ridden his horse in from the Texas border on April 22, 1889, staked a legal claim on the

Oklahoma strip, and then traded it for a horse and wagon before returning to Texas, where he accepted a job with the Texas Cattlemen's Association. For the next forty years he was the only lawman assigned to catch cattle rustlers and turn them over to state attorneys for prosecution. He was called "the Judge."

The Judge told me that before he was hired, cattle rustling was almost an accepted practice. A large ranch named the XIT dominated much of west Texas, covering ten counties on the west side of the panhandle. Its owners tried to collect a fee from folks traveling west on the Santa Fe trail—which the folks traveling west resented because they thought killing wild longhorns, buffalo, or XIT cattle for food was pretty much their right. Many XIT cowhands apparently felt the same way—their homestead farms on the edge of the XIT also were home to white-faced Hereford calves that closely resembled those owned by the XIT. A few years later, when the homesteaders' own cattle began to be rustled, they formed the Cattleman's Association and hired the Judge to catch the rustlers.

The "Judge" had built a sod house in the wide open plains halfway between Lubbock, Texas, and Roswell, New Mexico. While raising a family of six children, he spent his career examining cattle for altered brands and bringing rustlers to justice. He was a fine, proud man who had personally been a part of the opening of the West.

Francis Ormiston

It wasn't unusual in the late 1950s to meet farmers who had homesteaded their land, farmed it, and sent their kids to college. The entire Great Plains area seemed to me to be populated by honest, hard-working people who were close to and proud of their pioneering ancestors.

One year my wife Nancy and I visited Francis Ormiston, a DeKalb dealer who farmed near Plains, Kansas, which is near Liberal and Dodge City. His farm and the whole area around it were irrigated and prosperous. Francis was a born salesman who sold to a high percentage of his prospects and was one of DeKalb's best dealers, with annual sales in the range of 3,500 to 5,000 bags of seed. It was just after planting season, and he took us a mile or two from his house to an empty shed he had built at a highway intersection. Though almost empty then, earlier that season it had been stocked with more than 1,000 bags of seed (worth $10 to $12 per bag). Francis knew his customers well and also knew that during the planting season they would work their equipment night and day, often needing seed at night. To accommodate that demand, he had built this shed, leaving it open and unattended—customers who took seed at night wrote down how much they took and signed their names on a clipboard. He trusted them, and he sold more than 1,000 extra bags of seed that way nearly every year. Francis was truly an outstanding dealer, and his customers were honest, hard-working people we would all be proud to know.

Chapter 11

International Programs Begin 1950-1957

During the 1950s, Rus Rasmusen was often visited by foreign seedsmen, usually from Europe. They had heard about America's hybrid corn "revolution" and wondered whether DeKalb's products would work in their countries and whether DeKalb would consider a cooperative venture to market them. But Rus and Tom, Sr., had agreed that DeKalb had plenty of undeveloped sales potential in North America, and that, in Tom's words, "DeKalb should not be chasing rainbows overseas." In time, this policy weakened as opportunities overseas became more and more attractive.

SOURCE: DeKalb Genetics

Antonio Marchetto and Rus Rasmusen

ITALY

In keeping with the understanding Tom and Rus had about "not chasing rainbows," Rus did not encourage foreign seedsmen, though he was always polite and kept their names and addresses. Then, in late 1959, he was visited by a very persuasive Italian named Antonio Marchetto.

Antonio wanted to convince Rus that the Po Valley, which had a climate similar to that of the central U.S. corn belt, was a potentially big market for DeKalb seedcorn. As evidence, Antonio handed Rus yield data showing how well American "station hybrids" were performing in his country. In fact, he had built a modest business in Italy selling station hybrid seedcorn that had been produced in the United States. He argued that he should be selling the proprietary hybrids DeKalb was marketing in central Illinois because other Italian seedsmen had noted his success selling non-proprietary U.S. Experiment Station hybrids and were importing and selling the same hybrids at unacceptably low prices.

Rus was impressed and recommended to Tom that we continue discussions with Antonio. Tom agreed, and negotiations that led to the formation of DeKalb Italiana began.

ARGENTINA

In 1956, DeKalb's success with hybrid sorghum became widely recognized in the United States and abroad, so I was not surprised to receive a letter from an Argentine interested in testing DeKalb hybrid sorghum in the pampas, Argentina's temperate plains. Ramon Agrasar had studied agricultural engineering as a Fulbright scholar at Texas A & M and wanted samples to test on his country's farms and experiment stations because, as he put it: "Juan Peron has left our country, but he has left it so impoverished that the only decent piece of agricultural machinery our farmers have is the wheat combine harvester. They are very tired of picking corn by hand, so why not grow hybrid sorghum instead of corn? They can harvest sorghum with their wheat combines."

I thought his thinking was sound, so I sent him a sufficient quantity of DeKalb's line of grain sorghum hybrids to test throughout the Argentine pampas, charging him only 15 percent of the U.S. retail price for the seed—still a large sum for his small company. Six months later, in April of 1957, I received his report on our sorghum's performance. It was so enthusiastic that I promised not only to send him more seed but also to visit him in Argentina the following February, 1958, when our second test of DeKalb sorghum in the pampas would be ready for harvest.

DeKalb Grain Sorghum Impresses Argentine Campesinos

When I arrived, I was told that test plots of our hybrids had been distributed in the pampas among top farmers and government experiment stations. The growing season had been good and the appearance of the crop superb; the heads of our hybrids were so full of grain that Argentine farmers, who were accustomed to over-planted and un-cultivated Early Kalo, could hardly believe their eyes! Naturally, Ramon was eager to go into the hybrid sorghum seed business, producing and selling DeKalb hybrid seed.

My first impressions of Buenos Aires were confirmed by ten days of travel in the pampas with Ramon and Antonio Ruzo. Clearly, Argentina was a country blessed by nature. It had been developed well initially by immigrants who produced grain and meat for shipment to Europe, but its economy had floundered badly since the end of World War II. Most of the cars on the road in Buenos Aires, a city of more than 3 million, were at least ten years old. There was only one stoplight in the whole city, and nobody paid any attention to it. The water was so badly polluted that everyone used bottled water. The streetlights and buildings were dim, with many lights flickering. Obviously, Argentina had become a poor nation.

In the country, most of the good pampas land, which should have been growing crops like corn, was being used as pasture land. I even saw oxen being used to plow some very rich soil. Their economic problems had begun with the election of Juan Peron to the presidency in the early 1940s. Before the Peronistas came to power, average corn yields exceeded U.S. yields as the owners of very large estancias rented their land to farmers whose grain production had far greater value than the cattle that had previously grazed there.

"Exchange Controls" Tax Farm Exports

Juan Peron had promised to break up the estancias; but he did not impose meaningful income taxes or taxes on land in proportion to its productive potential. Instead, he imposed "exchange controls" that taxed exports but did not seem to the general public to be taxes. The early exchange controls were not a heavy a burden on farmers, but by 1958 a farmer exporting grain or meat received only 50 cents for each $1.00 paid by foreigners for his exported product. The remainder went to Peron's government.

Unable to afford the stiff export taxes, many landowners turned their land back to cattle grazing, which reduced productive output substantially but required very little labor. Hence many farmers and farm laborers sought employment in the cities, and the land that had been the nation's most productive asset produced food at much less than half of its potential. Farmers were poor, farm machinery rusted away and was too expensive to replace, and the nation sank into a serious economic depression. By the time Peron was voted out of office in 1956 the value of the peso had continued to decline, exchange controls remained, and the country was in a deep depression.

DeKalb Argentina Joins Forces with Agrosoja

The performance of the sorghum in the trials in 1958 was every bit as superb as Ramon had reported it in 1957. Farmers could harvest it easily and economically with their wheat combines, the only decent farm machinery in the country. Everywhere we went, we were encouraged to produce and sell sorghum seed in Argentina. Accordingly, after two weeks of chugging around in a relic Mercedes station wagon and becoming more and more impressed with the opportunities Argentina held for DeKalb, Ramon, Antonio, and I talked with Mr. Dighero, president of Agrosoja, their Argentine employer. Dighero shared Ramon's enthusiasm and wanted to import hybrid sorghum seed but did not have enough money to pay for it. To deal with this problem, we formed DeKalb Argentina, SRL, which received the seed (incurring a debt to DeKalb), and Ramon delivered it to Agrosoja customers, who paid DeKalb Argentina directly.

A "Finger-Burning" Experience with Inflation

Suddenly and unexpectedly in late 1959, Argentine President Frondizi devalued the peso by 40 percent against the U.S. dollar. The resulting loss to DeKalb Argentina exceeded the small capital of the company and threatened it with bankruptcy. Dr. Oscar Rosito, our new and competent attorney, advised Ramon to ask me for an immediate infusion of U.S. dollars. Ramon made the call, assuring me that the price of our remaining unsold seed would be adjusted upward to compensate for the devaluation, but advising that some had already been sold for pesos. The transfer was made, the crisis passed, and DeKalb Argentina incurred only a small loss, but we were awakened to the potential pitfalls of doing business internationally.

Ramon Meets a Greek Who "Must Have an Olive Orchard"

While Ramon and I were traveling in the pampas, he told me he had once been asked to appraise the value of a 1,000-hectare olive orchard a client was considering buying near Mar Del Plata, Argentina's "Miami Beach." His client told him, "I am a Greek, so I must have an olive orchard."

Ramon asked the operators to give him data on yields, costs, health of trees, customers, age and type of trees, etc. They gave him the information, but argued that he need not gather so much data, because his client was rich and could easily afford to pay a high price. Spurred on by their lack of ethics, Ramon prepared a thorough appraisal, reporting among other things that many of the orchard's trees were diseased. He valued the property at a much lower level than was acceptable to the seller, so no deal was cut, and Ramon sent his client a bill for his services. After several weeks went by with no payment from his client, Ramon went to the office of the client's business manager, who told him that no money was due because his boss had not bought the property. Ramon demanded to see the man's boss, to whom the business manager explained that they had offered the appraised value, which was much less than the asking price, and that their offer was rejected. Ergo, they owed nothing for the appraisal. The boss laughed and told his manager "Of course we owe for the appraisal. Pay the boy!" When Ramon received the check paying him in full, he noted that the man's name was Aristotle Onassis.

Chapter 12

Geologist Art Tiddens Joins DeKalb 1950-1959

By the mid 1950s, the costs of finding oil were soaring in the west Texas–New Mexico area DeKalb had considered its "playpen." New money had flowed in, and the fields were beginning to appear fully explored. Also, Paul Pugh, who managed our oil operations, had not had much success exploring outside of west Texas.

Accordingly, in 1955, when the Cities Service Corporation offered to farm out its properties in Montana to DeKalb, both Paul Pugh and Sam Marshall, our consultant geologist, recommended that we accept the offer.

Tom, Sr., and Charlie Roberts, his son-in-law who had joined DeKalb in 1952 and was assisting Tom in the oil business, also decided to hire a new geologist to manage the play. They chose Art Tiddens, who had extensive exploration experience with two of the major oil companies. Art was imaginative, intelligent, well trained in oil finding, and ambitious. He was destined to be the man who pulled DeKalb's oil business out of its postwar doldrums.

The Cities Service deal in Montana committed DeKalb to a $600,000 exploration program in return for a 50 percent interest in all of the Cities Service properties in Montana. Cities Service had spent the same amount on seismic exploration and leasing of the 250,000 acres in the area, so it was a fair deal for both parties. Cities Service was leaving Montana to concentrate its exploration efforts on the newly opened offshore deposits in the Gulf of Mexico.

Art jumped into his new assignment with enthusiasm and soon identified several attractive drilling locations. Unfortunately, he found very little oil. As a matter of fact, the most exciting thing that came out of our Montana exploration was a water "blow out" from a high-pressure subterranean aquifer that was penetrated by one of the company's contract drillers. Pure, drinkable water gushed out of the well under high pressure and flowed down the side of a mountain, attracting considerable attention, both from thirsty animals and from the state's drilling regulators, who required that the well be brought under control and capped. After several unsuccessful efforts, "Red" Adair, who was famous for fighting oil well fires, was brought in to cap the well.

In the end, the Montana Cities Service deal was a disappointment for DeKalb, except for the acquisition of Art Tiddens, who turned out to be considerably more competent than his Montana record would indicate.

After three years of drilling dry holes in Montana and enviously watching the flares from wells being drilled just across the border in Canada, Art was ready to move to Canada in late 1956. Tom, Sr., told him that if he were a young geologist he would want to be in Canada because it was a new frontier, a new oil province that was just starting to develop. Marion, Art's wife, overheard their conversation, and started making plans to move to Calgary.

ART "PARTNERS" WITH CREE

His first move was to commit to share equally in selected exploration efforts with the Cree Exploration Company, an "independent" headed by John Downing, who had for many years been exploration manager for Hudson Bay Oil and Gas, a large and successful Canadian firm. Cree was short on exploration dollars in the late 1950s and long on Canadian drilling prospects, making it an attractive partner for DeKalb. Art needed to work with knowledgeable Canadian oil finders as a first, sound step toward getting started in Canada. He was soon ready to establish DeKalb as an independent exploration company in Canada.

DeKalb purchased its first acreage in 1957, in partnership with Cree. DeKalb often was a more aggressive bidder than Cree and wound up with larger-than-half ownership in many plays. Nevertheless, Cree was often designated to be "the operator" because its experienced in-house staff knew how to efficiently license, survey well sites, drill, and let contracts. Within a year, DeKalb was selling oil and gas, and had made a good start building its own staff. About that time, the Cree company was sold to a larger operator, Northstar, which was, in turn, acquired by Shell.

ALBERTA: MORE OPPORTUNITY FOR INDEPENDENTS

Cree's familiarity with promising oil plays and developing fields fed Art's growing appreciation of Canadian exploration opportunities. Even more important were the exploration opportunities afforded by the Alberta Energy Board through what was called the "Crown Sales" system.

Crown Sales

The Alberta government owns nearly all of the petroleum "mineral rights" in its province and has developed an effective system of incentives for private development of these resources. Fundamentally, it grants every petroleum explorer an opportunity to make a bid for unleased land his company wants to explore. The bidding process grants any explorer a right to "post" (request a listing for an auction sale) Crown property. The auction process asks all interested explorers to bid for oil exploration rights on "posted" acres. The Alberta Department of Energy reviews the bids and accepts the highest bid it considers appropriate for the property.

The bids come in many forms. On "wildcat" acreage, for example, the bid might be to lease a large unexplored area (up to 100,000 acres), with the bidder undertaking to spend X dollars on seismic exploration, to be followed by spending Y dollars on exploratory drilling. The successful bidder is given a period of time (usually five years) to fulfill his exploration commitment. Upon fulfillment of his obligation, he is entitled to select leases on up to 50 percent of the original reservation area.

These leases could be as large as nine sections in a checkerboard pattern, with the other nine sections reverting to the Crown for future sale. Bids could, of course, be in dollars simply for the right to explore and develop the property. Royalties to be paid on hydrocarbons extracted usually were set at 12.5 percent, with some differences on a sliding scale based on either the quality of reserves or the production rate.

Well Information Made Public

When Art arrived in 1958, each explorer was required to submit his drilling logs and all pertinent geological data to the Alberta Energy Board within thirty days after discovering oil or gas. This information was made available to all bidders interested in the available sections the explorer had not earned by his discovery. The explorer could submit his own bid to be compared with competitive bids, with the highest bidder acquiring drilling rights under these sections.

Theoretically, everyone should have been bidding with the same geological information. However, the original explorer had a right to "post" the remaining available sections for bid auctioning. He could post nearby available Crown properties to come up for sale just after his drilling had been completed, but before then he had to release his technical data and logs. If he found oil or gas, and his timing was well planned, he would have inside information on the value of the adjacent posted property that he could use exclusively as the basis of his bid, to the disadvantage of his competitors, who would not have full knowledge of the nearby wells' productivity at the time of bidding.

Espionage?

On plays considered "hot," competing geologists used every device they could dream of to get information on the progress of wells being drilled, including making payments to rig hands for information, establishing base camps at the edge of drilling locations to observe operations, and identifying the depths at which known horizons have been reached. However, even the best industrial espionage agents would not have all of the information vital to the valuation of a well until its release after the well "came in," which could be several days after the posted property had been sold at auction. For example, they could not know the porosity or permeability of the drill cores, or whether oil or gas or water had been found, until the discoverer released the data.

In spite of the advantage possessed by the original explorer, competitors often submitted successful bids for adjacent leases. Sometimes the original explorer found itself outbid by smaller competitors bent on getting into the play. All in all, however, the system gave (and still gives) small independent explorers more opportunities to bid on good prospects than they have in the United States.

SOURCE: Corporate Records, DeKalb Energy

Cliff Heglin and Art Tiddens studying their first "Key Play".

Art's boldest early purchase in Canada was on January 16, 1958, in the Pembina Field, where he paid $50,595 for 320 acres (two locations) in the Cynthia area, and $2,142,106 for three sections sealed in the Berrymoor area and a 6,720 acre drilling reservation that included both Berrymoor and Lobstick acreage. These were relatively low-risk purchases because Art had done a good job of scouting. Nevertheless, paying $1,117,000 for our share of a little more than half of these Canadian prospects was a very big bite for DeKalb to take. The purchase announced that DeKalb was serious about operating in Canada and intended to grow its business aggressively. It was also a good example of the Crown Sales system working well, both by encouraging small independent explorers and by benefiting the people of Alberta, whose government was selling reserves at a high price.

Fortunately, all six Canadian wells Art drilled in 1958 were successful, giving him a batting average of 1000. Two were in Pembina and four were in Sundre. Over the years, both have been key plays; Table 12-1 shows just how fantastic the Pembina "key play" was. Table 12-2 displays the lifetime economics of Sundre; and Table 12-3 shows Art Tiddens' drilling activity during his first three years in Canada.

Table 12-1
Lifetime Economics of the Pembina "Key Play"
(This includes units at Berrymoor, Cardium Unit #7, Cynthia, Easyford, and Lobstick)

Cost	Income to 1992	Remaining Reserve Value	Ultimate Recovery
$16,722,000	$49,122,000	$9,834,000	$42,234,000

SOURCE: Corporate Records, DeKalb Petroleum Canada
Notes: DeKalb's first Pembina Cardium wells were drilled in March 1958. All data are from a DeKalb Energy Corporation (DEC) summary of operating results as of December 31, 1992. Cost is historic investment before general and administrative (G&A) costs of $16,722,000. Income of $49,122,000 derives from DEC corporate records. Remaining Reserve Value derives from total equivalent barrels remaining of 3,189M x SEC value of $3.10, equaling $9,284,000. Ultimate Recovery equals income plus remaining reserve value minus cost.

Sundre—Another Winner

DeKalb acquired its first leases in the Sundre area in 1957, splitting them equally with Cree. Thereafter, as we acquired more Sundre acreage, DeKalb was generally the designated "operator."

Art Tiddens was attracted to Sundre primarily because of its relatively shallow Elkton formation, which was an attractive oil play. The Sundre play might just be a "multiple zone" area, where the lower-cost shallow zones could be developed, establishing an operating leasehold whose deeper plays could be developed later. The Sundre wells produced oil from the Elkton, which had a small gas cap that flowed oil under gas pressure for many years before a waterflooding unit was formed to replace the oil that had been removed and keep the wells flowing. This is called "secondary recovery." Years later, oil and gas were found in large quantities in the Viking formation adjacent to Sundre. DeKalb held the rights to all oil under its Sundre leases (this is called "held by production"), so Sundre became another key play for DeKalb. Art's rate of success was phenomenal, and he had many more promising plays to consider for his next decade in Canada.

Art's success ratios were phenomenal, and he had many more

promising plays to consider for his next decade in Canada. He was sure to get support from Tom Roberts and Tom's son-in-law, Charlie.

Table 12-2
Sundre
(U.S. dollars)

Cost	Income to 1992	Remaining Reserve Value	Ultimate Recovery
$15,437,000	$34,939,000	$24,823,000	$44,325,000

SOURCE: Corporate Records, DeKalb Petroleum Canada
Notes: DeKalb's first Sundre wells were drilled to the shallow Elkton formation in March 1958. All of the data shown above are derived from a DEC summary of operating results as of December 31, 1992. Cost is historic investment before G&A at $15,437,000. Income of $34,939,000 is per DEC records. Remaining Reserves Value is derived from total equivalent barrels remaining of 7,071M x SEC value of $3.43, equaling $24,823,000. Ultimate Recovery equals income plus remaining reserve value minus cost.

Table 12-3
DeKalb's Canadian Oil Wells, 1958–1960

	1958	1959	1960
		Total Wells Drilled	
Gross	6.00	25.00	42.00
Net	4.60	14.83	26.74
		Success Ratio	
Gross	100%	64%	76%
Net	100%	83%	84%

SOURCE: Corporate Records, DeKalb Petroleum Canada

KEY PEOPLE

Art Tiddens was full of ambition, ability, imagination, and a drive to find oil and gas. His forte was being out of the office, consulting with experts, making friends, swapping ideas with geologists, and being out in the field when important wells were due to come in. He was well trained and aggressive, but a lousy bookkeeper. Keeping track of him was a challenge in 1958 and 1959, when he was living in the Palliser Hotel and roaming all over the Canadian "oil patch."

Art selected good people to help him in forming an effective cadre for DeKalb Petroleum Canada (DPC). His first choice was Cliff Heglin.

Cliff Heglin joined DeKalb on October 15, 1959, and was Art's indispensable right-hand man for the next twenty-five years. Cliff worked for Lewis Engineering, a consulting firm, in the same building where Art had an office. Art recalls that Cliff worked "a bit" at night and would occasionally go by Art's office to talk. His knowledge and enthusiasm impressed Art, as well as Tom, Sr., and Charlie, and four months after meeting Art, he went to work for DeKalb. Cliff was a petroleum engineer—the "numbers man" who converted Art's ideas into key calculations like "payback time," "return on investment," and "cost of finding and development." Art and Cliff made a terrific team. Basically, Art was the "idea man," and Cliff used his skills at mathematics and engineering to analyze and sort out the "best of Art," as they moved to make DeKalb a success in the oil business. Far from being bound to his desk, Cliff spent much of his time out in the field supervising completions, dealing with operating problems, and looking for new exploration opportunities.

Chapter 13

Hybrid Poultry Breeding 1950-1959

Having been so blessed by the success of hybrid corn, management and shareholders naturally began looking for other plants and animals that could be improved by hybridization. Tom considered hybridizing alfalfa, cattle, hogs, and chickens. Alfalfa was quickly rejected because its sexual reproduction system made hybridization impractical. Cattle breeding, too, would have been difficult because individual cows give birth to only one calf each year, making selection a lengthy proposition. Hog breeding and hybridization were more promising, because sows have two litters of seven to ten pigs per year, and crosses between breeds show considerable hybrid vigor.

DeKalb would develop hybrid pigs very successfully in the 1970s and 1980s, but hybridization of chickens was a logical first step into animal breeding because hens can produce as many as two hundred baby chicks per year, giving breeders many individuals to select from, making rapid genetic improvement possible. Poultry breeders had successfully improved strains within breeds but had undertaken little crossing between breeds or strains, even though some breeders had observed hybrid vigor in crosses between breeds. The possibility of "fixing" genetic traits by inbreeding had not been considered practical, because breeders knew that inbreeding brought out recessive genes in a pure (homozygous) form. These recessive genes were often not expressed in breeds or strains because their effectiveness was overwhelmed by dominant counterpart genes. Sometimes the recessive genes that expressed themselves in a pure form had undesirable effects. Highly inbred birds, for example, often showed too many undesirable recessive traits to be useful for breeding purposes.

Dr. J. Holmes Martin of Purdue, however, thought that the advantages of hybrid vigor might be exploited in crosses between partially inbred lines. After talking with many poultry breeders, Tom Roberts and Ray Nelson, who had joined DeKalb as Tom's assistant in 1943, offered Dr. Martin the funding he would need to determine whether hybrid vigor could be used to improve egg-laying strains of chickens. Martin accepted, taking a leave of absence from Purdue. He quickly designed and built the hatchery and poultry breeding farm he would need to inbreed, cross, and test hybrids made between strains within breeds as well as hybrids between breeds. He started with elite strains purchased from the best poultry "pure line" breeders, and recommended that DeKalb proceed to take the steps necessary to build a significant market share in the U.S. egg-producing industry.

SOURCE: T. H. Roberts, Jr.

Ray Nelson and Tom Roberts, Sr. honoring Edna Nelson

Upon deciding to go ahead with the program Dr. Martin had begun, Tom and Ray Nelson appointed Dr. E. E. Schnetzler ("Snetz"), Martin's protégé at Purdue, to direct DeKalb's poultry breeding program when Martin returned to Purdue in 1945. Snetz was soft-spoken, likable, astute, well trained for his job, and totally dedicated. More than any other person, he deserves full credit for leading the development of the hybrid chickens that support what came to be DeKalb's leading position in the United States.

DEKALB POULTRY ADAPTS

In 1950, when DeKalb introduced its birds to the U.S. market, most eggs were produced by small farm flocks, varying in size from 200 to 1,000 hens. Typically, the farmer's wife would feed the birds, as well as collect and market the eggs.

To serve that market, DeKalb signed on a network of the nation's best hatcheries, which would buy the DeKalb parent stock at comparatively low prices, grow the parents, collect and hatch their eggs, and sell the DeKalb Chix to farmers (or their wives) at 60 cents per chick, twice the price of non-hybrid chickens. A royalty of 30 cents per chick was then paid by the hatchery to DeKalb. This royalty was gradually reduced as competitive pressures grew. In corn-growing areas, DeKalb seed dealers were asked to sell baby DeKalb Chix, which were to be hatched and serviced by their nearest hatchery.

Some dealers did a good job; others did not.

In 1949, as DeKalb was gearing up to enter the poultry business, I graduated from Iowa State College. My first job with DeKalb was as assistant to Ray Nelson, assistant general manager of the company and general manager of poultry operations. I was charged with identifying the best hatcheries in the corn belt and signing them up to hatch and sell DeKalb Chix. The job was not easy, because many hatcherymen doubted that DeKalb's hybrid chicks would out-produce the improved strains they were hatching. But by 1952, when I accepted a job as district sales manager for both seed and chicks, we had signed on more than 150 hatcheries. That number reached more than 300 at its peak but declined rapidly as the efficiency of large integrated egg producers forced small, high-cost "farm flocks," who were the hatcheries' customers, out of the egg production business.

SOURCE: Corporate Records, DeKalb Poultry

E. E. Schnetzler, Poultry Research Director

Facilities

DeKalb's research data had convinced management that DeKalb's chicks would be superior to those on the market—enough better, in fact, to give the company a good chance of gaining a leading market share. To succeed, though, DeKalb would need sizable production facilities where "parent stock" chicks could be produced for sale to hatcheries, which would grow the parents that would produce the eggs they would hatch and sell as baby DeKalb chicks to egg producers.

In 1950 we took a big step toward providing quality parent stock from our own farms by purchasing three large wartime facilities from the U.S. government:

- The Scioto ordnance plant at Marion, Ohio. This plant, with six large warehouses and 1,900 acres of good farmland, cost $270,000
- The Sangamon ordnance plant at Illiopolis, Ill. This facility, situated on 1,300 acres of beautiful farmland, was priced at $223 per acre—total cost $290,000. It had thirty-eight warehouses (26,000 square feet each), many of which we converted to laying houses for parent stock.
- Camp Maxey, Tex. We bought this facility, with twenty-five warehouses (9,000 square feet each) plus 800 acres of grazing land for a total of $258,000 (Olson, "Genetics to Genius," pp. 214, 617).

In addition, we established, hatcheries at Sycamore and Illiopolis, Ill.; Marion, Ohio; Paris, Tex.; York, Penn.; Grinnell, Iowa; Fremont, Neb.; Effington, Ill.; and Dassel, Minn..

A Learning Experience

As Tom Roberts, Sr., and Ray Nelson set out to become the leading breeders of egg laying chickens in the United States, they learned on the job. One of their toughest challenges was planning the multiplication of parent stock chicks to supply their associate hatcherymen, who had to adjust to wide year-to-year swings in egg prices. These swings were the consequence of relatively constant consumer demand that was served by thousands of small farm flock egg producers who tended to buy more baby chicks when egg prices were high. This resulting expansion of egg production would cause drastic declines in egg prices. Unfortunately, the swings in prices were not regular, so predicting egg prices two years before having baby chicks for sale (the time required to increase or decrease parent flocks) was very difficult.

In the fall of 1953 egg prices had dropped precipitously, so our associate hatchery orders for parent stock were much lower than expected, leaving DeKalb with a big overproduction of parent stock. Tom and Ray believed that speculators were over-influencing the market for consumer eggs, forcing prices down to low levels, and then buying cheap "futures" contracts that they would sell at a profit a few months later when market supply and demand came back into equilibrium and prices rose.

I sat in on Ray and Tom's deliberations about how to avoid the losses they were bound to experience with their oversupply of parent stock chicks. Tom of course wanted to avoid heavy losses in DeKalb's new and growing poultry business, and he also did not want Ray blamed for something that was not Ray's fault. Tom suggested that if our overproduction was the consequence of egg prices being kept low by speculators, why not make up for our operating losses by buying large numbers of egg futures contracts at their current low levels and selling them a few months later when we and nearly all of our advisers were sure prices would be high?

I left for graduate school at Harvard the day after Tom made that proposal. The more I thought about it, the more convinced I became that it just wouldn't work. None of us was an expert in the egg futures market, and I believed that the "futures experts" we consulted had a conflict of interest: if we bought futures contracts we would do so through them, and they would get their commissions whether we had guessed right or wrong.

Before going to my first class, I wrote my dad a letter opposing playing the egg futures market, giving the reasons I have set forth here. Unfortunately, he had already plunged DeKalb heavily into egg futures. Even though he was not convinced by my arguments, he was tremendously pleased that I had taken a more conservative position than his. He wanted his son to be as conservative as he thought he was (but really wasn't, of course). The whole affair turned out to be a disaster. The egg market never increased, and the company took a heavy loss (I think it was nearly $500,000) when our contracts were sold. It was an expensive lesson, but one well learned. To the best of my knowledge, we never again tried to make up for operating losses by speculating in the futures market.

Getting Seed Dealers to Sell Chicks

In corn-growing areas, DeKalb seed dealers were asked to sell DeKalb baby chicks. At first, many of them saw a chance to increase their incomes. They asked for chick orders from their best seed customers, some of whom ordered simply because of their confidence in DeKalb. But many dealers were reluctant to sell chicks for fear of losing customers if the chicks got sick. Though understandable, seed dealers' reluctance to sell DeKalb Chix became a serious problem for DeKalb's district and regional sales managers. The company developed training programs to help DeKalb's sales force deal with poultry problems, but our baby chick sales increased slowly. Table 13-1(see page 141) records DeKalb's first five years of selling baby chicks.

The numbers may look good, but DeKalb's sales were only a small percentage of the U.S. total of 518,000,000 hens reported by the 1940 census. Sales were far short of our goals, and the poultry operation was still losing money in 1954. And Tom's efforts to push sales of chicks created friction because the sales organization was busy dealing with seed product performance problems at the same time. On June 26, 1954, at DeKalb's annual summer sales convention, Tom took the first step toward developing a separate sales organization for each product:

> "There comes a time when decisions must be made—when not all will agree. I have been thinking about this for five years, and I have spent most of the last two nights thinking about this. I think I am right, and that is the only bragging you'll hear me make. The fact that the DeKalb Agricultural Association as a whole has never operated in the red since I took over its management 34 years ago at the age of 28 when it had lost all its surplus and 60 percent of its capital, most of which I had sold, I believe qualifies me to make the decision I am making here. I have not talked with anybody about this because I thought it would lead to arguments or disagreements and in the end, I was going to have to make the decision anyway. The responsibility of the decision is mine.... Now, what should I do: set up two corporations or have two bosses?
>
> I have outlined here one concept of organization with a sales manager and three assistant sales managers—one on corn, one on chicks, and one on sorghum. And they in turn, all three of them would be on the necks of the regional sales managers and the dealers. Frankly, I don't like that. I'm going to say what I think, and this is my decision: We are going to have a chick manager of sales and a corn manager of sales, and we are going to have regional sales managers as we have had—we're going to have district sales managers as we have had, and we are going to have dealers as we have had. Maybe you are wondering what I meant by the hour of decision and what it is.
>
> The decision I must make is this—that the two most important jobs in our organization are going to be corn sales manager and chick sales manager. I'm going to pick the man who knows the most about corn sales for corn sales manager, and that's Rus Rasmussen. I'm going to appoint the man who knows most about chicks, poultry husbandry and hatcheries for chick sales manager, and that man is Ray Nelson. It's a promotion for both of them.... They are both big men. They work together beautifully. This is my decision and this is it." (Olson, "Genetics to Genius," pp. 630–31)

Olson reports that Rus and Ray were deeply hurt because Tom had not conferred with them before making the speech, but both stayed with the company and in later years agreed that Tom's decision had been proper and timely.

CHALLENGING CHANGES IN THE EGG INDUSTRY

In the late 1950s the egg-producing industry began turning to larger, more efficient operators. Recognizing the inherent economies of large egg-producing farms, feed-producing firms integrated forward by financing ever larger egg-producing operations. Some also financed specialists who produced twenty-week-old, ready-to-lay pullets, which were usually sold to large operations also financed by the feed producer.

Table 13-1
DeKalb Sales of Female (Pullet) Chix, 1950–1954

Year	Number
1950	985,708
1951	2,562,587
1952	3,308,786
1953	5,187,165
1954	8,823,551

SOURCE: Corporate Records, DeKalb Poultry.

Faced with the efficiencies of large operations, small flocks went out of business in droves, and the hatcheries set up to serve them went out of business just as fast. Likewise, gradually DeKalb moved from relying on its contract hatchery network and seed dealers to sell DeKalb Chix to a smaller, more highly trained group of salesmen—district managers. It was their job to sell and service the large, integrated egg producers, which had flocks of 100,000 to 800,000 layers and by 1980 constituted a very large portion of the U.S. egg production industry. These changes began in the late 1950s and accelerated into the 1960s, when DeKalb discontinued selling chicks through its seed sales organization. The poultry division became an independent part of the company, offering both knowledgeable service and low chick prices to those who bought large volumes of DeKalb Chix.

Jack Nelson

One of the key players in DeKalb's poultry business was Jack Nelson. He had graduated from Iowa State University with honors in poultry husbandry; he returned from military service in 1953 and jumped right into a series of jobs with DeKalb. His rapid rise in the company took him through six jobs in six years: trainee in the York, Pennsylvania, hatchery; midwest supervisor of associate hatcheries in Humboldt, Iowa; and district sales manager for both seed and Chix at Boone, Iowa, Charles City, Iowa, and Mankato, Minnesota; and eastern regional sales manager at York, Pennsylvania.

Financial Results - Part Four

OPERATING RESULTS, IN THE 1950s

Given all of the competitive challenges our hybrid corn and poultry businesses faced in the 1950s, the company's financial growth was surprisingly good. It is important to remember that DeKalb's oil business, which was increasing in value, contributed little to the bottom line because the drilling and dry-hole costs were written off as they were incurred. Hybrid sorghum's rapid earnings growth during the last three years of the decade helped a lot, of course, as did the acquisition of the Cornhusker Hybrid Seed Company. Table 13-2 shows DeKalb's growth in the 1950s.

Table 13-2
Shareholder Equity Growth in the 1950s

Year	Equity Reported	Equity (1990 $)
1950	15,485,788	83,983,000
1951	16,471,111	82,799,000
1952	17,469,265	86,160,000
1953	19,673,404	96,304,000
1954	22,860,422	111,071,000
1955	22,512,755	109,792,000
1956	22,598,834	108,591,000
1957	23,476,029	109,193,000
1958	25,142,800	113,708,000
1959	26,896,273	120,802,000

SOURCE: Records of Thomas H. Roberts, Sr.

Part Five

1960-1969

Chapter 14

The Changing of the Guard 1960-1969

In 1961, when I was thirty-seven years old, my father was ready to retire. After I had served one year as executive vice president in 1960, he chose to install me as president and chief executive officer in June 1961 at DeKalb's annual sales meeting. He retired from day-to-day management but remained chairman of the board. Here is what he told the board when he proposed my promotion:

> I am suggesting that the management of the company be turned over to Tom. I think it would be fair, perhaps, to review some of his activities with the company.
>
> He started as a water boy and worked there for two or three years. He then went out to Gunn's breeding plot and spent several summers with him. After he got out of the Army, he attended Iowa State College at Ames, and in his summers, while in college, he worked here in setting up a five-year budget program for our poultry operation. We needed the information, and I think that study in itself gave him a pretty thorough and complete knowledge of our poultry enterprise.
>
> He worked on signing up hatcheries after that for a period of time; went in as a district manager for two years, and then took over the responsibility of sorghum—its production and sale—and I think he did an outstanding job on that; and I think the cotton project which he was handling has progressed quite satisfactorily.
>
> From the standpoint of education, he has had seven to eight years of college work, and he came away with very high honors as far as grades are concerned. He is honest, and he probably has had as much experience and contacts in all branches of the company as anyone. He has been working hard, and I think the last year he has shown a lot of ability I did not know he had.
>
> At the moment, he is ten years older than I was when I became manager of the company. I think he is more conservative than I am; at least, that is what my brother tells me.
>
> I feel that he is qualified for the position, and I am going to recommend that I resign as President and be elected Chairman of the Board, and that Tom be elected President, effective July 1. I think the fact that my family owns about thirty percent of the stock places his interest and the company's in the same boat; and that is good for any company.

Upon a motion by Charlie Gunn, seconded by Ray Nelson, the board accepted the resignation of Thomas H. Roberts, Sr., as president of the corporation. Rus Rasmussen moved, and Frank Schweitzer seconded, that he be elected chairman of the Board of Directors. Both motions passed unanimously. Upon a motion by Gunn, seconded by Nelson, I was elected president of the corporation.

SETTING GOALS A FIRST PRIORITY

My Personal Goals

When I was elected to succeed my father as DeKalb's CEO, I set several goals for myself:

- To build and maintain a good relationship with Charlie Roberts.
- To build the company on proprietary products (hybrids) that no competitor could reproduce.
- To fully fund research, always remembering that it is the basic source of superior products.
- To market directly to consumers through sales people whose incentive is a percentage of income from each sale, and to provide them with territories large enough to solicit enthusiastically.
- To employ high-quality people, preferably with farm backgrounds; to live by high personal standards myself; to expect as much from them; and to pay them well.
- To give priority to markets we understood—farmers.
- To be willing to expand into promising foreign markets, employing local people who know their own markets, and to compensate them well, with emphasis on incentives based on profitable performance.
- To continue funding oil and gas exploration as long as its prospects look good, but to consider this activity to be a hedge against hard times in our basic agricultural businesses, which are often cyclical.
- To pay reasonable dividends to shareholders, keeping in mind that their long-term best opportunity lies in growth in the value of their shares.
- To nurture employee health and profit-sharing programs.
- "To make good, not to make excuses."

Establishing Objectives with Charlie

My first move as CEO was to confer with Charlie Roberts, my brother-in-law, regarding DeKalb's current financial position. We quickly agreed that the company was overcapitalized as a consequence of having minimized dividends and maximized earnings retention for many years. In fact, the company had no long-term debt, and its banks, which provided funding for our seasonal funding needs, were lending us money for only three or four months per year but were not paying us interest on the sizable funds we kept on deposit with them for the remainder of each year. Charlie and I agreed that our short-term financial strategies would be these:

- To give first priority to building our seedcorn business both domestically and abroad by being willing to fully fund research expansion and capital needs, and to fund aggressive multiplication of promising new hybrids.
- To build our oil business primarily out of its own cash flow, but to stand willing to invest "parent company" capital in expansion of our oil businesses as promising opportunities developed.
- To build our poultry business by being willing to fund its needs for cash to expand in a fast-changing industry.
- To persuade our bankers to pay us interest when they are holding sizeable sums of our money. This was quickly achieved.

Pulling Together Our Team

I thought that both Rus Rasmussen, seed vice president and sales manager, and Ray Nelson, administrative vice president and general manager of poultry, were better qualified than I was for the CEO job, but my dad did not agree. I realized, too, that after forty-five years with one CEO all of us would have to make adjustments.

My sister, Mary, was concerned that I might not be ready for the job. She was very supportive nevertheless. She said she thought I would do a good job if I could learn to listen more and talk less. Charlie Roberts, her husband, was also very supportive. Rus Rasmussen expressed a very similar opinion to Mary's—he thought I had done a good job so far and would likely do well in my new job if I listened carefully to key company people (which I understood to mean that I should listen to him). I would do that.

My first move, supported strongly by Charlie, was to clarify lines of authority. Charlie had drawn up the company's existing "Table of Organization." The drawing resembled a wheel with Tom Roberts at the center and spokes connecting him with forty people who reported to him. Somehow, the organization had functioned reasonably well with Tom's ambiguous delegation of authority, most likely because of his personal charisma and the respect he richly deserved for having made the company a huge success.

Two Immediate Priorities

I thought my first priorities should be the creation of solid working relationships with Rus Rasmussen and Charlie Roberts.

My biggest initial challenge was to make friends with Rus, who was a proud, intelligent, soft-spoken, and sensitive man as introverted as my father was extroverted. Rus knew our seed business better than anyone in the organization, so I immediately appointed him vice president for seed operations.

Equally important was the development of a solid understanding with Charlie Roberts, my brother-in-law, whose family possessed exactly the same number of shares in the company as mine. I appointed Charlie administrative vice president and vice president of oil operations. Charlie's responsibilities would be general administration of the corporate staff and continued responsibility for our oil business. We both realized that our direct responsibilities would probably change from time to time as the company grew, and we agreed that we needed to work closely together. Charlie was my age, very capable, personable, and conscientious. I did not want him ever to resent being the number-two man, so I resolved to confer with him regularly, to give him responsibility and authority over important corporate functions, to acknowledge his successes both inside and outside the company, to avoid criticizing him when things did not go well, and, in general, to let him know that I considered him a full and welcome partner in the management of our business. I reserved the right to make the final decision when we did not agree, but I did my best to behave in ways that would avoid the buildup of resentment.

Executive Committee Formed

To be certain I was kept informed of the fundamentals of each of our businesses—their achievements, their problems and their plans for dealing with them—I established an Executive Committee consisting of Rus Rasmussen (seed), Ray Nelson (poultry), Charlie Roberts (oil and administration), Harold Noren (seed sales), Harold Nolin (seed production), and myself. At regular Monday morning meetings, each member discussed the state of affairs in his area of responsibility. The need for better executive communication was well known to everyone on the new Executive Committee, so the concept of improving communication was well received by all.

GETTING STARTED

Charlie Roberts and I sought to develop a consensus of the board and our operating executives that DeKalb was overcapitalized and that we must either invest more aggressively in our existing agricultural and oil businesses or pay much larger cash dividends. It was easy for us to agree that we should not increase dividends substantially because by doing that we would limit future growth. The board agreed. Accordingly, we would focus on building our existing businesses.

Dick Holland: Seed Research Director

Because, amazingly, the job of seed research director at DeKalb had not existed before 1961. We took immediate steps to create and fill that new position. After talking with several leading USDA Experiment Station administrators and plant breeders, I came to believe that Dick Holland was our man and suggested to the Executive Committee that we appoint him to the new position. Dick's brought both impressive professional and personal credentials to the job:

- He was the scientist who had shown how to hybridize sorghum.
- His gentle, persuasive personality was deemed "right" for the job.
- In 1956 he had quietly but determinedly convinced us that we were positioned to stake out a leading position in the promising new hybrid sorghum business. In fact, that position was his own creation: he had multiplied his parent lines of grain sorghum in the winter of 1954–55 and followed that in the summer of 1955 with another increase, which gave us a much larger supply of parent seed than our competitors had to produce hybrids in the summer of 1956 for sale in the spring of 1957. This could have been done by our competitors, but they didn't have Dick's perspective and good judgment.
- His alertness had positioned DeKalb to be an industry leader in both hybrid cotton and hybrid wheat.
- He had selected an outstanding plant breeder in Bruce Maunder and had positioned him to take over DeKalb's hybrid sorghum research program without a hitch.
- And he would be accepted by our squabbling corn breeders.

In addition, we held once-a-month staff meetings on Saturday mornings, at which each administrator reported on his area of responsibility. These meetings were not particularly popular with the staff, because DeKalb had abandoned the five-and-a-half-day work week in the late 1950s, and many rightly believed that Saturdays should be family days. We gradually abandoned those Saturday-morning meetings

Bold Seedcorn Marketing

DeKalb's seedcorn sales declined by 25 percent between 1959 and 1962, partly because U.S. acreage planted to corn declined 20 percent during the same period and partly because the popularity of our Nebraska-bred "3X" hybrids declined as well. Nevertheless, our seedcorn business was poised on the brink of sales increases matched only by the sales explosion we had experienced between 1936 and 1942, when DeKalb had moved from obscurity to prominence in the hybrid seedcorn industry.

This time, we moved boldly forward with single-cross hybrid seedcorn production and sales. But we needed a few more years of testing to identify a full line of truly outstanding “singles” for every maturity zone. We had test marketed single-cross seed with DeKalb 805 in the late 1950s and had enough confidence in XL45 (a single cross) to release it for sale in the north-central corn belt in 1963.

Simultaneously, while waiting for an across-the-board product line offering single-cross hybrids in every maturity zone, Hank Slade came up with three beautiful three-way crosses, XL361, XL362, and XL363, which fit well in the central corn belt. When planted thickly, these introductions all had outstanding ability to increase yield.

The addition of Hank’s three hybrids to DeKalb’s line beginning in 1963 was timely and important, as they replaced the Cornhusker 3X hybrids that could not survive either the corn diseases they encountered in the humid areas east of Nebraska or the higher populations that farmers were planting across the corn belt. Table 14-1 shows the record of Hank Slade’s XL361, XL362, and XL363 as nearly as I could estimate.

Table 14-1
Three Excellent Three-Way-Cross Hybrids

	XL 361		XL 362		XL 363	
Year	Total Autumn Supply	Estimate of Spring Sales	Total Autumn Supply	Estimate of Spring Sales	Total Autumn Supply	Estimate of Spring Sales
			(Bushels)			
1963*	33,365	29,512	663		0	
1964*	233,876	170,384	28,370	20,578		
1965*	289,342	213,384	68,849	62,684		
1966	447,573	288,000	243,328	155,000		
1967	442,000	354,000	191,096	153,000		
1968	484,000	387,000	103,000	82,000	72,000	58,000
1969	534,000	377,000	21,000	16,000	187,000	150,000
1970	340,000	272,000			165,000	132,000
1971	205,072	164,000			121,000	97,000
1972	104,000	83,000			100,000	80,000
1973	64,000	51,000			64,000	51,000
1974	52,000	42,000			13,000	13,000

SOURCE: DeKalb production records.

Notes: The Estimate of Spring Sales columns show volumes of sales realized the spring following the Autumn Supply. Sales records through 1965 were as reported here, with asterisks marking the years when we found accurate data showing sales by variety. Sales records for these three hybrids were not available, but we found good records of seed production by year, so I have estimated sales by hybrid to have been 80 percent of each year’s springtime supply (carryover seed plus prior year production) of each hybrid, with the exception of two years (1966 and 1969), in which XL361 was overproduced and required time to work out of an oversupply. The Total Autumn Supply columns present new production plus carryover seed left over from the prior year. Multiplying this by 80 percent is, in my opinion, a reasonable estimate of each year’s sales, as DeKalb during my tenure as CEO aimed to have a “pipeline” of approximately 20 percent greater supply than would be sold each year, in order to maximize sales and customer service. The unsold seed in the pipeline could usually be carried over and sold the next year.

Stringfield Suggests a Single-Cross Tester

Glen Stringfield, an outstanding corn breeder who had retired from government service, had joined DeKalb as a consultant and part-time corn breeder in 1959. He told Rus Rasmussen that a single-cross hybrid between two Experiment Station lines, OH43 x W64A, had performed well as a "test hybrid" (a proven performer against which all experimental hybrids were compared) in USDA trials, and recommended that it be used as a test hybrid in DeKalb trials. Hank Slade had grown it on his own station in DeKalb, Illinois, and endorsed Stringfield's suggestion that it be entered in DeKalb's nationwide trials because he knew it had short, sturdy stalks and low ears that could be easily harvested and that it would resist major corn diseases and produce a high yield when planted thickly.

However, Stringfield did not believe the production risk of any single-cross hybrid would justify large-scale commercial production, and Charlie Gunn agreed with him. Armed with their opinion, Rus in turn consulted with our "foundation" seed production managers, who had grown inbred parent seed for years. They thought single crosses could be produced economically in large volume if we priced them sufficiently high and produced enough seed to build up carryover inventories that would ensure adequate seed supplies for customers in years that followed bad seed production conditions.

Rus discussed the pros and cons of single crosses with Harold Noren and me and many others, including Dr. Sherret Chase, Dr. Basil Tsotsis, Hank Slade, and Tom Roberts, Sr. We all believed that DeKalb should produce the hybrid in large commercial volume if it performed well in our nationwide tests. In 1961 DeKalb tests, we saw how well it performed at high plant population density, so we decided to "bet the farm" on this fine hybrid, which we called XL45. It was first produced on a commercial scale in 1962 for sale in the spring of 1963.

XL45—AN OUTSTANDING HYBRID

Hank Slade, who was Charlie Gunn's assistant for many years, reported on the evolution of XL45 in a letter he wrote to me in July 1994:

> "In the early 1950s we were having lots of complaints about 423, so your dad sent me out to find out what the problem was. I found 423 could not keep up to the population that some farmers were planting, and that it was very susceptible to the European corn borer. I was told to start testing our lines for corn borer and disease resistance, and so I had my first breeding program.
>
> In 1956, I planted my nursery in 30" rows, high popula-

tion, and applied corn borer and diseases to it. It was at this time that I sent for seeds of the inbreds OH43 and W64A from the Illinois Foundation Seed Co. I received enough ears to plant 30 rows of each. At harvest time, I learned OH43 and W64A were both very good at high populations. W64A had a problem with standability, but there was one row that stood up well. That one row was our source of W64A from then on.

It was after crossing W64A and OH43 that I realized I had a hybrid that would out-yield Pioneer 371. But I also realized it was adapted to 30" rows, and I thought it was the only hybrid that was.

Two years later, in 1959, I had enough seed to plant it with other hybrids that were planted in 30" rows. My problem was there wasn't a 30" row combine harvester around. That summer I spent 3 days with John Deere & Co. in the hope that they would be interested in building a combine to harvest 30" rows. They told me that they couldn't do it because most farmers could not afford to change their equipment, and 30" rows would not go. Shortly thereafter, I met a farmer who had some influence with Allis Chalmers, and he persuaded the company to build a 30" row combine. We got the first 30" combine at that time, just in time to harvest our plots.

By 1960, the problem for DeKalb was to decide on taking the production risk involved in producing single-cross corn, so your dad called a meeting of our breeders. Mr. Gunn said no because he thought our inbreds would be stolen. Mr. Stringfield said no because he felt single crosses would be like shooting a rifle at a problem, and he thought it would be better to use a three-way because it would be like shooting a shotgun. Loring Jones said he didn't know, but he thought we should probably continue with three-ways, etc.

It was my turn next and I told the group that unless we went with single crosses, we would soon be selling to only 15 to 25 percent of the farmers, because farmers were ready for single-cross corn.

That summer a big push for 30" rows came in Ohio, where a meeting was held to show the farmers 30" row tests. They had a breeder from Canada who gave a talk on the success of narrow rows in his plots. At that time, I knew we would have the only hybrid for 30" rows if we produced OH43 x W64A.

The next spring (1960), Harold Noren got a letter from Wilbur Watson, a DeKalb County farmer, asking if we had a hybrid that would yield and also stand up, and if not, why didn't we? Harold called me and asked if I had a hybrid for Mr. Watson. I gave him a bushel of what was to become XL45. He didn't have the plates to plant it, so his field was planted at seeding rates well over 30,000 plus plants per acre. I watched

> this field and took your dad out to see it. After that, he would come out to look at the field about twice a week. He was very excited about its possibilities. If it had not been for his support of it, I doubt XL45 would have ever come out.
>
> The company tried other versions of the inbreds used to make XL45, but they did not work out. During its heyday, I attended a meeting with other companies. At this meeting, the breeder for Pfister Associated Growers got up and said he wanted to congratulate DeKalb for the outstanding hybrid XL45, and that Pfister was going to have to work harder!
>
> As proof that my OH43 x W64A was different, all the other companies tried to copy it, but were unable to do so."

Some of our most astute observers, including Rus Rasmussen, Harold Noren, Basil Tsotsis, and Hank Slade, thought it might perform even better in farmers' fields than it had in our two-row research tests, where its short stature often meant that it grew in the shade of taller adjacent hybrids. After receiving DeKalb research test data, knowing Hank's enthusiasm for his version of OH43 x W64A and having observed its performance on Wilbur Watson's farm where it had been planted extremely thickly, Rus was confident that many farmers would like XL45 just as much as Wilbur Watson liked it. He was absolutely right.

The pure hybrid vigor of XL45 was superb. It out-yielded everything our competitors threw at it and initiated a decade of sales breakthroughs with DeKalb single crosses that doubled our market share and tripled our profit margins. All of those factors, plus the fact that we introduced many more single cross hybrids, added up to a compound growth in DeKalb annual earnings of 20 percent per year for the next ten years. Table 14-3 presents an estimate of XL45's sales history, based on DeKalb's seed production records and the assumption that 80 percent of the unit (bushel equivalent) volume of XL45 seed available was sold each year. This is a reasonable assumption and is the best I can do without the exact sales records of the company.

A Remarkable XL45 Field Day

DeKalb had a remarkable field day at Illiopolis, in the heart of Illinois, in mid-September of 1965. The day started slowly, as rain began falling over the assembly building where more than a thousand farmers had gathered. Lunch was served, but the rain continued, and it soon became evident that viewing DeKalb's plots would be impossible.

Harold Noren, DeKalb's sales manager, had slides to show, but the feature of the day was Clyde Hight, a boyhood friend of Harold's. He told the assembled farmers that he had just finished harvesting 300 acres of DeKalb XL45 growing in thirty-inch rows planted at a rate of 30,000 seeds per acre that produced an average yield of over

200 bushels per acre; a remarkable record! Thirty thousand plants per acre was a very high planting rate, and the thirty-inch rows were also innovative—the standard row width for corn was traditionally forty inches. Before the introduction of XL45, there would have been a lot of barren stalks in any fields planted that thickly. Most farmers were still planting in forty-inch rows, and few were planting at seeding rates in excess of 20,000 seeds per acre.

Table 14-2
XL45—DeKalb's Biggest Winner

Year	80,000 Kernel Units
1963	46,000
1964	174,300
1965	349,000
1966	521,000
1967	1,008,400
1968	1,136,400
1969	1,255,000
1970	1,015,700
1971	448,500
1972	313,000
1973	254,000
1974	127,000
1975	63,000

SOURCE: XL45 seed production data, the primary source of the above estimate of sales, was provided by DeKalb's Seed Production Department.
Note: all of DeKalb's single-cross hybrids were sold in 80,000-kernel "units," which contained approximately the same number of kernels as a bushel of medium-flat kernels, such as the seed parents of three-way and four-way crosses.

Clyde Hight's tremendous yields from DeKalb's short, strong-standing single cross were astounding. Very few who heard Clyde Hight that day failed to plant XL45 the following spring, and Clyde became a famous farmer. Coffee shop conversations extolled XL45, and we at DeKalb knew we had a winner on our hands.

MORE GREAT DEKALB SINGLE CROSSES

Harold Noren challenged our corn breeders to enter promising single-cross experimental hybrids in performance tests in all of the major U.S. maturity zones. XL45 was classified as a 105-day hybrid, which fit DeKalb, Illinois, perfectly, and performed well as far south as Clyde Hight's farm in south-central Illinois near Taylorville, which is considered to be in the 115-day maturity zone. Harold realized that to fully serve the U.S. corn belt we would need to offer single crosses in six maturity zones, beginning with the 90–95 day zone in the north and ranging southward to the 115–120 day zone.

DeKalb's corn breeders responded quickly to Harold's challenge, and by 1966 DeKalb was offering single-cross hybrids in all of the major maturity zones. The most notable were XL25, XL45, XL54, XL64, and XL66, which served the corn belt from Wisconsin in the north to southernmost Illinois.

PUBLIC RELATIONS AND PROMOTION OF THE "XL" HYBRIDS

Positive word-of-mouth reports about DeKalb's XL hybrids were wonderful, but Harold Noren and Leo Olson, DeKalb's advertising manager, agreed that a well-planned advertising and sales promotion program would be needed to change favorable coffee shop conversation into orders for DeKalb's top-performing, but expensive, new XL single-cross hybrids.

Leo did a great job of organizing and administering an effective public relations program and coordinating it with advertising and dealer sales campaigns that both sold our XL hybrids and showed farmers how to maximize their yields. Working with Rus and Harold Noren in the early 1960s, when DeKalb's single-cross high population hybrids were introduced, he developed DeKalb's Five Point Program:

1. Maximize fertilizer application.
2. Increase plant-per-acre populations by using narrower rows.
3. Control weeds with herbicides.
4. Plant as early as possible.
5. Plant DeKalb XL hybrids.

Lloyd Zeman of *Successful Farming Magazine* wrote several convincing articles advocating row width reduction from forty inches to as narrow as twenty inches after observing DeKalb's demonstration plantings at Dayton, Iowa. As a result, implement manufacturers spent large sums changing planter and cultivator designs to accommodate narrower rows. It was Leo Olson, Rus Rasmussen, and Harold Noren who made those things happen.

The promotion of thick planting and heavy fertilization was, in fact, a critically important factor in XL45's success, because its yield at low to medium planting rates was only mediocre. Table 14-4 shows the results their efforts, backed up by great single-cross hybrids, had on DeKalb sales between 1960 and 1969

OFF-GRADE KERNELS INCREASE PROFITS

The tripling of our profit margin as we introduced single crosses occurred partly because we had to find a way to plant the small kernels produced by inbred seed parents. We solved this problem by providing plastic planter plates for our customers to put into their corn planters (the planter manufacturers had installed metal planter plates that would plant only medium-flat kernels). Because our inexpensive plastic planter plates would plant small kernels, we sold nearly 100 percent of the kernels produced by our inbred seed parents, whereas we had normally sold only the medium-flat and large-flat kernels produced in the past by four-way-cross seed parents, which constituted only 55 to 60 percent of the total kernels they produced.

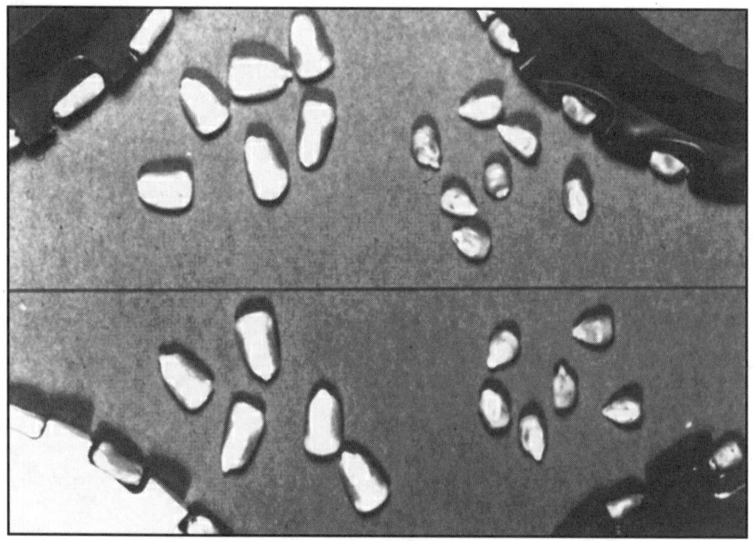

SOURCE: Corporate Records, DeKalb Genetics

Small corn kernels fitting plastic planting plates.

Our single-cross profits were also high because the demand for them was so strong, allowing us to sell odd-shaped kernels that germinated well, but that would not ordinarily be accepted by farmers. In addition, we priced them high because we feared crop failures would occur more frequently when the seed parents were inbreds. That fear proved unfounded.

Our "bet-the-farm" decision to switch our product line as fully as possible to single crosses was the most important decision DeKalb's management had made since the decision in 1923 to produce hybrid seedcorn. I personally was pleased that my father, Tom Roberts, Sr., lived long enough to experience once again the groundswell of praise from farmer customers when they realized DeKalb had created another truly better hybrid.

Table 14-3
DeKalb's North American Seedcorn Sales, 1960–1969

Year	Units
1960	1,988,500
1961	1,607,000
1962	1,530,000
1963	1,755,000
1964	1,839,700
1965	2,157,800
1966	2,217,000
1967	2,789,000
1968	3,158,000
1969	3,511,000

SOURCE: DeKalb's Seed Production Department and personal records of employees who kept track of sales data.
NOTE: These sales are expressed in bushel-equivalent units of 80,000 seeds per bag for single crosses.

A POIGNANT TRIP

Rus Rasmussen and I became close friends, partly because he was doing such a remarkable job of increasing seed sales and profits, but mostly because we respected each other. Rus had a heart attack in 1963; he recovered and returned to work but asked me to travel to Europe with him in 1964 in order to "develop a feel for" our European seed business. At the time, he was the only person in the DeKalb office who knew our growing European seedcorn business well. I felt honored to be asked to travel with him.

Our trip was a poignant experience, marked by the tremendous affection and respect shown him by his European colleagues. Throughout the trip, I often asked Rus to stop and rest with me, pretending that my attache case was too heavy to carry at the pace he was setting. He was always willing to stop, at least for a minute or two. On one such occasion, near midnight after a wonderful dinner at Antonio Marchetto's home in Venice, Rus and I decided to walk across Venice to the Danielle Hotel, where we were staying. Our final rest stop for me and my "heavy" attache case was on the steps of the cathedral in St. Mark's Square, where we were surprised by a woman who approached me asking, "Do you want me?" I, in surprise, replied in two of the few Italian words I knew, "No, grazi," and when she turned to Rus, who was a very handsome and distinguished-looking man; he replied sternly, "No, thank you." She disappeared into the night.

In Paris, Paul Duvivier, president of R.A.G.T., held a dinner party for us in a five-star restaurant, complete with two interpreters. Despite the fact that we declined his invitation to finish the evening at Paris's Cowboy Bar (we had a 6:00 a.m. flight the next day), Duvivier later completed a contract with DeKalb that provided a sound beginning for a long and happy relationship between our company and R.A.G.T. in France.

Farewell, Good Friend

Rus and I had a great trip, and our mutual respect and affection grew day by day. Saying our goodbyes in Madrid at the end of the trip brought tears to my eyes and to his as well.

Rus died of a heart attack a week later, on October 2, 1964. He ranks with Tom Roberts, Sr., and Charlie Gunn as the men who created DeKalb. Tom and Charlie started research in 1924, and Rus joined the company in 1935, creating the sales organization that made it an industry leader.

After Rus' death, I talked with Charlie Roberts about men within the company who should be considered to succeed Rus as vice president for seed operations. Both Harold Noren and Harold Nolin were well qualified to move into the job, but were needed in the jobs they were doing—Noren in seed sales and Nolin in seed production. We concluded that both of these good men deserved more recognition for the fine jobs they were doing, so after discussing the matter with the Executive Committee I assumed the general management of seed operations in addition to being president, Charlie became executive vice president, Harold Noren was made vice president of seed sales, Harold Nolin became vice president of seed operations, and Ray Nelson remained vice president of poultry and animal sciences.

TOM ROBERTS, SR., PASSES AWAY

Tom Roberts, Sr., died in the spring of 1967 a few months after experiencing a devastating stroke. He was seventy-five years old. He was mourned not only by his own family and his DeKalb family but also by people throughout the world of agriculture who had come to admire and respect his entrepreneurial zeal and his devotion to farmers. He was truly a great leader and a fine example for all of us. Indeed, this book is my tribute to him. The following recognitions are selected from many we received:

The Directors of the DeKalb Agricultural Association, Inc., wrote: "[We] deeply regret the loss of our honored Chairman, friend, and associate, whose integrity, vigor, and abilities were inestimable sources of strength to our company, whose affairs he so ably directed for 48 years as Secretary, General Manager, President, and Chairman of the Board, and whose interests he was ever ready to serve and defend. We record, therefore, the loss of a leader of exceptional honor and ability."

John Strohm, a well-known agricultural editor, wrote: "He was one of the real giants of the middle west whom I came to know and respect and love as a great American and a real agricultural pioneer. The legacy he leaves, of course, is all around—what an example he has set for all of us."

Earl Butz, then dean at Purdue University and later secretary of agriculture, stated: "American agriculture will always owe a tremendous debt for the leadership he gave in farm credit, in hybrid seeds, in agribusiness, and on a wide variety of beneficial fronts. It was my privilege first to know Tom back in the 1940s when he was taking the leadership in the battle to save a free farm credit system for American agriculture. Without his leadership and vision, I am sure that our great cooperative farm credit system would have 'gone down the drain.' It now serves agriculture magnificently, thanks to the fight he waged a quarter century ago."

SOURCE: Roberts Family Records

Tom Roberts, Sr.: Revered leader for 48 years

Tom's strengths were his intelligence, imagination, and determination, his understanding of his farmer customers, and his willingness to take the risks necessary to achieve success. His decisions to bet his career on hybrid corn and to go into the oil exploration business in 1942 are prime examples of his daring.

Trust was another of Tom's characteristics that endeared him to those who worked for him, but it sometimes backfired. For example, the first manager of DeKalb's oil exploration business responded positively to the freedom of action Tom gave him during the war years of 1942 through 1946, and the farm-outs he negotiated were tremendously successful for many years. But Tom's willingness to "let his managers manage" with minimal supervision resulted in eight postwar years of disappointing results from our oil operations. I believe that the lesson here is that if the general manager's style is to be over-trusting, he needs to be careful to appoint aggressive managers who will instinctively know when to consult the boss.

Perhaps Tom's greatest strength was his genuine interest in the well-being of his employees, as was manifested in his early installation of profit-sharing and hospitalization plans. His regular reports to employees at annual meetings endeared him to everyone in the organization.

Tom was an old-fashioned, tight-fisted manager who for a long time would not allow radios to be installed in company cars because he wanted his people "thinking about business" while driving. He was appalled by the wasted time he associated with coffee breaks and insisted on five-and-half-day work weeks for many years after most companies had cut back to five days. When he finally gave in to employee demands for five-day work weeks, he did so in exchange for dropping coffee breaks. He rejected telephone credit cards for at least ten years after most other companies had allowed their traveling salesmen to have them. He had many more such ideas, but instead of resenting them, his employees understood and respected him for his thrift and his high expectations.

Tom would not allow the hiring of known "drinkers," and never allowed cocktail parties at sales conventions or any other company function. On the other hand, he had patience with able employees who developed drinking problems and stood by them while they made real efforts to get well.

These are just a few of the straight-laced ideas that Tom combined with compassion. His employees loved him for his conscientious demands as well as for his obvious concern for their personal welfare.

My Greatest Day

Two years after Tom died in 1967, Harold Engh, a very successful businessman who had been my father's lifelong best friend and golfing partner, called me to his office for a talk. After we had taken care of business matters and I was about to leave, he said to me, "Tommy, for quite a few years I thought you might be a bit too big for your britches, but I've recently learned what has happened to DeKalb in the nine years you have been its boss, and I want you to know that I think you have been doing a great job. Your dad would have been very proud of you."

That was the greatest moment of my business life.

Chapter 15

New Vigor in Corn Research 1960-1995

As competitive pressures increased and farmers realized that most four-way crosses looked and yielded about the same, we became convinced that our future would depend on pure, higher yielding single crosses.

At first, many of our corn breeders were nervous about single-cross hybrids. They were concerned that single-crosses could not be produced in consistent volume because of parent line weaknesses, but by 1960 most would admit that strong-stalked, disease-resistant inbreds could be good seed parents, and they knew that hybrid vigor would be maximized in single crosses.

In the end, the phenomenal success of single-cross XL45, together with Harold Noren's clear and urgent request for single-cross hybrids to be made available in all major maturities caused our breeders to accept that single-crosses were the wave of the future. Major changes were made at all of our research stations, with emphasis on single-cross performance at high plant population levels.

The significance of our decision to swing strongly into single-cross hybrids is dramatically illustrated in Table 15-1, which shows how yields increased between 1935 and 1990, when the entire industry had followed our leadership into predominately single-cross production. Table 15-1 also suggests that as plant breeders developed hybrids that would reliably produce ears on every plant at high plant populations, farmers became more confident of achieving higher yields at higher plant population rates.

As farmers witnessed the yield performance of single-crosses that would yield well at high plant population rates, they increased their use of fertilizer, herbicides and insecticides to maximize their yields, and, in the process, to provide more food for an exploding world population.

"Hybridization Did Much More Than Just Increase Yield"

Richard Crabb, in his 1947 book The Hybrid Corn Makers: Prophets of Plenty, writes:

> "Hybrid corn did much more than just increase corn yields. In the corn belt, it is in the process of revolutionizing our agriculture as completely as the steam engine revolutionized the industrial world. It is changing not just methods of farm

management and farm operation, but also the social pattern of the farm family and the rural community.

Ever since the American industrial achievement that accompanied our participation in the First World War, there has existed a strong movement toward mechanized farming in our most concentrated and highly productive farming areas. Tractors were introduced along with a host of machines that were more efficient than the old horse-drawn implements.

One job, however, could not be done successfully by machine, and that was the harvesting of corn. Our farmers had to keep their horses for harvesting corn in the fall, and since they could not afford to let the horses remain idle for the rest of the year, they were forced to cling to much of their horse-pulled equipment. Inventors had tried in vain, especially after the great success of the McCormick reaper had banished the need of harvesting small grain by hand, to develop a practical corn picker, but their best efforts produced nothing of much more than novelty value until the coming of hybrid corn.

The new corn provided two things that had prevented mechanical corn pickers from being successful. It would stand in the field long after the regular harvest time if necessary, and the ears of hybrid corn were so uniform in size and position on the stalk that it became simpler to develop successful corn pickers.

With the coming of the successful corn picker, many a farmer sold his last pair of horses and swung over completely over to a mechanized type of farming. This put his farming operations on a basis of greater efficiency and resulted in his producing the greatest number of pounds per man in all the long history of agriculture. He soon discovered that he could handle a larger acreage, and this accelerated the trend toward fewer and larger farms.

The mechanical corn picker, its effectiveness and wide use made possible by hybrid corn, was quickly adopted by corn belt farmers. In 1935 only fifteen percent of the corn in Iowa was harvested by machine, but in 1945 approximately seventy percent of the Iowa corn crop and fifty-five percent of all of the corn in our corn belt was mechanically harvested.....our farmers in 1942 produced the greatest volume of corn ever raised in the United States, a record 3.2 billion bushel crop, and did it with one-fifth less corn ground than was planted in 1917 to raise our greatest corn crop of the First World War. This "surplus" land, amounting to nearly twenty million acres, was planted to soybeans and other war crops. (Pp. 290–94)"

PROBLEMS MANAGING RESEARCH

Managing an expanding research program turned out to be more difficult than it should have been, given our willingness to finance whatever research budget increases were necessary to maintain or expand our market share. In 1960, after Virgil Welch threatened to resign if Sherret Chase were appointed director of corn research, Chase accepted the newly created position of director of international corn research, where he did a great job. I had planned to wait a few years for Chase's talent to be demonstrated before making him head of all of our seed research, but that plan fell apart when he resigned in 1966. His letter of resignation was the biggest disappointment of my career with DeKalb.

Figure 15-1
Average U.S. corn yield increase per year for kinds of corn

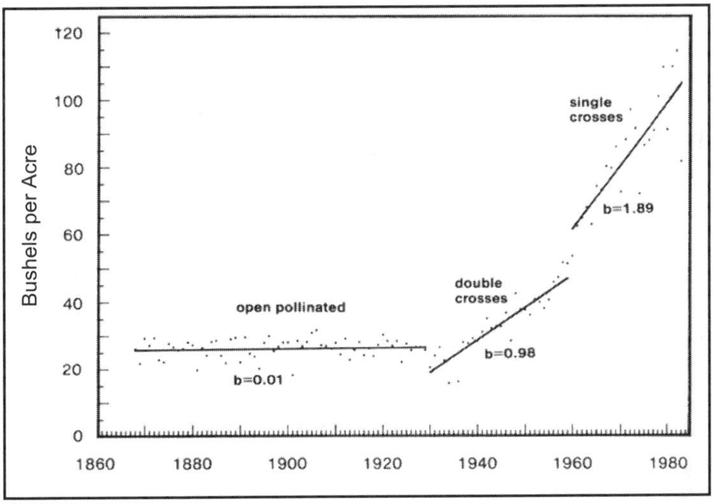

SOURCE: Forest Troyer

Dr. Basil Tsotsis Takes Over in the U.S.

After Sherry took over international corn research in 1960, Basil Tsotsis began coordinating domestic corn research and was named U.S. corn research director in 1964. Until then, Basil had organized our first pathology lab in 1958 to assist breeders in the identification and elimination of disease vulnerabilities; he had organized the statistical evaluation of data from our testing program (computerizing it in 1961, the first in our industry to do so); he had also participated in germ plasm and hybrid development in Chase's breeding program. After 1962 he was responsible for the advancement of hybrids XL64 and XL66, both of which were developed in Chase's program. They would be big DeKalb winners.

The program that Sherry set up in 1954 and in which Basil participated after 1958 covered all eleven maturity classes (0 to 1200) serviced by DeKalb hybrids. This was consistent with our objective of having their program influence our overall breeding effort. Shortly after being appointed corn research director, Basil informed Dick Holland that there were still more than a thousand unevaluated inbred lines, a substantial number of which could be used in areas with seasons either earlier or later than that of DeKalb, Illinois.

Basil volunteered to sort out the best lines and send them to breeders in locations where the lines were best suited. He crossed them with "tester" lines of the Reid x Lancaster heterotic pattern, planting them and evaluating their performance in hybrids after harvest. After conducting his evaluations, Basil made a practice of offering all DeKalb corn breeders (including those who were newly hired) free choice of any of these tested inbreds to include in their own breeding programs. In that way, many of the lines became widely used by our breeders and were key to the development of hybrids like XL43, XL54, XL66, XL64, XL75, XL 81, and others that supported DeKalb's sales surge in the early 1970s.

Basil Tsotsis' Approach to Corn Breeding

Basil recognized that there were two fundamental approaches to breeding, both of which should be utilized by breeders. The differences of opinion he would encounter with his breeders were in degree of emphasis. The alternative approaches were population breeding and line improvement:

Population breeding involves collecting elite lines on each side of the well-respected Reid x Lancaster heterotic pattern, inter-crossing the lines within each germ plasm "pool," and selecting among the segregating progeny for superior traits. The improved germ plasm pools are then used as elite sources for the initiation of inbreeding. Outstanding inbreds such as Iowa's widely used B73 were selected from this sort of elite germ plasm pool.

Many theoreticians think this system has the greatest long-term potential because it encourages genetic diversity through gene recombination. Basil Tsotsis believed in the soundness of population breeding and insisted that DeKalb's breeders include it in their breeding programs.

Line improvement starts with the breeders' most elite inbred lines and aims to improve them by out-crossing to other germ plasm known to contain genes that may correct weaknesses in the elite line. This is usually followed by backcrossing to the elite line, inbreeding, and selecting in subsequent segregating generations for retention of the desired genes. This may be followed by another cycle of backcrossing to the elite line, again inbreeding, and selecting for both the desirable characteristics of the elite line and the improvements the breeder is aiming to incorporate into the line. This approach tends to make small incremental improvements in well-established parental lines.

Line improvement had been emphasized by Pioneer, whose

breeder and research coordinator, Dr. Forrest Troyer, claimed "Population breeding is for show, and line improvement is for dough." Their success suggests that the line improvement system must be emphasized by hard-competing firms, whose competitive survival depends on the more rapid improvements available from the line improvement system. For breeding programs as large as Pioneer's and DeKalb's, the best solution appears to be to insist that every corn breeder utilize both systems but put greater emphasis on line improvement. It is interesting to note that Bob Siefert, a believer in population breeding and developer of the outstanding Pioneer 3369A, was appointed Pioneer's corn research director in 1976.

Our Goal: Singles in All Maturities

DeKalb's breeders responded quickly to Harold Noren's request to develop single crosses for all major maturities. XL43, XL66, XL64, and XL81 all used inbreds out of Sherry Chase and Basil Tsotsis' breeding program and were winners as XL43 succeeded XL45 in the north central corn belt; XL64 and XL81 were behind DeKalb's big sales gains in the central and south central corn belt in the late 1960s and early 1970s. Until then, the central corn belt had been dominated for many years by Pioneer, Funk, and PAG (Pfister Associated Growers).

Other DeKalb breeders contributed both single and three-way crosses to our product line as our market share of the U.S. hybrid seedcorn business doubled between 1960 and 1970. Needless to say, we encouraged Basil to hire all the breeders he needed and to establish research stations to maintain or increase our market share even more. Table 15-2 shows the location and leaders of the breeding stations established between 1960 and 1969.

Table 15-2
New DeKalb Corn Researchers, 1960–1969

Year	Location	Responsibility
1960	DeKalb, Ill.	Glen Stringfield, sr. research adviser
1962	Mt. Olive, N.C.	Dr. Dave Alvey, new station manager
1963	Dayton, Iowa	Bob Christensen, test station manager
1964	DeKalb, Ill.	Dr. Bill Crum, new station manager
1965	Illiopolis, Ill.*	Dr. R. G, Johnson, new station manager
1967	Leesburg, Ga.	Dr. Jack Duclos, new station mgr.
1967	Mason, Mich.	Dr. Gary Beil, new station manager
1968	DeKalb, Ill.	Dr. John Eastin, corn physiology
1969	DeKalb, Ill.	Dr. Marvin Lindsay, genetic resources

SOURCE: Dr. Basil Tsotsis.

* Illiopolis research moved to Thomasboro (near Champaign, Ill.) in 1977.

Basil Tsotsis hired a number of new corn breeders in the 1970s. The following chronology lists their research station locations and responsibilities:

1970	Hired Dr. Jerry Arnold to replace Dr. Dave Alvey, who had resigned, at DeKalb's Mt. Olive, N.C., location. Initiated DeKalb corn research in Mexico under the direction of Dr. Lindsay and the participation of a Mexican corn breeder, Oscar Cota, at two locations, where we could make two breeding cycles per year.
1973	Hired Dr. Dave Smith to manage the DeKalb, Ill., pathology program that Basil had established in 1958. Approved Dr. Smith's recommendation that a new plant pathology program be set up at Mt. Olive and managed by Dale Dowden. Hired Dr. John Snyder to direct a new program for specialty corns, genetic studies, and tissue culture. Established a corn borer lab in Michigan to produce corn borer egg masses for all DeKalb corn breeders. Hired Dr. Ron Castleberry to replace Dr. John Eastin, to direct our corn physiology program. Hired Dr. John Pfund to assist Dr. Crum at the DeKalb, Ill., research location.
1975	Opened a new breeding location for the early maturities at Glanworth, Ontario, under local breeder Ron LeDrew.
1976	Hired Dr. Craig Cowley to manage a new corn research program at Marion, Ohio. Hired Dr. Tom Morgan to direct Mount Olive station, transferring Dr. Jerry Arnold to a new corn research station at Union City, Tennessee. Dr. James Overman hired and located at Union City primarily to develop resistance to the southwestern corn borer.
1977	Converted Dayton, Iowa, corn testing station to a full breeding station under the direction of Dr. Marv Lindsay, who relinquished his role in Mexican breeding to others he had trained.
1978	Hired Dr. Keith Kauffman to replace Dr. Lindsay in directing the germ plasm resources program. Basil leaves temperate corn research to direct the tropical corn research effort.

TROPICAL CORN RESEARCH

By the end of the decade, Basil Tsotsis' strengthening of research on tropical corn was paying off handsomely for DeKalb in such far-away places as Thailand, Indonesia, Brazil, Mexico, and Central America:

1973 Established a new research location near Guadalajara, Mexico, with our Mexican partners, the Bohrer brothers of Ciudad Obregon, Sonora.

1974 Hired Dr. Ramon Godoy as corn breeder and elevated Osçar Cota to general manager in Mexico.

1978 Established a DeKalb corn breeding effort in Brazil. Developed nursery operations and research facilities at Barretos, Sao Paulo, and at Paso Fundo, Rio Grande do Sol, with new buildings and labs. Hired an outstanding young corn breeder, Dr. Ofiro Solferini, for the Barretos location, and another good man named Liberto Puzzar for Passo Fundo.

1979 Acquired a research location near Puerto Vallarta, in Mexico, to allow for efficient breeding operations of two cycles per year. Hired Carlos Levy as breeder-pathologist. Built lab facilities at both Guadalajara and Puerto Vallarta.

Established a research farm at Solongpan, Thailand, under Dr. Sutat Sriwatanpougse (1979–1982) and Dr. Anek Silapepun (1982–present). Our Thai location is a valuable one for all DeKalb research because it is in one of the few places in the world where segregating corn can be selected in the certain presence of downy mildew, which is often a serious corn disease in the tropics. Segregating germ plasm from all DeKalb tropical research locations (and some temperate locations) is routinely planted there to identify plants resistant to downy mildew.

Basil Tsotsis' development of DeKalb's U.S. corn research team was consistent with management's goal of expanding research whenever it was justified. We were fully aware that our research was the key to our future. Basil deserves credit and appreciation for his many contributions to DeKalb's growth. In my opinion his most notable achievements were as follows:

- his leadership role in developing hybrids that propelled us to U.S. industry leadership in the late 1960s and early 1970s.
- his many contributions to the improvement of our hybrid corn testing programs;
- His hiring, training, and development of many of the corn breeders we depend on today and who were essential to our competitive survival in the U.S. seed corn market in the 1970s and 1980s; and

- his organization and development of the tropical corn breeding program that has become the basis for a steadily growing DeKalb seedcorn business in many tropical countries.

SOURCE: Basil Tsotsis

Dr. Basil Tsotsis

By 1978, it was apparent that the reason for DeKalb's decline in corn market share was our lack of truly competitive hybrids. This implied that our research and development effort needed major changes and redirection. To make a major change was gut-wrenching for me and all of my advisers because it would mean a heavy swing in temperate areas in the direction of line-by-line breeding, which had been making steady progress. However, we needed new and better hybrids as quickly as they could be developed, so we gave the leadership of our vital temperate corn research leadership to Charlie Krull, a man who would give greater emphasis to line-by-line breeding.

Basil Tsotsis remained director of tropical corn research, where his thorough knowledge of tropical corn and his familiarity with population breeding were needed. He would, for example, cross elite populations of our best temperate and subtropical lines with tropical lines to broaden the base populations behind a line-improvement system. He accepted his new assignment and went about his duties with vigor that substantially improved our tropical germ plasm and ultimately produced very good hybrids for his area of responsibility. Basil resigned on July 15, 1985.

DR. CHARLIE KRULL: TEMPERATE CORN RESEARCH DIRECTOR

Dr. Charlie Krull was selected to overhaul our temperate corn research program. Charlie had joined the company in 1968, working on both hybrid wheat and hybrid corn. He showed considerable versatility when he became our research director in Argentina, where he and his assistant, Fabio Nider, had significant success crossing the best U.S. dent corn into lower-yielding Argentine flints and selecting for both flint kernel characteristics and high yield.

Flint corns had been required by the Argentine government for many years because shippers of dent grain had run into spoilage problems shipping dent corn to Europe in the early part of the century. Although flint corn kernels were harder than dent kernels and stood shipment better than the dents, dents nearly always out-yielded flints in farmers' fields. Charlie and his assistant, Fabio Nider, were convinced that yields of Argentine flint hybrids could be significantly increased by crossing our best dent inbred lines onto Argentine flints, selecting in subsequent segregating generations for the flint kernel character in combination with the high yields of dents. This breeding system was very successful—indeed, so successful that it produced many outstanding hybrids well adapted to Argentina.

SOURCE: Charlie Krull

Charlie Krull, Temperate Corn Research Director

Charlie's Plant Breeding Record

Most of the U.S. corn research group considered Charlie to be a wheat breeder rather than a corn breeder, which caused some consternation when he was put in charge of our U.S. corn research. We were concerned that we might lose some breeders over this change, but in practice, none left. This was probably because the breeders recognized that change was needed and perhaps also because they respected Charlie's plant breeding ability. Charlie's management style was to convince his breeders that changes in their breeding methods were necessary, leaving final decisions up to each breeder. His background with Rockefeller was probably helpful, where he also had to rely on convincing, rather than ordering, local scientists to make needed changes.

Charlie arrived in the United States from Italy in May of 1978, after the research plantings were essentially finished. He spent most of the summer analyzing programs in depth, talking with our breeders, and developing a series of changes. Some of these were made for the 1978–79 winter nurseries, and several were made for the 1979 field season, but most were made in the 1980s.

Changes Made by Charlie

In 1988, after ten years on the job, Krull wrote a memo summarizing his work at DeKalb and the changes implemented on his watch. I have incorporated parts of his memo into this book. His work has been used in various company presentations to establish research credibility with employees, dealers, customers, and the investment community.

In short, Charlie did three things: (1) He shifted our emphasis from population breeding to line-by-line breeding; (2) he and his breeders greatly increased the amount of material being yield-tested by increasing the crossing done at each station and by opening new breeding and testing stations; (3) he slowed the tempo of hybrid releases to allow for more thorough testing of hybrids before they went on the market.

Line-by-Line Breeding

Charlie suspected that a large part of our problem resulted from an overemphasis on breeding from broad-based populations, a practice that had developed in a well-justified move by Chase and Tsotsis to broaden the selection base over what had been done in the 1940s and early 1950s, when a lot of effort was put into reselecting within inbred lines. The lure of broad-based populations was that they contained the variability needed to make progress in breeding. Their disadvantage, however, was that the frequency of desirable combinations was low. That is, it was difficult to get truly outstanding inbred lines directly from a population. This problem was behind the hiring of Dr. Marv Lindsay in 1968 to develop a "genetic resources" program to provide truly elite populations to be used by breeders who were reluctant to work with such materials directly but needed to work elite germ plasm into their line improvement programs.

Line-by-line crosses between commercially useful lines or between population-derived lines and commercially useful lines give a much higher probability of finding an outstanding new inbred. As Dr. Forrest Troyer said, "Population breeding is for show, line-by-line breeding is for dough." Eventually, progress must come from a broad population, but the primary emphasis must be on breeding from crosses between the best available lines. Unfortunately, population breeding may have been overemphasized in the late 1960s and early 1970s

Given his history, everyone expected Charlie to make this change, and he did. Doing so did not, however, require much pressure from him, because our breeders realized the change was needed. He was asked frequently if line-by-line breeding was now the approved method. His reply was generally that they had the freedom to use populations, line-by-line crosses, exotics, or any combination of them, but that they would be judged on results. But most of our breeders switched to Charlie's preferred method, line-by-line crosses.

Breeding and Testing Volume

While the needed emphasis on line-by-line breeding was fairly well understood, Charlie concluded that too few plants were being worked in segregating generations, particularly the first segregating generation (S1), and too little testing was being done.

We had certainly not been reluctant to support research and had thought that our research volume was as high as any in the industry, including that of Pioneer. Our breeding stations were generally larger than Pioneer's, and we had about the same number. Stations that had been used primarily for testing had been expanded to full-blown breeding stations even before Charlie Krull's arrival. These included Union City, Tennessee in 1976, Dayton, Iowa, in 1977, and Marion, Ohio, in 1977.

DeKalb did a good deal of testing "on station," while Pioneer breeders did most of their testing at off-station locations. Consequently, they were using more testing locations than DeKalb. This required time for us to correct, but in the early 1980s Charlie significantly increased the number of DeKalb stations, the volume of work per station, and the amount of off-station testing.

Much of the first segregating generation (S1) of the line-by-line crosses had been handled in two-row blocks, which in Charlie's opinion didn't have enough plants to select for the segregating characters. In the mid-1970s, Dr. Bill Crum had begun producing test hybrids in "scalars" (making test crosses by using an elite male pollinator on several rows of different female lines that had been detasseled). Charlie had used this system successfully and inexpensively in Argentina and persuaded his breeders that it permitted more test hybrids to be produced and tested each year than had previously been possible. Our breeders agreed that larger populations should be handled, and most used the "scalar" method extensively by 1980, often using 10-row blocks, moving to 20, 40, and even 300-row blocks per breeding cross as they experienced the advantages of scalars. On Charlie's watch, production of experimental hybrids for testing was tremendously expanded, using scalars for crossing in both summer and winter blocks.

Segregating Material Is Given More Emphasis

In Charlie's opinion, the total amount of segregating material also represented too small a percentage of the total nursery work. He addressed this in two ways: first, by greatly increasing the amount of segregating material being handled per station, and second, by decreasing the amount of hand-pollinated nursery work devoted to hybrid makeup and observation. The amount of segregating material could be doubled in this way, with only a 5–10 percent increase in budget, which was quite cost-effective.

The amount of segregating material being worked was also expanded when we opened new stations. Charlie and Dr. C. W. (Bill) Crum, associate director of our corn research program, opened a series of breeding and testing stations in the early 1980s, concentrating primarily west of the Mississippi River, where we had done less work. The new facilities included breeding stations at Owatonna, Minnesota (1981), North Liberty, Iowa (1982), Marshall, Missouri (1982), and Glenvil, Nebraska (1986), as well as major testing stations at Canandaigua, New York, and Garden City, Kansas (1981). All of these changes ballooned the amount of segregating material ten times in the decade after 1978. The additional amount of material being evaluated obviously increased greatly the probability of surfacing better lines and hybrids.

Mechanizing

An even greater challenge, however, was to increase yield testing fast enough to fully evaluate the numbers of new hybrids we would be producing. The main obstacle to the expansion of our testing program was the almost complete lack of plot mechanization that prevailed in the late 1970s, when virtually everything was planted by hand. The lack of mechanization limited the testing volume, made depth of planting difficult to control, and caused the planting season to drag out far too long. Pioneer had mechanized planting several years earlier.

Charlie and Bill urged us to buy specialized plot seeders, which we quickly did. Today, a greatly increased volume of nursery and yield trials is now planted in 20 percent of the time it required in 1978.

Another bottleneck was our harvesting of yield tests, so Charlie and Bill also convinced us to purchase specialized plot combines, which are now fully automated, one-man machines. The combined effects of mechanization and additional stations have allowed the amount of our yield testing to be expanded enormously, and we are now are testing more than 700,000 replicated entries per year. This is probably the largest testing effort on any crop by any company in the world.

Charlie Krull urged me to discuss this increase in nursery and testing volume here at some length because he believes it to be as important as the shift to line-by-line breeding in increasing breeding productivity from 1980 onward.

Hybrid Release Tempo Slowed

Hybrids must be adequately tested before release to ensure that they fit market needs. When a company's hybrid is not performing well in the marketplace, it is tempting to jump to something new without adequate data. But there is really no substitute for multi-year testing. Additional testing does not, of course, make a bad hybrid better, but additional data are often needed to be sure that a new hybrid is truly superior.

Occasionally, DeKalb sales executives became overly enamored with a new pedigree based on observation or sketchy data, and urged its release to meet a sales need. To the best of my knowledge, this practice was never approved by either our scientists or our top executives, but it nevertheless happened in a small number of situations. In the late 1970s and early 1980s, the success of Pioneer 3780, our primary competitor, hastened our release of hybrids with insufficient information. To meet the 3780 challenge, XL25, a good hybrid that was essentially defensive, was released, followed by XL23, XL25A, XL28, XL31, and the infamous XL36, which was the only one released without approval by our research people. XL25A was probably the best of these. It did not really keep up with 3780 in yield, but it had salable advantages in stalk strength, disease resistance, insect resistance, test weight, and grain quality.

DEKALB-PFIZER GENETICS: A JOINT VENTURE

Although the changes Charlie Krull and his group made in corn research were solid and we supported them fully, progress was going to require time, so our market share continued to slip alarmingly to Pioneer and the look-alikes marketed by other companies. We could not use the look-alikes ourselves because the foundation seed company selling the inbred parents would not deal with the major producers, Pioneer, DeKalb, and Funk. Nevertheless, we needed at least short-term access to better germ plasm in the late 1970s and early 1980s. Pfizer was able to fulfill many of our needs.

Ultimately, the joint venture with Pfizer had these three advantages:

- Pfizer had commercial quantities of promising hybrids like T1100 that would help us immediately in the marketplace.
- Pfizer's twelve breeders had been trained for six years by Dr. Forrest Troyer, who had been a key man at Pioneer for many years. Many of them had developed promising new hybrids that would most probably be released for sale soon. We knew

that corn breeding was to some extent a "numbers game," meaning that the more good breeders we employed, the better our chance of developing superior hybrids would be.

- Pfizer had launched a biotechnical corn research program that seemed to fit well with our own. Pfizer had better laboratories, and we had more testing facilities and knowledge of on-the-farm needs.
- Pfizer's FACT testing system, comparing hybrids under final tests in strips of six or eight rows, has had an important impact; hybrids sometimes behave differently in strips than in standard two-row tests. Adding the four-row FACT test in one more year of testing has prevented us from advancing hybrids that aren't ready. Dealers like it too, not only because it gives them more confidence in our decisions but also because it gives them a chance to view candidates for commercial release in their area.

Pfizer's Corn Research Program

Starting with stations at Olivia, Minnesota, and Mason City, Illinois, Dr. Forrest Troyer had established his own breeding work at the St. Louis headquarters for Pfizer Genetics and 12 corn breeding stations across the corn belt in the mid-1970s. This included stations at Madison, Wisconsin; Windfall, Indiana; Tifton, Palmyra, Pennsylvania; Georgia; Story City, Iowa; Farmville, North Carolina; Kingston, Ohio; Doniphan, Nebraska; and Blenheim, Ontario. He also directed soybean breeding stations at Beaman, Iowa and Terre Haute, Indiana.

Opening such a large group of stations in a short time was difficult, and the stations were not well financed, but Forrest assembled a group of fine breeders. Many of the stations in this network supplemented the expansion already under way within DeKalb.

Charlie and Forrest encouraged the exchange of inbreds and the making of breeding crosses within a few days after the merger. Initially, the Pfizer and DeKalb research groups operated separately, but they were consolidated under Charlie's leadership in 1986. Forrest continued his own program near DeKalb, and also carried out a number of specific projects for the company until his retirement in 1993.

The ex-DeKalb and ex-Pfizer stations complemented each other well in some areas. For example, DeKalb had a station in Tennessee, but Pfizer did not; while Pfizer had a station in Indiana, and DeKalb did not. But there were two stations in Georgia, North Carolina, and Ohio, which is more than the acreage planted by farmers justified. Other duplications were in major corn states such as

Minnesota and Iowa. These stations were streamlined and consolidated, and the net effect was a larger network that did a better job of covering the important U.S. corn areas. Of the twenty-one DeKalb stations operating in the United States in 1994, six had come from the Pfizer group along with a number of good breeders.

Our corporate "marriage" was not consummated rapidly. Some breeders resigned from both companies and found corn breeding work elsewhere. On balance, however, I am convinced that the most capable breeders stayed, probably partly because DeKalb's stations were well funded, and partly because our combined farmer-dealer sales organizations were deemed to be capable of selling much larger quantities of an outstanding new hybrid than would have been the case with smaller companies. There is no greater thrill for most DeKalb corn breeders than to see the "winged ear" flying beside corn fields for mile after mile throughout the Midwest.

Charlie Krull Resigns, John Pfund Takes Over

In July of 1993, Charlie Krull left DeKalb. He was not immediately replaced, probably because DeKalb's regional research organization was well established and effective. However, Dr. John Pfund, who had been slowly but surely turning out good hybrids, was made DeKalb's research director in 1995. John's newest hybrids made market share increases possible in the key north-central corn belt area.

Thus ends my report on the growth and development as well as the trials and tribulations of DeKalb's corn research program. It grew steadily from the late 1950s through the 1980s, and the excellent performance of recently released hybrids and the company's recent market share gains stand as tribute to the effectiveness of both its research and its dedicated management team, which is headed by Chairman and CEO Bruce P. Bickner and President Richard Ryan.

Chapter 16

Hybrid Sorghum 1960-1992

A note to readers: This chapter covers thirty-two years instead of the usual ten because I believe the sorghum story can best be told with reference to events over the longer period.

As our hybrid sorghum business grew, it became apparent that Dick Holland was being overworked. He suggested that we look for the best young breeder we could find. In an extensive search, we found Dr. Bruce Maunder, who had been an outstanding graduate student at Purdue. Bruce became one of the most dedicated, energetic, hard-working, and effective plant breeders DeKalb has ever had. He stepped into his new job in 1960, assisting Dick where help was needed, and demonstrating strong interest in being involved with the overseas sorghum breeding that was getting under way in Argentina, Mexico, and other parts of the world.

In late 1961, I asked Dick Holland to move to DeKalb to assume responsibility for all plant breeding, and only twenty-two months after joining DeKalb, Bruce stepped into Dick's sorghum shoes.

1964: THE INTRODUCTION OF THE HETERO-YELLOW HYBRID

Over the years, Bruce has been very active in identifying new and promising germ plasm from USDA's world collection, where he has found varieties of yellow-seeded sorghums and crossed them into his seed parents, producing the outstanding hetero-yellow hybrids that came to be a significant part of DeKalb's product mix. These hybrids were more drought resistant than the rest of our sorghum product line. Along with yellow-by-yellow crosses, he developed hetero-yellow hybrids E57, F61, and F64, which were introduced to the market in 1964. These hybrids excelled in dormancy (going dormant during dry spells and recovering to produce good grain yields when it rained), had more disease resistance and root strength, higher test weight, higher yields, and more tolerance to stalk rot. They were, in fact, a step upward to a new plateau of excellence for our sorghum product line.

Bruce was one of the first to identify developing problems with sorghum headsmut disease in south Texas, and to successfully seek headsmut resistance in the "world collection." Varieties retained in this collection were usually low yielding but were retained because they carried genes resistant to diseases and/or insects. Having found resistance of the kind he wanted, Bruce quickly crossed it into his better lines and developed resistant hybrids for areas where headsmut was a problem. He also succeeded in incorporating resistance to downy mildew disease into DeKalb hybrids.

In the 1960s, Bruce expanded research and testing, both domestically and internationally. His tutoring and the diversity of his sorghum germ plasm were tremendously helpful to Fabio Nider of DeKalb Argentina, as well as to Dr. Glen Robison, the head of the new sorghum research facility we had established in central Nebraska. The yeoman work done by this team has kept DeKalb well ahead of its competitors.

1968: THE YEAR OF THE GREENBUG

As sorghum acreage and yields increased, insect problems became more difficult, especially from the greenbug, which had first attacked sorghum in the United States in 1968. Bruce's vigorous use of the world collection of sorghum germ plasm made possible his pioneering release in 1972 of the first greenbug-resistant hybrids, giving us yet another edge on our competitors; his effective breeding effort, coupled with successful seed multiplication, enabled DeKalb to have enough greenbug-resistant seed to plant 4 million acres in 1976, a full year ahead of competitors, who were depending on Texas A & M for their seed stock. The greenbug is prone to mutation, and so it continued to be a major project for Bruce, who quickly developed new hybrids resistant to the new races of greenbug that came along.

SOURCE: Bruce Maunder

Bruce Maunder shooting down a huge greenbug.

A new generation of DeKalb hetero-yellow hybrids was introduced in 1969, and C42Y, a true yellow, began its growth in popularity on the immense dry land acreage of our western Great Plains. It became DeKalb's leading sorghum hybrid in the 1970s.

Bruce has also developed a comprehensive sudan grass breeding program. His objective is to find male parents for sorghum–sudan grass (Sudax) hybrids that will keep us ahead of the generic sorghum–sudan grass hybrids our competitors came out with after they observed our success with Sudax.

DEKALB SORGHUM RESEARCH GOES INTERNATIONAL

Bruce Maunder established a sorghum research program in Argentina, working with Fabio Nider, who had begun breeding corn for us in the pampas in the mid-1960s. Their sorghum program developed sorghum hybrids for subtropical Argentina, South Africa, and Australia, as well as for tropical areas like northern Argentina, Brazil, and Colombia. Bruce also took full advantage of the opportunity DeKalb Argentina gave him to accelerate temperate sorghum breeding: he can grow two crops in one year by alternating research plantings every six months between the northern and southern hemispheres.

DEKALB HYBRID SORGHUM: NUMBER ONE IN THE WORLD

Dr. Bruce Maunder, responding to my request for information about DeKalb's sorghum business, wrote:

> Tom, I think that we probably want to emphasize that in the 1960s and 1970s our advantages were most obvious in dry years where the germ plasm we were using gave us more root, more resistance to water loss, more dormancy, more heat tolerance, and more of the various traits needed to tolerate stress. In the last 5 to 10 years [1982 to 1992], we have been much stronger on the high yield end with hybrids like DK-48 in the medium maturity class and DK-56 and DK-66 in the irrigated or favorable rainfall class. I think in the upper Panhandle of Texas DK-66 has likely won the Texas A&M trial five or six times out of the last seven years and won again in 1992. We also had very strong results in the Halfway test near Plainview....
>
> Until the late 1970s, Northrup King more or less owned the early maturity market, but their hybrids were high in tannin or had a subcoat and they also had poor stalk quality. Glen Robison, who came with us in Nebraska in 1965, was able to work with a 4-dwarf early female which gave a strong dominance for maturity without using a brown type germ plasm. This gave us high yielding hybrids of far better stalk quality, so the market switched rather rapidly to DeKalb, which gave

us a much improved market share which we have maintained ever since.

SOURCE: Bruce Maunder

Bruce Maunder "At Home"

I think Bruce just about said it all in those two paragraphs. In another letter, however, he made these points about important events in the history of our sorghum business:

- In 1975 farm trials of some 250 comparison plots, we showed that C42a+, C42y+, and E59+, all of which were greenbug-resistant hybrids, would outperform their counterparts even in the absence of the greenbug. When the greenbug was present, they were much stronger than their counterparts.
- In 1976, we had enough greenbug-resistant seed of the hybrids named above to plant 4 million acres. The impact of that seed is apparent in the sales data presented in Table 24-1.
- In 1980, biotype E of the greenbug came to the Great Plains, and the race to develop hybrids resistant to the new biotype began.
- In 1983, our first E-resistant hybrid was developed, and our whole product line was converted to this resistance, thanks to some Russian and Spanish germ plasm Bruce had already been "working," and which already had resistance to both C and E..
- In 1989, DeKalb made the first sale of sorghum seed strongly resistant to sorghum midge, an insect that can

devastate grain yields of sorghum in hot, moist climates. It was a success, but was only needed in the Mississippi delta.

- In 1990, DK40y and DK56 joined DK37, giving us three new hybrids with earlier maturity and much higher yields than the hybrids they replaced. These hybrids were early enough in maturity and high yielding enough to perform well with minimum irrigation in dry areas.

Finally, and most appropriately, the Farm Industry News chose DeKalb's greenbug work and the hybrids that had been developed by our staff as one of the nineteen best products developed over the previous twenty-five years of U.S. agricultural products. The reward was based on polls taken of farmers and readers. This, I think, is the finest ending I can give to a story about a fine organization headed by one of the finest plant breeders I have ever known.

SOURCE: Bruce Maunder

A Sorghum Field Day in Nebraska

CORN YIELDS THREATEN, BUT HIGHER SORGHUM YIELDS ARE AHEAD

On February 28, 1992, Bruce Maunder had both good and bad news for me. The good news was that he had some new sorghum germ plasm that had shown as much as a 20 percent yield increase over our current commercial product. The bad news was that the U.S. sorghum industry was in chaos because acreage planted had declined to only 9 million from a 1960 level exceeding 15.5 million, in spite of average yields having increased from 22 to 73 bushels per acre during the same period.

The decline in sorghum acreage was attributed to new corn hybrids, which had been outperforming sorghum on irrigated farms. Bruce was nevertheless encouraged by his own research results and believed we could ride out the storm because he thought that the performance of his new hybrids would soon cause farmers to plant more sorghum.

Very unfortunately, Bruce tendered his resignation from DeKalb in late 1996. The fundamental reason behind his decision, in my opinion, was the decline in acres planted in the United States and the cost reductions DeKalb felt forced to make. I consider him to be the best sorghum breeder in the world, and I feel certain my opinion is shared by sorghum researchers everywhere.

Table 23-1
DeKalb's U.S. Sorghum Sales Record, 1970–1992

Year	Grain and Forage Seed	Sudax
1970	437,822	260,718
1971	403,341	264,425
1972	367,745	267,000
1973	490,877	257,589
1974	462,273	219,443
1975	469,472	184,308
1976	642,652	201,700
1977	505,795	197,971
1978	488,067	184,200
1979	400,033	189,026
1980	396,900	160,841
1981	441,387	202,997
1982	439,000	155,000
1983	285,000	227,,000
1984	399,000	106,397
1985	393,000	132,281
1986	334,396	157,629
1987	258,000	153,639
1988	233,000	147,643
1989	294,482	152,817
1990	194,000	123,486
1991	235,000	103,484
1992	286,000	96,876

SOURCE: DeKalb corporate records as explained in the Preface.

Chapter 17

Our International Seed Business Grows 1960-1969

In March of 1961, Tom Roberts, Sr., and Rus Rasmusen met Antonio Marchetto and his brother Sergio at the Great Verona Fair in Verona, Italy. Both of the Marchettos were alert, impressive men. Their interest in DeKalb was so great that Tom and Rus agreed to send them DeKalb hybrid seedcorn for testing in the Po Valley in the summer of 1961 and to begin discussions that could lead to the formation of some kind of joint venture.

DeKalb's four-way-cross hybrid 624 proved to be outstanding in Po Valley tests in 1961, so 8,100 bushels were shipped to the Marchetto brothers for the 1962 planting season. They renamed it DK666 and sold it to selected farmers whose farms were well located throughout the Po Valley. Also, negotiations aimed at forming a new company to produce and sell DeKalb hybrids in Italy progressed well, and the DeKalb Italiana company was established in 1962.

DEKALB ITALIANA

The DeKalb Italiana company was formed on January 30, 1963; 50 percent was owned by DeKalb, 30 percent by Antonio Marchetto, and 20 percent by Sergio Marchetto. The new company appointed A & S Marchetto, SNC, exclusive agent for DeKalb in Italy, which was paid 20 percent of DeKalb Italiana's sales revenues for organizing and managing marketing activities. When sales rose to the 6,000-ton level annually in the mid-1970s, the Marchetto families, in accordance with the terms of their contracts, received more than 60 percent of net pre-tax profits, considerably more than the 50 percent share originally intended.

In 1976, Roger Rasmusen (Rus' son), who was then in charge of DeKalb's international seed operations, negotiated successfully to equalize sharing of profits between the Marchettos and DeKalb. He achieved his objective by purchasing a one-half interest in A & S Marchetto, SNC, for DeKalb.

ANTONIO DRIVES DEKALB ITALIANA INTO A LEADING ROLE IN ITALY

Antonio Marchetto, the brother chosen to manage his family's relationship with DeKalb, was a dynamic man who fully understood the value of his opportunity and approached it with tremendous vigor, taking personal interest in learning the strengths of the hybrids he would select for production. He listened carefully to the advice of

DeKalb's geneticists and also often visited test plots, developing a knowledge of his product that would enable him to propel it quickly into leadership.

SOURCE: DeKalb-Italiana

Antonio Marchetto

His vigor, imagination, product knowledge, and customer awareness combined to help him make decisions that exceeded even the wildest imaginations of DeKalb's best marketers. For example, knowing that Italian farmers would not accept "off grades" (kernels that were small or misshapen because they came from the tips or butts of parent-line ears), he developed a special market for them in Albania, where, because most corn fields were planted by hand, seed kernel shape did not matter.

Antonio's drive moved DeKalb Italiana rapidly into leadership in the Italian hybrid seedcorn market. Between 1963 and 1970, a combination of good hybrid performance and the excellent management team of Antonio and Sergio Marchetto resulted in this growth in sales of DeKalb seed in Italy:

Three-Way and Single Crosses Introduced

The successful introduction of DK666, a four-way cross, in 1962 was gratifying, but Antonio and Sergio did not want to be limited to four-way crosses. They were aware of DeKalb's 1963 decision to push single and three-way crosses hard in the United States, so they insisted on testing them in Italy, too. They did not expect all of DeKalb's newest hybrids to perform as well in Italy as they had in the states, but they hoped to identify a few that would perform well there. Their hopes were fulfilled, as DK805 and XL361 performed very well, and were readily accepted by Italian farmers. On the other hand, XL45 did not perform well in their tests and was never popular in Italy.

Table 17-1
DeKalb Italiana Sales, 1963–1970

Year	Sales (000 tons)	Sales (50-lb. units)
1963	337	14,828
1964	743	32,692
1965	1,340	58,960
1966	2,027	89,188
1967	2,608	114,752
1968	3,037	133,628
1969	3,855	169,620
1970	5,352	235,488

SOURCE: DeKalb Italiana records.

XL361, a three-way cross introduced in 1965 (one year after DK805), was more enthusiastically accepted than single-cross DK805 because it performed better at the high seeding rates used by most Italian farmers and was more resistant to the corn diseases encountered in Italy. XL71, a full-season hybrid in the central Po River Valley, was successfully introduced in 1968. The fine performance of DK666, DK805, XL361 and XL71 was reflected in DeKalb Italiana's outstanding sales growth in the '60s.

Seed Production Begins in Italy

In 1965 the Marchetto brothers anticipated rapid sales increases and recommended that DeKalb establish a seed production facility in Italy. We agreed and built a seed processing plant at Chiarano, about forty miles from Venice in an area where tax incentives were available. At the time the plant was built, local costs were much less than the cost of importing seed from the United States. But when new and considerably higher EEC subsidies for (grain) corn grown in common market countries were established in 1970, the cost advantage shifted back to U.S. seed production because very high EEC tariffs on imported grain corn (to finance the subsidies) did not apply to seedcorn imports.

Much lower U.S. grain corn prices made DeKalb Italiana's costs of purchasing seedcorn from American contract-growers only one-third of the costs it had to pay contract growers in Italy. Nevertheless, for political reasons as well as because DeKalb sales increased very rapidly in Italy between 1965 and 1985, we continued to produce seed at Chiarano, supplementing it with low-cost seed produced in the states. We also established a research station at Chariano, because selection of segregating breeding material is best done in the environment where its hybrids are grown.

In 1969 a unique and honorary club was created to recognize the achievements of Italian farmers who produced corn yields in excess of 150 "quintals per hectare" (more than 200 bushels per acre). There were many such farmers, and the best were awarded a free trip to DeKalb, Illinois, where they were honored. This club still exists and continues to create goodwill for DeKalb Italia (our new name) in Italy.

DEKALB AND RAGT, PARTNERS IN FRANCE

The relationship between DeKalb and R.A.G.T., which began with completion of an exclusive license agreement signed on May 9, 1963, was happy and successful. (The name R.A.G.T. consists of the first initials of the four provinces of France that surrounded Rodez, the city where R.A.G.T. was founded as a co-op.) Our joint efforts have produced a steadily growing hybrid seed business that has greatly exceeded our forecasts.

Our initial expectations were modest because corn plantings in France at the time were small and limited to the southern part of the country. Few corn breeders expected production to increase much because corn grows so slowly in the mild summer temperatures that are typical in most of France. Nevertheless, Rus Rasmusen and Paul Duvivier realized that the corn belt in the United States had been pushed northward nearly two hundred miles since hybrid corn was introduced in 1936, so they agreed to a joint research effort aimed at developing early-maturing hybrid seedcorn adapted to northern France.

There were remarkable similarities between DeKalb and R.A.G.T., among them:

- Both had started as farmer cooperatives, DeKalb in 1912, and R.A.G.T. in 1919.
- Both were owned by farmer-members and had similar objectives: teaching farmers, supplying farmers' needs, and helping to market farm products.
- Both became companies whose shareholders were mostly the same farmers who had originally founded the cooperative. Ultimately, both came to be controlled by families. At R.A.G.T., the controlling families were Duvivier, Singla, and Fabre. At DeKalb, they were the Roberts and Rasmusen families.
- Finally, and most important, the leaders of both organizations had faith that they could develop hybrids that would perform well and expand corn plantings in France.

Great People!

The owners of DeKalb and R.A.G.T. were all educated in the best agricultural colleges, and all had based their business success on serving farmers. Our French colleagues are outstanding people, so it is fitting, I believe, to introduce them here.

Paul Duvivier was R.A.G.T.'s chairman and CEO from 1957, when he succeeded Pierre Fabre (Gabriel Fabre's father) until his death in the early 1970s. Paul started the company's seed business in 1945, chose Louis Gayraud to manage it in 1946, and encouraged Gayraud to create the DeKalb-R.A.G.T. joint venture. Paul was a man of vision, a good judge of talent, and a beloved bon vivant. He signed the original licensing agreement with DeKalb on May 9, 1963.

Emile Singla succeeded Paul and presided over nearly two decades of growth and development until his sudden death on December 1, 1991. He was especially responsible for the seed division's prominence and was universally loved and respected by staff, friends, and associates. Extremely hard working, he continued to manage his farm throughout his career. This gave him an instinctive feel for his farmer-customer's point of view. His service to France and to European agriculture were recognized when France awarded him its highest award, the Legion d'Honneur.

Gabriel Fabre joined R.A.G.T. in 1970 as general manager, reporting to Emile Singla, and succeeded Emile after his death in 1991. He worked alongside Singla, his first cousin, as both sales manager and general manager. His nephew, Alain Fabre, an engineer, joined R.A.G.T. as general manager in 1989 and started its biotech business. He became the company's CEO in December 1994 when Gabriel retired.

Louis Gayraud was general manager of the seed division from the end of World War II until his death in 1983. He was looked upon as the father of the seed division. He oversaw the construction and development of the company's huge seed processing plant near Rodez, which was the first plant in the worldwide DeKalb organization to dry corn seed successfully using cobs as fuel. Louis was a thorough man and one of Europe's most respected seedsmen.

Pierre Llaurens, succeeded Louis as general manager of the seed division in October 1983. He was highly regarded by both his French and his American colleagues, especially by Dr. David Curtis. In 1994, he was president of the European Union's Seed Trade Association.

Jacques Coquerel started the seed sales department in 1960 and was the national seed sales manager for many years. He and Gayraud were more responsible than most for the DeKalb-R.A.G.T. relationship. They came to DeKalb in 1964, negotiated the first license, and were always thereafter active at the interface between the two companies.

Dr. Daniel Segonds joined R.A.G.T. as a corn breeder in 1972 and has played a key role in the development of both corn and sunflower product lines. His abilities and contributions were rewarded in 1994 by his appointment to the research leadership of the company.

Finally, I thank *Patrick Gregoire*, the company's marketing manager, whom I visited Rodez in 1994, for the marvelous work he did on behalf of the preparation of this book. His careful work and his enthusiasm for his job surely make him a great marketing manager.

GROWTH OF THE R.A.G.T. SEEDCORN BUSINESS

At the end of World War II, the United States came to the assistance of France with the Marshall Plan, which encouraged the formation of the National Institute of Research Agronomy (NIRA), whose purpose was to develop more productive crops and cultural practices. NIRA encouraged passage of a "breeders' rights" law, which gave plant breeders the right to collect royalties from users of the improved seeds they had created. This opened the door to private development of self-reproducing plants such as small grains and soybeans. We hoped that an effective breeders' rights law might offer DeKalb and R.A.G.T. plant breeders opportunities to develop and profit from the sale of self-reproducing seeds, but our primary objective was to develop adapted corn hybrids.

NIRA Performance Testing

In the early 1960s, the French Ministry of Agriculture with the help of NIRA, developed a performance testing program to approve new varieties for sale. The Comité Technique Permanent de la Sélection (CTPS) is a public committee composed of breeders from NIRA and the private seed companies, plus official representatives from the ministry. They decide whether a variety should receive marketing approval (official registration) on the basis of several agronomic and genetic diversity tests. The testing and approval process takes from one to two years.

Linking R.A.G.T. and DeKalb

In 1961, NIRA breeders were developing corn hybrids from very-early-maturing parent lines that were adapted to France. Louis Gayraud, manager of seed operations for R.A.G.T., wrote to U.S. developers Pioneer, DeKalb, Northrup-King, and Cargill asking if they would be interested in forming a joint venture with R.A.G.T. for the development of hybrid seedcorn for sale in France. Pioneer said no, Rus Rasmusen of DeKalb said maybe, and the others did not reply.

After checking into R.A.G.T.'s reputation, Rus decided to pay Louis Gayraud a visit at Rodez in September of 1961. In those days, a traveler to Rodez had to be a bit of an adventurer, because the best way to get there was to take a fifteen-hour train ride from Paris that dropped one off at Rodez in the middle of the night. Rus spoke no French at all but somehow managed to find R.A.G.T. and Gayraud and to begin negotiations.

On their first trip to DeKalb, R.A.G.T. officers Gayraud and

Coquerel asked a man who was laying new sod on a church lawn how to get to the DeKalb office. He smiled and told them how to find it, and then identified himself. By sheer coincidence, that man was my father, DeKalb's founder. I have absolutely no recollection of his ever working in the church yard (when I was a boy that was my job). Perhaps the French people were wrong—he was more likely looking for a golf ball. Anyway, they were impressed to have met DeKalb's founder, and he sent them on their way to our office thinking he was a faithful member of the church.

Table 17-2
R.A.G.T. Hybrids

Name	Pedigree	Life Span
204	0314 x 7060 / F7 x F2	1966–1974
202	SD-5 x W33 / F2 x F7	1968–1978
216	W153xSD102 / F2 x F7	1970–1980

SOURCE: David Curtis

Figure 17-3
FRENCH CORN AREA EVOLUTION, 1966 THROUGH 1994

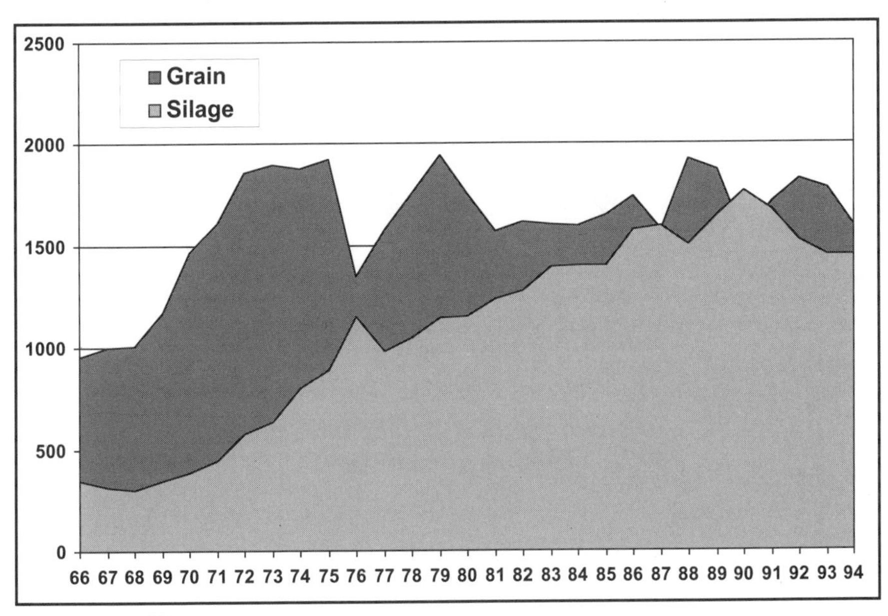

SOURCE: RAGT

Louis Gayraud was an acknowledged gourmet, so he was shocked by his first breakfast at McDonald's. He swore then to teach Americans visiting France what good food was really like, and he followed through with his vow, much to the pleasure of DeKalb people who visited him in Rodez.

Despite—or because of—these minor cultural adventures, the two companies negotiated a contract to jointly develop, produce, and sell hybrid seedcorn in France.

Joint Corn Research Begins

Dr. Sherret Chase, who was responsible for DeKalb's international corn research programs, suggested that DeKalb and R.A.G.T. enter three four-way crosses in NIRA trials in 1962. These were "open pedigree" hybrids, in that all of the inbreds had originated in either USDA or NIRA Experiment Stations. The new hybrids, 202, 204, and 216, passed the NIRA tests, were approved for sale, and became fully competitive with other hybrids available in the late 1960s. They were all good four-way-cross hybrids (see Tatble 17-2), and by 1972 R.A.G.T.'s sales volume had grown to almost 9 percent of their market.

SOURCE: DeKalb Argentina

Ramon Agrasar, Amelia Labastie, Antonio Ruzo in 1960.

ARGENTINA: HIGH IMPORT COSTS REQUIRE LOCAL PRODUCTION

We had never planned to build our Argentine business on seed imported from the United States because we knew that costly shipping and handling would put us at a disadvantage against local producers. Moreover, our experience with the monetary devaluation as well as the increasing demand for our product reminded us that it made sense for us to produce our hybrids in Argentina in large quantities as soon as possible.

As early as the summer of 1959–60, we produced small quantities of seed in Argentina and processed it at a jerry-built plant near Buenos Aires, but demand was growing so fast that for the 1960–61 season we would need to invest large sums to build a seed processing plant, dry and bag seed, pay a sizable labor force, and compensate contract growers. Credit was hard to come by in Argentina, so most of the necessary pesos would have to be provided by DeKalb and Agrosoja, our new partner. Unfortunately, Agrosoja was unable to raise its share of our new capital requirements, so structural changes in our relationship were necessary.

Building DeKalb Argentina's Seed Business

Ramon Agrasar and Antonio Ruzo talked with the president of Agrosoja, Mr. Dighero, pointing out the importance of producing hybrid sorghum seed in Argentina as soon as possible, and told him that I had authorized them to invite Agrosoja to be our partner in our sorghum effort if he would match the capital DeKalb would be advancing to DeKalb Argentina. They told him we would build the business without Agrosoja for a year or possibly even two, to give him time to come up with his share of the necessary capital. He agreed to this arrangement and permitted Ramon and Ruzo to be compensated by DeKalb Argentina as well.

Ramon's next move was to employ Amelia Labastie, a very good accountant. Conflicts developed almost immediately between Mr. Dighero's accountants and Amelia, who found a lot of improperly posted accounts, nearly all of which showed Agrosoja's financial strength to be greater than it really was. Amelia became a key employee for us almost immediately by unearthing these past irregularities.

I had absolute confidence in our Argentine tests, which told us we could expect superior performance from our sorghum hybrids. As executive vice president of DeKalb, it was easy for me to persuade DeKalb's board of directors to approve the expenditure of the thousands of dollars for the seed drying and processing equipment necessary to produce quality seed in Argentina. Their only concern was that Argentina's high inflation might eat up our profits. I was equally concerned but believed we had a unique opportunity to build product loyalty in Argentina, just as we had a few years earlier in the United States. I wanted DeKalb sorghum seed to be the first hybrid sorghum planted by as many Argentine farmers as possible, because I believed they would become long-term friends of our product. Our directors agreed.

Preparing for Seed Production in Argentina

We estimated we with could sell 1,600 tons (64,000 25-kg. bags) of seed during the 1960–61 season, and that this could produce a net profit of about $300,000. Clearly, we should "go for it," but it was also clear that to produce this much seed we would have to build a modern seed plant. The jerry-built seed processing plant at Palermo we had used for our first crop clearly could not handle 1,600 tons of seed.

Accordingly, we sent Stan Bozdech, our most knowledgeable expert on the planning and construction of seed processing plants, to Argentina to construct a plant that would be ready for processing by April of 1961. Of course, we sent the money necessary to do a good job. Stan and our Argentine colleagues did a fine job planning an expandable, efficient plant to be built thirty miles northwest of Buenos Aires. It was built both well and on time and was continually expanded throughout the 1960s, as sales of both grain sorghum and Sudax (a forage sorghum made by crossing grain sorghum and sudan grass) grew steadily. Hybrid corn, a major new product, was added to our product mix in 1965.

In the summer of 1959–60, DeKalb Argentina produced and processed 300 tons of hybrid sorghum seed, and 100 tons were shipped from DeKalb in the United States, totaling 400 tons for sale in the September–October 1960 planting season in Argentina.

Argentine Farmers Begin Production

Our first serious attempt to produce seed was in the summer of 1960–61 at these locations: on the farms of Juan Guidobaldi, Juan Carlos San Martin, and Enrique Killmoory in Buenos Aires province near Norberto de la Riestra; on the Frederico Becker farm near Canals in Cordoba province; and on the farm of a man named Juan Banus near Calchaqui in Santa Fe province.

All of these contracted farmers were carefully selected for their good farms and great interest in the potential of DeKalb sorghum. We limited each of them to a production goal of less than 100 tons (4,400 50-lb. bags), both to hedge against planting errors and to be reasonably certain that none would produce more seed than he could handle in his first year.

We also selected and trained five college students to help each seed grower properly “rogue” to prevent off-type pollen from contaminating the quality of our seed. Two of these students, Fabio Nider and Miguel (Mike) Goyenechea, returned to work for us after they finished college, as managers of research and seed production, respectively. Mike became a permanent employee in 1960, and Fabio joined the company as assistant breeder in Sherret Chase’s Argentine corn breeding program in 1961.

Dealing with Dighero

When it was time for Mr. Dighero to decide whether to join us in the hybrid sorghum seed business, Antonio Ruzo, whose financial interest in Agrosoja equaled Ramon’s at 5.13 percent, asked Ramon to let him conduct final negotiations with Dighero. After several long visits with our exceptional lawyers, Oscar Rosito and Julio Cipriani, followed by a meeting with Dighero and Rosito, Ruzo convinced Ramon that their small interests in Agrosoja were worthless, and Dighero agreed to release both of them from their jobs in return for their shares. Their employment contracts with Agrosoja had expired, and Ruzo was eager to end his association with the company. Ramon agreed. Also, DeKalb bought out Dighero's interest for a reasonable sum.

SOURCE: DeKalb Argentina

Juan Carlos San Martin & Antonio Ruzo in 1960-1961 Seed Field.

Mr. Dighero's problem was that he had prospered when the Peronistas were in power but had serious financial difficulties after Juan Peron left Argentina. He did not have either the money or the experience to make meaningful contributions to DeKalb's effort to get started in Argentina.

Shortly thereafter, Ramon and Antonio moved DeKalb Argentina to an office on the sixth floor of 960 Cordoba Avenue. Antonio built the office furniture himself. Amelia and their new secretary Elvira moved in and were followed a few days later by Orlando Fagioli, who was destined to be one of the most effective sales managers in the history of all of DeKalb.

Their full allegiance was to DeKalb Argentina, in which Ramon and Antonio were allotted 3.85 percent of common-share ownership in addition to employment contracts they accepted without reservation. Ramon's final comment was, "Thanks to Ruzo, Rosito, Murphy, and Cipriani, DeKalb was out of that mess."

DeKalb's "Best and Brightest" Support Our Argentine Effort

Dick Holland had accompanied me to Argentina in March of 1959 to observe maturing sorghum in plots. The leading Argentine agricultural leaders he visited knew him by reputation, and he took time to talk with newly employed DeKalb Argentina people who were eager to start growing sorghum seed in Argentina. In late 1960, Dick sent Archie Campbell, our Lubbock, Texas, sorghum plant manager to train the Argentine people who would be processing and bagging sorghum seed for the first time in their new seed processing plant.

Bruce Maunder Sets Up DeKalb Argentina and the U.S. with Two-Generations-per-Year Breeding

In 1962, Dick Holland was appointed DeKalb's seed research director and moved to our home office in DeKalb to assume his new responsibilities. Dr. Bruce Maunder, Dick's successor as sorghum research director, started traveling to Argentina every year to help Ramon, Fabio Nider, and Orlando Fagioli select hybrids for advancement to commercial production in Argentina, and to set up a system of breeding based on establishing two generations per year of sorghum breeding by planting research nurseries in the alternate spring seasons in each hemisphere.

Dr. Chase Adds Hybrid Seedcorn to Argentine Product Line

A few years later, Sherry Chase, who was in charge of DeKalb's international seed research, recommended we add DeKalb hybrid F880, a four-way-cross of four flint inbreds, to our Argentine product line. F880 grew in sales volume to nearly 6,000 tons (240,000 25-kg. bags) by 1969, five years after its introduction. Our hybrid seedcorn sales in fact exceeded hybrid sorghum sales as early as 1967 and the corn lead as grown to nearly 50% of the market.

Hence, our best geneticists, well-trained Argentines, our best seed processing experts, two excellent product lines (hybrid seedcorn and hybrid sorghum), and adequate financial support came together at the right time to make our Argentine sales a dramatic success, but inflation made profits only so-so (see Table 17-3). The decline in grain sorghum sales in 1964 occurred because weather problems led to low yields of marketable seed, we doubled our prices, and Northrup-King, a competitor, introduced NK300, a good new hybrid. Sky-rocketing inflation between 1964 and 1967 was the main reason for losses during that period, even though our sales increased rapidly.

F880: A Unique Corn Hybrid

Our most notable achievement during the last half of the 1960s was the successful addition of hybrid seedcorn to our product line.

The excellent performance of F880 was behind the remarkable sales growth. It was developed by Sherret Chase from four Argentine government Experiment Station inbred lines.

Sherry noted that there was very little communication or exchange of inbred lines between corn breeders at Pergamino BA, Argentina's most important station, and its corn breeders, who were located at outlying stations in Entre Rios, Santa Fe, and Cordoba provinces. He collected seed of the best lines at each of the four stations, crossed them in many different combinations, and tested their hybrids at DeKalb Argentina test fields throughout the pampas. F880 was a four-way flint hybrid made of three inbreds from the government's Pergamino station in Buenos Aires province, and one outstanding inbred from the Parana station in Entre Rios province.

Table 17-4
DeKalb Argentina's Sales and Earnings, 1960–1969

	Sales in Metric Tons			
Year	Corn	Sorghum	Sudax	Net earnings (000 U.S.$)
1960		331	69	(3)
1961		1,323	277	88
1962		2,518	308	137
1963		2,065	432	150
1964		982	857	(104)
1965	643	1,284	1,454	(179)
1966	1,813	1,606	1,715	(66)
1967	4,083	1,502	1,463	(123)
1968	8,136	3,641	1,779	967
1969	7,303	3,858	1,110	636
Total	21,978	19,110	9,454	1,503

SOURCE: DeKalb Argentina's corporate records.
Note: One metric ton equals forty 25-kg. (or 55-lb.) bags.

While F880 was earning respect among Argentine farmers for DeKalb Argentina's corn breeding abilities, Fabio Nider was being trained in corn breeding techniques, first by Sherret Chase and later by Basil Tsotsis and Charlie Krull, all of whom were directors of research for DeKalb during the thirty-year period from 1960 to 1990. Our corn breeders were impressed by the hybrid vigor they saw in flint-dent crosses and agreed that our Argentine corn breeding should be based on strengthening the heterotic (hybrid) vigor in flint corn hybrids by crossing the best Argentine flint male and female inbreds with our best "dent" inbreds, and selecting for flint kernel types in subsequent segregating generations of inbreeding. By using dent inbreds that were the parents of our highest yielding dent hybrids, we succeeded, in due time, in substantially increasing the heterosis (hybrid vigor), and, therefore, the yields of our Argentine flint corn hybrids

The corn breeding abilities of Fabio Nider and Raoul Mella, assisted by our U.S. corn breeders, made DeKalb Argentina the clear leader in hybrid corn sales in Argentina by 1995. Having two breeding generations each year in each hemisphere helped us, too.

How a Good Argentine Lawyer Is Paid

As I close out the story of the exciting decade of the 1960s in Argentina, I must tell about a tense moment with Dr. Oscar Rosito, our beloved Argentine friend and lawyer.

One of the first tasks Ramon and I had to perform in Argentina was to find a good lawyer. Blair White of Sidley and Austin, DeKalb's Chicago law firm, suggested that I talk to Dr. Oscar Rosito of the Buenos Aires law firm Rosito, Cipriani, and Fornatti, who had considerable experience helping beginners start up new businesses. We liked him very much and asked him to help us get started in Argentina, keeping in mind that we would be going into business with Agrosoja, which employed Ramon and Ruzo but seemed to be on the brink of bankruptcy. He suggested that we form DeKalb Argentina, SRL, to be the depository of funds DeKalb would need to get started in Argentina. This would assure us of having control of our funds, and in the long run it could become an independent subsidiary of DeKalb in the event that Agrosoja was unable to match our capital contributions. We followed his instructions and constantly sought his advice on corporate legal and financial matters.

Oscar Rosito turned out to be both a good friend and a wise counselor. We came to realize that we were rather special to him and that he had truly taken us under his wing, so we always followed his advice, which was invariably good. There was one problem, however. He never sent us a bill, and we did not have a firm understanding of how he would charge us. Year after year for five years I asked for his bill, and on my fifth year of traveling to Buenos Aires he told me his bill was ready and that he would deliver it after Ramon and I joined him for lunch at the Jockey Club, which I knew was the most exclusive club in the city. Ramon and I were therefore very uneasy when he told us that he was a horse breeder (this was a requirement for Jockey Club membership) and that he owned Manganga, which Ramon knew was the best stud in Argentina. Since horse breeding at any level, much less his, is extremely expensive, I began to fear that he was about to hand me a bill for perhaps as much as $100,000 for his five years of excellent advice. You can imagine my relief when I opened the envelope to find a bill for only $5,000! I felt as though he regarded Ramon and me as family, and we, of course, felt the same about him.

SOURCE: DeKalb Argentina

Dr. Oscar Rosito: attorney, consultant, friend.

INDIA

A Sincere Effort Fails

In early 1960 I answered my telephone to the challenge of a distinguished stranger. It was Dr. Ralph Cummings, head of Rockefeller Foundation operations in India. He told me that the foundation's scientists had developed hybrid corn that was well adapted to the northern half of India but that farmers had been slow to plant hybrids because there was no organized seed business there; nobody was "pushing" hard enough to persuade them to plant hybrid seed.

Farmers traditionally simply saved some of the grain they harvested each fall and planted it the following spring, so they were reluctant to buy the new hybrid seed. Several state-owned seed companies had been formed, but they were not very effective, so Dr. Cummings had sought and received approval from the highest levels of the Indian government to encourage an American hybrid seed-corn producing company to begin operations in India. He wanted that company to be DeKalb.

My initial response was conservative; I pointed out that DeKalb had no experience with either tropical agriculture or with the problems of doing business in India. Dr. Cummings was persuasive, however, pointing out that similar challenges had faced American hybrid seedcorn producers when they introduced hybrid corn to American farmers. He acknowledged that we would face difficulties, but assured me that we would be supported wholeheartedly by both the Rockefeller Foundation and by officials at the highest level of the Indian government. Dr. Cummings most compelling argument was a suggestion that perhaps DeKalb had an ethical obligation to society to help the underprivileged farmers of the third world, after the astounding success we had achieved in the introduction of hybrid corn to American farmers. I told him we would give it our best effort.

Accordingly, we organized a joint venture with an Indian partner and dispatched Pete Olson to India. Pete had been a successful district manager in Nebraska who had served his country well in Russia for several years after World War I. He went to India assured of full support from DeKalb, the Indian government, and the Rockefeller Foundation. He built a small seed processing plant, contracted with Indian farmers to grow hybrid seedcorn, and organized a small sales organization in the state of Punjab.

Every year for the first five years of Pete's efforts in India, he sold essentially all of the seed he had produced. Unfortunately, however, the more he produced and sold, the greater were his company's financial losses. This was partly due to the high marketing cost of selling to farmers whose farms were so small that each one needed only a few pounds of seed, but mostly it was due to competition from a seed producing competitor owned by the Punjab government, which was willing to fund its losses as long as it kept the price farmers had to pay for their seed very low. India was at that time close, philosophically, to becoming a socialistic country.

DeKalb seedcorn sold at somewhat higher prices than its subsidized competitor, but at only half the price we charged in developed countries. We managed to sell out each year because our seed was of much higher quality than that produced by our state-owned competitor, but we could not push our prices high enough to make a profit. Ergo, the more hybrid seed we produced and sold, the higher were our losses.

The final blow to our hopes for profitability came in the fifth year of our Indian operations, when the state-owned seed company produced more seed than it could sell, and the state government decreed that no competitor could sell any more seed until its company was sold out!

A Visit with the U.S. Secretary of Agriculture

That decree was the straw that broke the camel's back as far as I was concerned, so I went to Washington, D.C., to tell Dr. Orville Freeman, the U.S. secretary of agriculture, that we at DeKalb believed we had responsibly fulfilled our ethical obligations to India, that our losses had risen to close to $500,000 dollars per year, and that I saw little prospect of our ever becoming profitable. Secretary Freeman's reply was, "We can't let you pull out, because you are too important a part of our efforts to increase India's food production." I retorted that I was not willing to lose one more dollar in India, and he suggested that we could use some of the many "Public Law 480 dollars" that were at the time "blocked" in India. I replied that although I did not understand fully what a blocked PL480 dollar was, when DeKalb borrows money it intends to pay it back, so I could not be comfortable borrowing PL480 dollars that had very little prospect of ever being repaid out of our Indian operations. I did agree, though, to keep our operations going, with PL480 financing, for one more year, during which DeKalb would do its best to maintain a good operation and to prepare to turn over ownership of the company either to our own Indian partner or to some other suitable Indian company.

Secretary Freeman accepted my proposal, and after one more year of operations we sold our interest to our Indian partner at a very low price and left India.

A "WILD IDEA" IN INDONESIA

By 1962, Tom, Sr., had dropped his opposition to "chasing rainbows overseas" because he was comfortable with our decisions to go into business in both Italy and Argentina. Tom was very imaginative, so it was not surprising that he developed an interest in yet another overseas operation when, while on vacation, he struck up a friendship with Harold Hutton, a successful entrepreneur. What was surprising, however, was that the country he became interested in for DeKalb was Indonesia.

Hutton was an experienced oil executive whose early business experience with the oil industry had been with Atlantic-Richfield. He had resigned in 1945 to become an entrepreneur. His first big success was completion of a contract with the U.S. Army Air Corps in the Pacific theater of operations to remove all aviation fuel and gasoline that had been left behind when bases were closed at the end of the year, dividing the profits from the sale of the fuel with the Air Corps.

While performing that task, Harold learned that a small Indonesian island near Sumatra still had large underground reserves of high-quality oil (distillate). This field had been one of the first major pre-war discoveries of the Royal Dutch Shell Oil Company, but during World War II it had been sabotaged several times; first by the Dutch when the Japanese invaded, next by the Japanese when they were driven off, and last by Indonesian guerrillas fighting to drive the Dutch out of their country. The net result was that nearly every oil well on the island had been sabotaged.

Production Sharing

The new Indonesian government, under President Sukarno, had very little cash and wanted desperately to revive its oil fields. Harold

Hutton seized the opportunity that the Indonesian government's need for hard currency created and negotiated a "production-sharing" deal to attempt to revive oil production from the small island's sabotaged wells as fast as possible. His terms were simple. He would provide all the equipment and capital needed to revive oil production and would have a monopoly on its sale. For as long as Hutton had unrecovered capital invested in the project, he would be entitled to 80 percent of the income from sale of the oil, and 20 percent would go to the Indonesian government. When he had recovered his capital, the sharing of income would be reversed, with 20 percent going to Hutton and 80 percent to the government.

Harold bought huge pumps, attached them to the damaged well bores, and pumped the highly salable oil directly into tankers lying offshore. It was a very successful operation for both parties to the contract. In fact, the U.S. Department of State advised us that it was one of the few good ways of doing business in Indonesia.

Where did DeKalb fit into Harold Hutton's Indonesian business? The answer to that question lies in his concern that the success of his production-sharing agreement began to attract envy from the desperately poor native population and their representatives in the Indonesian government. Hutton saw and appreciated the rising resentment, so he proposed to Tom, Sr., that DeKalb, with its agricultural know-how, send a team of people to Indonesia to clear out some large rubber plantations that had been ruined by the war and produce corn to feed the Indonesian people. Hutton's proposal was sufficiently attractive that we asked Rus Rasmusen to visit Indonesia to evaluate the business opportunity he had offered.

Rus started with a journey from Singapore to Sumatra on a converted World War II mine sweeper manned by a former U-boat captain. Upon arrival, they were convoyed to the ravaged rubber plantations by two jeeps bristling with guns and soldiers. Rus studied the property and returned home to report that he did not believe corn could be raised economically on the properties he had seen. Further, even it were a success, there would not be enough profit in the project for DeKalb to justify sending its most talented people to supervise the job.

A Deal a Methodist Bishop Would Approve Of?

We agreed with Rus, and told Hutton that there was not enough potential profit to justify our efforts to manage it for him. His reply was to offer DeKalb a "piece of the action" in his very profitable production-sharing oil scavenging deal. He showed us his numbers, and we could see that the deal he was offering us would pay back all capital and operating expenses in two years. It was a very tempting offer.

Accordingly, Tom, Sr., Charlie Roberts, and I, and Blair White, our newly appointed attorney, met in Los Angeles with Mr. Hutton to discuss the deal. Ultimately, we decided not to go forward because we didn't feel comfortable with the ethical aspects of some of the production-sharing operations. He obviously disagreed with our evaluation, because he stormed out of the room thundering, "This was a deal a Methodist bishop would approve of!"

Chapter 18

Hybrid Cotton and Hybrid Wheat Begin and End 1960-1969

DeKalb's efforts to hybridize cotton and wheat were serious attempts to extend hybrid vigor to them, as we had to corn, sorghum, and chickens. Our efforts spanned approximately fifteen years, centering on the 1960s.

After succeeding so spectacularly with hybrid corn, DeKalb turned to hybridizing chickens and sorghum as well. Their efforts were successful and received the wholehearted support of both shareholders and management. Accordingly, in 1957, when Dick Holland learned that the Rohm & Haas (R&H) pharmaceutical company had developed a chemical gametocide that would sterilize the male portion of developing cotton flowers, he realized that hybrid cotton might be possible if pollen from adjacent male-fertile cotton could be used to fertilize male-sterile plants.

DEKALB'S EFFORTS TO HYBRIDIZE COTTON

Dick advised me of the new gametocide and suggested that we take two steps to determine whether hybridizing cotton would be practical:

- Spray samples of R&H's new gametocide on cotton plants under farm conditions to (a) find out if it would sterilize the male part of cotton flowers completely, and (b) determine how much of the chemical to apply and what the cost would be.
- Make crosses by hand of genetically diverse cotton varieties to produce a few pounds of pure hybrid seed for planting in research fields to see how much more cotton lint yield we could expect from hybrids than from parental varieties.

Dick set aside a small part of his Lubbock, Texas, nursery for spraying and hand-crossing cotton. The gametocide spray produced complete male sterility, and his tests of handmade hybrids showed that the best ones would yield up to 20 percent more than the average yield of their parents.

Having determined that cotton hybridization might be achievable, we addressed the obstacles we would have to overcome to make hybrid cotton an economic success:

- We would have to learn how to sterilize pollen of the plants in our designated "female" rows without reducing the productive potential of the plants.
- We would have to find a way to move pollen from the adjacent designated "male rows" in sufficient quantities and in a timely enough manner to fully fertilize the sprayed "female rows" in our seed production fields. Complete fertilization would be vital: the costs of producing hybrid seed would be enormously increased if our contract growers had to endure a loss in the volume of the valuable cotton lint that would be produced on the female parent rows.

The problem of achieving normal yields in hybrid cotton seed production would be further complicated by the fact that cotton flowers in an indeterminate manner. That is, one or two flowers are produced each day, and pollen must be carried to the new blossoms each day during the pollinating season. In addition, cotton pollen is heavy and must be carried by insects (predominantly bees) from male-fertile plants to the male-sterile "female" plants. This would be nearly impossible in major cotton producing areas like the Mississippi delta, where boll weevil infestations must be controlled by heavy spraying with strong insecticides, which kill boll weevils and boll worms as well as the bees that carry pollen from male rows to the female rows.

Hybrid cotton seed would have to be produced where farmers did not spray insecticides on their cotton to control weevils, and where natural bee populations could perhaps be supplemented by hives of honeybees. We thought that we might find places on the fringe of the cotton belt where natural insect activity had been noted—perhaps in northern Georgia, near the city of Athens, where University of Georgia cotton specialists had reported considerable insect activity in farmers' cotton fields.

GEARING UP

The obstacles were formidable, but so had they been when DeKalb started trying to produce hybrid corn. Dick and I discussed the pros and cons with Tom, Sr., Sherret Chase, Rus Rasmusen and many of the nation's best cotton breeders. Having weighed their advice, we decided to make cotton hybridization a serious corporate objective.

Dr. J. B. Weaver, chief of cotton breeding at the University of Georgia, was hired in 1958 to head our cotton breeding effort, and we purchased a farm close to Athens, Georgia, on which to begin our efforts. J. B.'s objectives were to develop hybrids for the major cotton growing areas of the United States—the Mississippi delta, the high plains of Texas, and the irrigated, intensively cultivated valleys of Arizona and California. J. B. set out to identify cotton varieties that would produce the best hybrids, and to overcome the seed production problems associated with producing hybrid cotton.

J. B. established breeding and testing stations in each of the three major U.S. cotton growing areas and hired Dr. Jack Duclos and an experienced technician named Bill Ramsey to man the new stations.

J. B.'s cotton breeding efforts progressed steadily for several years, and we soon began holding field days to demonstrate our methods and our hybrids to cotton breeders and cotton farmers. I participated in most of these, admittedly nervous because the people I was talking to knew a lot more about growing cotton than I did, and also a bit nervous about how well southern farmers would accept my Yankee accent and my decision to invite black farmers to join in field days with a predominantly white group. All went well, however.

In a way, the progress we made in our cotton breeding had an almost seductive effect on us. J. B.'s hybrid test plots revealed some very attractive, high-yielding hybrids we were sure farmers would readily accept—if only we could produce hybrid seed on a large scale at reasonable cost. On that score, very little progress was made because we had continuous problems with inadequate bee activity in our seed fields.

We began to suspect that inadequate seed set in our seed fields might also be occurring because the gametocide spray we applied to our "female" rows might also be damaging the female (stigma) part of the sprayed plants. In any event, our seed yields in hybrid production fields were consistently unacceptably low and costly. We learned the bitter lesson that while our best hybrids would out-yield non-hybrid varieties by approximately 20 percent, the cost of the hybrid seed would exceed the value of the hybrid yield increase.

One Last, Exciting Gasp

The beautiful, extremely high-yielding cotton fields of Arizona gave us hope that expensive hybrid cotton seed would be accepted by Arizona farmers because cotton was grown there as a three-year perennial, a practice called "stubbing," and was very profitable for all three years; non-hybrid varieties often yielded as many as four bales (worth $2,000) of cotton per acre per year. We had hybrids that would increase that yield by 20 percent, so we believed we could show farmers that DeKalb's hybrids were well worth the high price we had to ask for our pure F-1 (first-generation) hybrid seed; they could amortize their seed costs over three crops of very high-yielding cotton.

Equally promising was the possibility of producing pure hand-crossed seed in Mexico and exporting it to Arizona farmers who could grow it just as they grew their regular perennial cotton, without any spraying with the FW450 gametocide. The pure F-1 hybrid plants would out-yield the Arizona varieties by 20 percent, and DeKalb would not charge them for their pure hybrid seed, except to ask them to sell us the cottonseed they harvested at the going commercial price of cottonseed, which typically sold for the value of the oil that could be pressed out of it. The seed produced from our very expensive, pure hand-crossed F-1 hybrid seed would be second-generation (F-2) seed. When planted by farmers, the hybrid yield advantage of the F-2 hybrids would be only one-half of the yield advantage of the pure F-1 seed, but it would still out-yield varieties by 10 percent and could be offered at acceptably low prices to cotton growers in California's large San Joaquin valley.

These opportunities to utilize Arizona's perennial cultural practices looked practical to us but proved to be entirely impossible after the first year we tried it in Arizona. The pink boll worm, a stubborn cotton predator, was found in Arizona cotton fields that year for the first time, and state entomologists declared that stubbing, or the production of cotton on fields that were reseeded only once every three years, would not be allowed in the future because the trash left in the stubbed cotton fields harbored the pink boll-worm larvae over the winter.

Thus ended a serious effort to create hybrid cotton. Many good people who had labored long and hard to make it a success had to redirect their careers. J. B. Weaver returned to the cotton breeding programs of the University of Georgia, and Jack Duclos was transferred into DeKalb's corn breeding program, but other good people had to find work elsewhere.

I estimate that DeKalb spent 4 to 5 million dollars over the years we labored to create hybrid cotton. To the great credit of the DeKalb shareholders who had risked so much with the creation of hybrid corn, they voiced no criticism when our efforts to produce hybrid cotton failed.

HYBRIDIZATION OF WHEAT—ANOTHER NOBLE FLOP 1961

When scientists found a sterile-restorer system for wheat that was similar to the one that had worked so well for sorghum, Dick Holland told me that hybrid wheat could be produced. His main concern was that farmers might not be willing to pay the same high prices (about $15 per bushel) for hybrid wheat seed that they were willing to pay for hybrid seedcorn, for these reasons:

- Wheat seeding rates averaged 60 pounds (or about one bushel) per acre, whereas corn seeding rates averaged only 20,000 seeds (or about 14 pounds) per acre.
- The average per acre yield of wheat in the United States was less than 30 bushels per acre, but average corn yields were nearly 100 bushels per acre, or more than triple the average yield of wheat.

In marginal areas wheat farmers would likely be reluctant to pay much of a premium for hybrid wheat seed. Even in high-yielding areas, the cost of wheat seed per bushel of production of grain would likely be substantially higher than the cost per bushel of corn production, so wheat farmers would necessarily be more price-sensitive about their per unit seed costs than corn farmers. Accordingly, hybrid wheat seed producers would likely have to accept lower margins per unit of hybrid wheat seed than they had become accustomed to realizing per unit of hybrid seedcorn.

Getting Organized

Dick and I sought the advice of many leading wheat breeders, including Dr. Norman Borlaug, seeking their views of the feasibility of hybrid wheat. Their comments were nearly always the same. They would admit they were intrigued by the possibilities inherent in wheat hybridization but that their wheat breeding budgets were fully utilized, primarily with keeping their varietal wheat resistant to the rapidly mutating diseases of wheat. They seemed to be saying that the idea of hybridizing wheat was interesting but not sufficiently attractive to shift funds from their own budgets to develop hybrids.

Dick Holland and I disagreed with them. The conservative attitudes of conventional wheat breeders reminded us of the attitudes of conventual corn breeders and sorghum breeders when hybrid corn and hybrid sorghum were new and seemingly wild ideas. We felt wheat breeding was the kind of opportunity (or risk) that DeKalb should be willing to take. Tom, Sr.. agreed, so we set about building and equipping a staff of wheat breeders.

Dr. James Wilson, wheat breeder for the Kansas Agricultural Experiment Station, was chosen in 1961 to head up our wheat breeding program. Jim established DeKalb's first wheat breeding station just outside of Wichita, Kansas. The new station was soon manned and equipped to face the challenge of producing hybrids of hard red winter wheat, which is the kind that is grown in the vast central plains area stretching from the Gulf of Mexico to Nebraska. Dwight Glenn and Bill Burrow, two of DeKalb's best young men, were assigned to handle production and sales when Jim's breeding program appeared to be on the verge of having hybrids to offer for sale to farmers (about five years after it was begun).

Dr. Gregorio Vasquez was one of the first geneticists added to Jim's breeding program. His assignment was to develop hybrids of hard red spring wheat, which is grown in the northern plains area of the United States as well as in the prairie provinces of Canada. We had the wholehearted support of Norman Borlaug and the Rockefeller Foundation, as is suggested by Dr. Borlaug's willingness to permit us to hire Dr. Vasquez, who was one of his best breeders. In addition, Dr. Borlaug was very generous and helpful, providing valuable advice as well as the best of his spring wheat varieties, which were emerging as the phenomenally successful new varieties that would soon win Dr. Borlaug the Nobel Prize for creating the "Green Revolution" that made a significant contribution to the world's food supply.

Encouraged, we added Dr. Henry Shands, an outstanding young plant breeder who was finishing his graduate work at Purdue University, and stationed him outside of Lafayette, Indiana, near Purdue, where he worked at developing hybrids of soft wheat, which is widely grown in the east-central United States.

An Afternoon at Purdue

Shortly after we hired Henry Shands, he and Dick Holland and I met with the chairman of the Purdue Agronomy Department and a Purdue wheat breeder to seek release of their best unreleased wheat varieties to Henry. We told them we knew our hybrid wheat breeding program was risky and that it might fail for many reasons, but we did not want to start it with "two strikes" against us, which would be the case if we started with the wheat varieties farmers were currently growing instead of the unreleased experimental lines they were multiplying in their nurseries and would likely be competing with our hybrids three to five years in the future. If our hybridization efforts were successful, we wanted to start with the best parent lines we could find.

SOURCE: Corporate Records, DeKalb Genetics

DeKalb's Spring Wheat Breeders and Friends: From Left to Right: Dick Holland, Tom Roberts, Jr., Tom Roberts III, Dwight Glenn, Juan Munoz, Gregorio Vasquez, Jose Fuentes, Person Unknown.

Another man came into the room and listened quietly for about thirty minutes before excusing himself. As he left, he said, "I think the young man is right," referring to me. I thanked him, and asked who he was after he had left. He was Dr. Earl Butz, Purdue's dean of agriculture and one of the leading agricultural economists in the world. His opinion clearly influenced the agronomists we were talking to, who shortly thereafter agreed to release their most promising breeding material to us.

That experience had an unexpected personal bonus for me. Two weeks later Dr. Butz telephoned to ask me if I would like to become a director of IMC, the world's largest producer of phosphate and potash fertilizers. I accepted his offer and served on the IMC board for more than thirty years.

Breeding for Overseas Markets, Too

Our breeding efforts in the United States gave us reason to believe that hybrid wheat could be a success, so we contacted some of the leading wheat breeders worldwide about forming joint ventures to breed hybrid wheat adapted to their areas. Among those chosen were Wiebel's in Sweden and Nickerson's in Great Britain. In areas where DeKalb had corn or sorghum research stations, such as Argentina and Italy, we also began hybrid wheat breeding programs. In fact, Dr. Charles Krull of the Rockefeller Foundation in Mexico (where he was an assistant to Dr. Borlaug), was hired and assigned to DeKalb Argentina, where he developed an excellent wheat breeding program. Later, he became director of all of DeKalb's European plant breeding. Still later, Krull took charge of all DeKalb corn breeding.

High Costs and Minimum Hybrid Vigor Force DeKalb to Abandon Hybrid Wheat

All in all, we had considerable success developing wheat hybrids that out-yielded non-hybrid varieties. However, we did not have much success producing these hybrids cheaply enough to price it low enough for farmers. The most difficult problem turned out to be low yields in seed production fields, where we had counted on the wind to carry pollen from "male" rows to adjacent male-sterile "female" rows, as we had been doing for many years in hybrid sorghum and hybrid corn seed production fields. Wheat pollen seemed to be shed all at once rather than over a period of several days, and all too often the seed set on our male-sterile female plants was not complete, so yields of hybrid seed harvested was low.

DeKalb had to compensate the contract grower for his low yields, and the cost of the hybrid seed forced us to set the price unacceptably high. We never were able to resolve this problem. We also had difficulty achieving the 20 percent yield advantages in wheat hybrids that we had experienced with hybrids of corn or sorghum, probably because most of the varieties we found to be acceptable parents were closely related. The combination of high production costs and limited hybrid vigor forced us to conclude that hybrid wheat seed could not be economically produced, and that our wheat hybridization effort must be closed down.

The financial cost of our effort to hybridize wheat was considerable, as was the emotional cost to many of our best young people, who found that their years of hard work were not productive. We sold our wheat breeding business to Monsanto, which continued it on a much reduced scale. I estimate that our effort to develop hybrid wheat cost 5 to 6 million dollars.

Chapter 19

DeKalb Develops an Oil Exploration Strategy 1960-1969

CHARLIE ROBERTS ASSUMES OIL RESPONSIBILITY

The understanding Charlie Roberts and I reached when, in 1961, we agreed that he would supervise our oil operations was a good one. It was clear that our oil business must be coordinated with our other businesses and supervised by a top executive headquartered at DeKalb. Charlie was the logical man to assume that responsibility because he fully understood the company's financial needs and had become familiar with our oil operations while training under Tom Roberts, Sr.

SOURCE: Corporate Records, Depco

Art Tiddens, Charlie Roberts and Cliff Heglin

Table 19-1
Oil and Gas Prices in Canada and the United States
(U.S. dollars)

	Oil and Liquids ($/bbl)		Gas ($/Mcf)[b]	
Year	U.S.	Canada	U.S.	Canada
1958	2.88	2.44		xxxx
1959	2.82	2.31	n/a	0.17
1960	2.74	2.36	n/a	0.19
1961	2.73	2.32	n/a	0.20
1962	2.70	2.29	n/a	0.20
1963	2.77	2.33	n/a	0.19
1964	2.76	2.33	n/a	0.16
1965	2.75	2.33	n/a	0.18
1966	2.68	2.33	0.09	0.12
1967	2.92	2.34	0.06	0.12
1968	2.67	2.42	0.11	0.12
1969	3.73	2.62	0.13	0.17
1970	2.95	2.67	0.12	0.13
1971	2.95	2.89	0.10	0.15
1972	3.10	2.69	0.14	0.16
1973	3.31	3.05	0.19	0.16
1974	6.56	4.75	0.27	0.19
1975	9.00	6.76	0.29	0.42
1976	9.91	7.97	0.65	1.03
1977	10.26	8.88	1.01	1.23
1978	10.05	9.84	1,22	1.50
1979	12.30	10.33	1.53	1.46
1980	22.50	12.03	2.02	2.01
1981	32.12	14.46	2.37	2.19
1982	32.07	17.97	2.88	2.26
1983	28.62	22.96	3.22	1.90
1984	25.59	24.15	3.32	1.93
1985	24.09	23.60	3.03	1.87
1986	18.18	17.18	2.01	1.58
1987	14.96	14.83	1.76	1.29
1988	15.15	13.63	1.62	1.31
1989	15.98	15.64	1.88	1.36
1990	20.39	20.50	1.83	1.37
1991	17.58	17.68	1.67	1.22
1992	15.94	16.76	1.58	1.16
1993	14.45[a]	14.45	1.44[a]	1.44
1994	13.73[a]	13.93	1.53[a]	1.53

SOURCE: John Leteta, DeKalb Energy's Chief Financial Officer

a. U.S. operations were so small that we reported the same prices in the U.S. as in Canada in 1993, 1994, and 1995 in Canada.

b. Mcf = million cubic feet.

OIL OPERATIONS IN CANADA

Gas was so plentiful and pipeline capacities so limited in Canada in the 1960s and 1970s that new gas discoveries often could not be marketed for several years. Gas prices followed the rise and fall of oil prices, but the long delays in pipeline "link-ups" made gas uneconomical in most cases until prices started rising in the mid-1970s.

Art Tiddens in the 1960s

Enthusiastic about his Canadian success and confident of receiving more financial support, Art continued to search for promising Canadian oil plays, with phenomenal success. In fact, Art was most productive as an oil and gas finder in the thirteen years beginning in 1957, when he moved to Canada. This was a period of continuously low oil and gas prices, which meant that he could usually lease the properties he most wanted to explore. And it was the period that established DeKalb solidly in Canada. Indeed, seven out of nine key plays, constituting close to 70 percent of the total value created by DeKalb in its entire Canadian oil exploration history, were first leased between 1957 and 1969. Many of these plays were expanded by adding leases, drilling for deeper geologic horizons, and exploiting opportunities made attractive by rising oil and gas prices.

Table 19-2
Pembina - Lifetime Results
(U.S. Dollars)

Cost ($000)	Income to 1992 ($000)	Remaining Reserve Value ($000)	Ultimate Gain ($000)
16,722	49,122	9,384	42,234

SOURCE: DeKalb Energy Records

Table 19-3
Sundre - Lifetime Results
(U.S. Dollars)

Cost ($000)	Income to 1992 ($000)	Remaining Reserve Value ($000)	Ultimate Gain ($000)
15,437	34,939	24,823	44,324

SOURCE: DeKalb Energy Records

I was surprised when I realized that such a significant percentage of the value of our Canadian oil properties stemmed from the creative development of these plays. Our success with them says a lot, I think, about the importance of key geologists taking into consideration both short- and long-term geologic opportunities.

Five More Key Plays in the 1960s

Following his late 1950s successes at Pembina and Sundre, Art's geological training and experience continued to pay off. He purchased five more properties that we classify as key plays in Canada: Leafland, Sylvan Lake, Garrington, Harmattan East (Caroline), and Judy Creek.

Art frequently bid for the properties because he was aware there were deeper strata beneath the shallow primary targets that were known to be productive. Leafland, Sylvan Lake, and Garrington are good examples of "multiple zone" areas, where the lower-cost shallow cardium zone could be developed first, establishing an operating leasehold with deeper strata that could be developed later.

Leafland

Section 28 in the Leafland play was purchased for $25,000 in July of 1962, but that section was only the beginning. Success finding oil in the shallow cardium zone caused Art to buy many more leases near Section 28. Leafland turned out to be a multiple-zone play that eventually became one of DeKalb's best properties. Our original wells were cardium oil producers that held all of the deeper zones in DeKalb's possession. The "modest" Leafland play was destined to become one of DeKalb's biggest fields in Canada; deeper glauconite formation gas discoveries during the 1980s would yield ultimate recovery of 60 billion cubic feet of gas, yielding the equivalent of 15,478,000 barrels of oil, or 13 percent of DeKalb's "ultimate recovery" in Canada, at the very low average finding cost of $1.25 per equivalent barrel of oil.

Art quickly became an expert at finding oil in the shallow cardium zone. He was aware of deeper formations that appeared to be good gas prospects, but gas was in oversupply in Canada, and its price was so low that drilling for gas was often not an attractive proposition. In fact, Art found more gas than he wanted as he explored for oil. Over the thirty-year period between the completion of its first well at Leafland and 1992, DeKalb's investment there totaled more than 17 million well-spent dollars (see Table 19-4).

DeKalb exploration began in the Leafland cardium area in 1963. It was followed in November 1963 by the company's first deep test to the Peskisko, which encountered twenty feet of glauconitic gas-bearing sand, which was not economical at the time.

Table 19-4
Leafland - Lifetime Results
(U.S. dollars)

Cost ($000)	Income to 1992 ($000)	Remaining Reserve Value ($000)	Ultimate Gain ($000)
17,744	43,638	27,973	53,837

SOURCE: Corporate Records, DeKalb Energy
Notes: Cost is historic investment before G&A. Cost data as well as Income to 1992 are derived from data developed by DEC. Remaining Reserve Value is derived from total equivalent bbls. remaining (9,060M) x SEC value of $3.09 per bbl. Ultimate Gain equals Income plus Remaining Reserve Value minus Cost as of December 31, 1992. Source: All of the data above are derived from the DEC Summary of Unrecovered Investment as of December 21, 1992, in U.S. dollars.

Sylvan Lake

Sylvan Lake has been a remarkable area for DeKalb, too. It is in a geologically complex area, where almost every time we drilled a well we discovered a new pay zone. DeKalb exploration began at Sylvan Lake in 1963, and our original objective was oil, but we kept finding gas, gas, and more gas. In 1966 we participated in construction of a gas plant in order to strip the valuable liquids from our gas production. Subsequently, DeKalb drilled a series of successful farmouts and increased reserves to the point that in 1992 we needed more gas processing capacity.

Sylvan Lake's ultimate recovery of oil is expected to total 2,699,000 barrels plus 6,477,000 barrels of oil-equivalent gas. Obviously, Art's 1963 oil play turned into a great play for both gas and oil. It is expected to produce nearly 8 percent of DeKalb's total production, making it clearly a key play. Table 19-5 tells the economic story of Sylvan Lake.

Table 19-5
Sylvan Lake - Lifetime Results
(U.S. dollars)

Cost ($000)	Income to 1992 ($000)	Remaining Reserve Value ($000)	Ultimate Gain ($000)
17,405	24,949	15,493	23,037

SOURCE: Corporate Records, DeKalb Energy
Notes: Cost is historic investment before G&A. Income is derived from net equivalent bbls. sold. Remaining Reserve Value is derived from 5,230M equivalent bbls. remaining x SEC value of $3.36 per bbl. Ultimate Gain equals Income plus Remaining Reserve Value minus Cost.

Garrington

Art's romance with oil plays with multiple-zone possibilities led him in 1963 to the Garrington area, where he acquired leases that had geological potential for producing oil from the cardium zone. Drilling resulted in twelve marginal wells that produced oil for three years before being put into larger water flood units. A few years later, in 1971, DeKalb's Garrington cardium interests and several marginal Pembina wells were sold to New York Oils for 800,000 Canadian dollars.

DeKalb retained its deeper rights at Garrington, however, and in the late 1970s and early 1980s Garrington became a key play when huge gas reserves were discovered in its glauconite zone. All told, DeKalb has invested $26,358,000 at Garrington. Cost of finding has been $4.26 per equivalent barrel. Table 19-6 shows the lifetime economic results for the Garrington play.

Table 19-6
Garrington - Lifetime Results
(U.S. dollars)

Cost ($000)	Income to 1992 ($000)	Remaining Reserve Value ($000)	Ultimate Gain ($000)
26,368	45,166	5,768	24,566

SOURCE: DeKalb Energy records at end of 1992.
Notes: Cost is historic investment before G&A. Income is derived from DEC corporate records. Remaining Reserve Value is derived from DEC records showing total equivalent bbls. remaining (1.444M) x SEC value of $3.99 SEC per bbl., equaling $5,768,000. Ultimate Gain equals Income plus Remaining Reserve Value minus Cost.

Judy Creek

In early 1962, Art bought a 50 percent lease in the extreme northeast corner of the developing Judy Creek field. Our first well there was the best in the field, and its core was the best by far that our geologists had ever seen. As it turned out, this well was the highest formation in the huge Judy Creek field, which was owned mostly by Esso. A major company that owns most of the wells in a large field usually has the upper hand in forming water flooding pressure maintenance units; but in this case, Esso needed our well very badly, so Art was positioned to negotiate from strength, and did so. If we had not joined the Esso unit, Esso would have had to drill a ring of wells around ours to protect their position. DeKalb's share of the Esso unit well continued producing for many, many years.

In his effort to maximize our share in the unit, Art drilled two more wells. They were not especially good producers, but Esso allowed them into the unit. On the night the last of these was being completed, the casing collapsed in the hole. It had to be repaired immediately in temperatures fifty degrees below zero. Cliff Heglin stayed in the rig for seven days while the casing was repaired. Needless to say, It was the longest week of his life.

Since 1962, total DeKalb investment at Judy Creek has been $2.942 million, with a very low finding cost of 97 cents per oil-equivalent barrel.

Table 19-7
Judy Creek - Lifetime Results
(U.S. dollars)

Cost ($000)	Income to 1992 ($000)	Remaining Reserve Value ($000)	Ultimate Gain ($000)
2,942	12,262	2,312	11,632

SOURCE: DeKalb Energy records at end of 1992.
Notes: Cost is historic investment before G&A. Income is derived from DeKalb Energy records. Remaining Reserve Value is derived from 734M total equivalent bbls. x $3.15 SEC value per bbl. Ultimate Gain equals Income plus Remaining Reserve Value minus Cost.

Harmattan East (Caroline)

The Harmattan East play began with the objective of finding oil in the relatively shallow Viking and Elkton zones. Located close to the Sundre field (and often referred to as the "Caroline" play), the first wells, drilled in 1968, produced more gas than oil. DeKalb's Sundre and Westward Ho fields were nearby and also were capable of producing more gas than oil.

Table 19-8
Harmattan East (Caroline) - Lifetime Results
(U.S. dollars)

Cost ($000)	Income to 1992 ($000)	Remaining Reserve Value ($000)	Ultimate Gain ($000)
6,387	43.416	19,160	56,109

SOURCE: DeKalb Energy records at end of 1992.
Notes: Cost is historic investment before G&A. Income is derived from DEC records. Remaining Reserve Value derives from total equivalent bbls. remaining of 5,049M x SEC value of $3.79 per bbl. Ultimate Gain equals Income plus Remaining Reserve Value minus Cost.

In order to market the gas, liquids, and oil from this area through pipelines, DeKalb participated in construction of a "gas" plant at Caroline in 1968. The function of the plant was to separate out valuable liquids (propane and butane) from the gas. The liquids were marketed as produced, and the gas was sold to pipeline markets. Table 19-7 showed the lifetime economics for Harmattan East (Caroline).

Spurred by the opportunity to market its Harmattan (Caroline) production through the Caroline gas plant, DeKalb drilled and fully developed the Harmattan East field in 1969. It turned out to rank close behind Leafland in ultimately recoverable BOE's (barrels of oil-equivalents), but it is arguably our most profitable field because our investment at Harmattan was less than half as much per BOE discovered at either Leafland or Pembina, as shown in Table 19-9.

Table 19-9
A Comparison of Harmattan, Leafland, and Pembina Investment per Barrel of Oil-Equivalents (Before G & A)

Field	Reserve Life Index (Years)	Ultimate Recovery (BOE)	Investment $U.S.	Investment Per BOE
Harmattan	16.5	12,694	6,387	$0.50
Leafland	16.8	14,233	17,774	$1.25
Pembina	23.5	12,639	16,722	$1.32
Totals		39,566	40,883	

SOURCE: DeKalb Energy records at end of 1992.

Key Plays after 1970

DeKalb's two key plays after 1970 were Nevis (see Table 19-9), in 1975, and Bingley (see Table 19-10), in 1982. (In addition to these, both Leafland and Garrington, which began as shallow cardium plays before 1970, had by far their most significant finds in deeper gas-producing formations developed after 1970, when Bob Johnson was chief geologist for our Canadian operations.)

Nevis

The Nevis field became a key play after several dry holes had been drilled in an attempt to find hydrocarbons in the Leduc, Basil Quartz, and Belly River formations. The first four wells were for the most part deeper and unsuccessful tests of the Leduc, but they revealed gas potential in the shallower Basil Quartz and Belly River zones. Bob Johnson, DeKalb's chief geologist in Canada, subsequently determined that the Belly River zone covered a large area of low-pressure gas; if a sufficient number of wells were drilled, the "blanket sand" (a continuous blanket of oil-bearing sand) of the prospect turned out to be a successful commercial venture.

Table 19-10
Nevis - Lifetime Results
(U.S. dollars)

Cost ($000)	Income to 1992 ($000)	Remaining Reserve Value ($000)	Ultimate Gain ($000)
45,618	38,905	196,501	2,937

SOURCE: DeKalb Energy records at end of 1992.
Notes: Cost is historic investment before G&A. Income is derived from DEC records. Remaining Reserve Value is derived from total equivalent bbls. remaining (7,540M) x SEC value of 2.61 per bbl. Ultimate Gain equals Income plus Remaining Reserve Value minus Cost.

Bingley

The last developed key play was discovered at Bingley in 1982 by our geologists, who were working under Bob Johnson's leadership. Table 19-10 shows its numbers. Other smaller fields that did not qualify as key plays were nevertheless important to DEC's profitability, as the summary in Table 19-11 shows.

Table 19-11
Bingley - Lifetime Results
(U.S. dollars)

Cost ($000)	Income to 1992 ($000)	Remaining Reserve Value ($000)	Ultimate Gain ($000)
18,834	20,8434	10,673	12,682

SOURCE: DeKalb Energy records at end of 1992.
Notes: Cost is historic investment before G&A. Income is derived from DEC records. Remaining Reserve Value is derived from total equivalent bbls. remaining (3,010M) x SEC value of $3.56 per bbl. Ultimate Gain equals Income plus Remaining Reserve Value minus Cost.

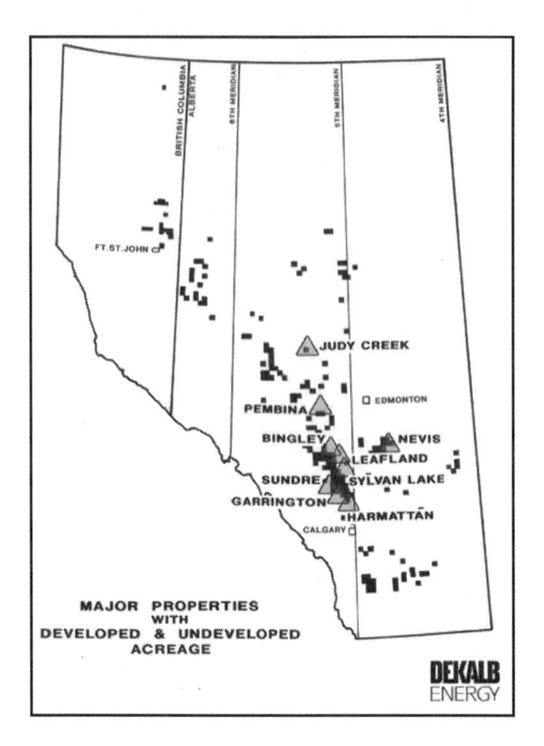

Map of Major DeKalb Properties in Canada

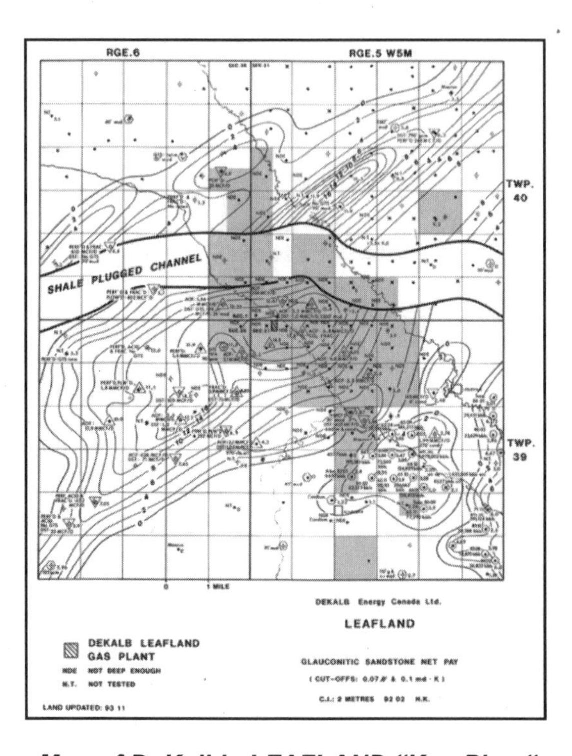

Map of DeKalb's LEAFLAND "Key Play "

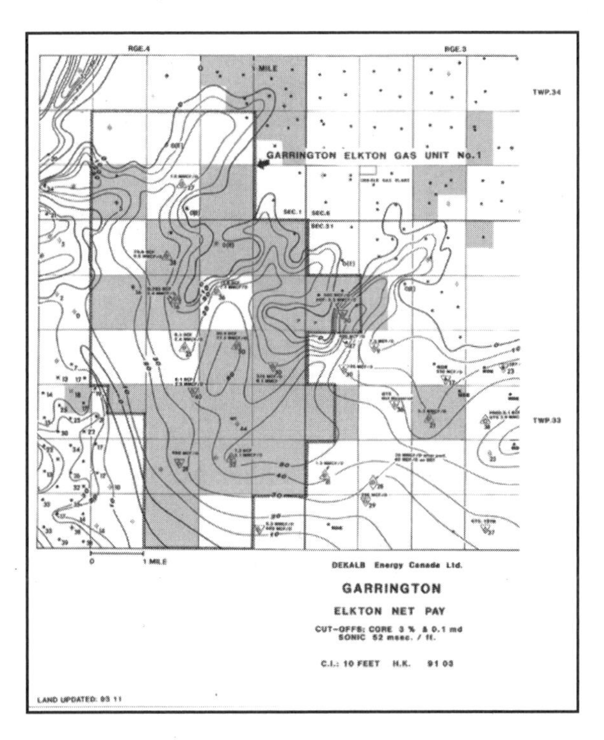

Map of DeKalb's Garrington "Key Play"

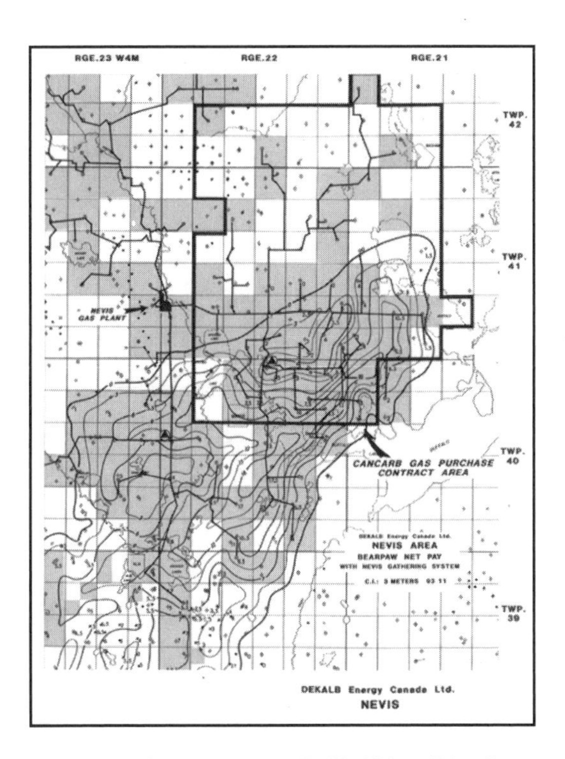

Map of DeKalb's NEVIS "Key Play"

Summary of Value Created at Nine Key Plays

If past successes at lower levels are suggestive of the future for our key plays, it would not be surprising if further success awaits us at even greater depths in these areas. Table 19-12 shows the enormous significance of "other fields" not listed separately.

Table 19-12
Other Fields - Lifetime Results

Cost ($000)	Income to 1992 ($000)	Remaining Reserve Value ($000)	Ultimate Gain ($000)
94,377	47,739	69,508	22,870

SOURCE: DeKalb Energy records at end of 1992.
Notes: Remaining Reserve Value is derived from total equivalent bbls. of 23,514M bbls. times SEC value of $4.09/bbl. Ultimate gain equals Income plus Remaining Reserve Value less Cost.

DEKALB PETROLEUM CORPORATION FORMED FOR ALL CANADIAN HOLDINGS

The DeKalb Petroleum Corporation was formed in 1959 to hold all of DeKalb's properties in Canada. On advice from consultants, all of the properties were gradually sold to the new corporation, and by 1965 all had been transferred. Later, in the 1980s, as we prepared to take our oil companies public, we named the combined companies the DeKalb Energy Company. Still later, after most of the U.S. properties had been sold, the name was changed to DeKalb Energy Canada, or DEC.

Excitement at Swan Hills

Swan Hills is located in the northern half of Alberta, where the winters are brutally cold, but all drilling must be done during winter when the swampy muskeg underbrush is frozen solid by temperatures that are often as low as –60 degrees Fahrenheit. In 1962, DeKalb acquired an oil lease at Swan Hills that became a center of interest for many competitors after an excellent well was brought in near our lease. There were open Crown lands adjacent to us that would have great value at the next Crown sale if our well was successful (we had posted them for bidding to coincide with competition of our well, so we could expect to have an advantage in the bidding).

We kept our drilling a closely held secret as the bit moved closer to our deep objective (almost 8,000 feet down), going so far as to work out a code system for telephone reporting of each day's drilling.

Knowledge of the potential oil-bearing strata was very important to prospective bidders for adjacent leases. Our competitors posted geologists in tents near our rig with binoculars, recorders, and listening devices that could identify certain geological formations by the squeal of the machinery when it hit the marker formation. These "spies" living in heated tents calculated how deep we were by counting the number of drill stems we had in the hole and so knew whether key formations were higher or lower than their own nearby wells. And it worked! DeKalb's geologists back in Calgary knew exactly how deep the drilling bit was from coded telephone calls, but they heard at the Petroleum Club at lunch each day what the latest news from the spies was, and they found it to be amazingly accurate. If we struck oil, the spies would know it. But they could not know the permeability and porosity of our cores, information that would be crucial in determining the size of our sealed bids. Unfortunately, the well was a dry hole, so we announced it, and nobody bid for the adjacent leases. Our announcement was in accordance with the unwritten "rules of the game."

Table 19-13
Lifetime Value of Nine Key Plays
(U.S. dollars)

Field	Cost ($000)	Income to 1992 ($000)	Remaining Reserve Value ($000)	Ultimate Gain ($000)
Harmattan (Caroline)	6,387	43,416	19,160	56,189
Leafland	17,774	43,548	27,973	53,837
Sundre	15,437	34,939	24,823	44,325
Pembina	16,722	49,122	9,834	42,234
Garrington	26,368	45,166	5,768	24,566
Sylvan Lake	17,504	24,949	15,493	23,037
Nevis	45,618	38,905	19,650	12,937
Bingley	18,834	20,843	10,673	12,682
Judy Creek	2,942	12,262	2,312	11,632
Other fields	94,377	47,739	69,508	22,870
Totals	261,864	360,989	205,194	304,309

SOURCE: DeKalb Energy Canada

Notes: The numbers presented above include: actual drilling and equipping costs for producing wells and dry holes; lease acquisition and seismic expenditures; cost of gathering and gas processing facilities; operating overhead costs through 1992.They do not include non-operating expenses and income taxes, which totaled $182,658,000 for the life of our Canadian company through 1992, leaving $178,321,000 ($360,979,000 less $182,658,000) net income after taxes and operating costs through 1992. These funds were largely reinvested in DEC exploration. The Remaining Reserve Value of DEC on December 31, 1992, using SEC after-tax valuation was $160,490,000 ($205,194,000 pre-tax) compares closely with its Remaining Reserve Value of $159,600,000 on December 31, 1994, five months before the sale of the company to Apache (see supporting Summaries of Unrecovered Investment.

Further Development in the 1960s

In 1968 we drilled eleven wells in Manitoba on an extension of the Williston Basin, which was at that time an interesting play in North Dakota. Also in 1968, DeKalb joined with Reserve Oil & Gas and Clark Oil & Refining to earn an interest in 270,000 acres in the Yukon area, which was the closest Canadian onshore land to the big Prudhoe Bay oil discovery in Alaska. In the long term, wildcat tests were dry and nothing came of this property..

All in all, DeKalb and its people in Canada were enthusiastic and optimistic as the 1960s came to a close. The only significant cloud on our horizon was the election of Pierre Trudeau as prime minister in 1968. Many U.S. oil men feared his anti-Americanism, and some would pull out of Canada, but in the long run his administration did not harm smaller companies like DeKalb.

Key DeKalb Employees, 1960–1969

John Leteta came on board in 1960. He had roughnecked for a drilling company for five years, transferred to his employer's main office in the contracts department, and moved from there to their production accounting department. John answered Art Tiddens's ad for a clerk and got the job. He arrived to find Art's office drawers loaded with invoices. He dove into them and straightened things out while the rest of the company was very heavily involved in drilling. He recalls that wells in those days cost $35,000 to $45,000—a small fraction of today's costs, even after adjusting for inflation. During his first six years with DeKalb he took accounting night courses at the University of Calgary and graduated as a certified management accountant in 1966.

Jack Irwin came to DeKalb in July of 1964 to head up the land department. He became a valuable member of the management team, heavily involved in originating exploration ideas, negotiating with partners and competitors, and managing the properties after the wells were brought in. Jack writes of his early days with DeKalb as follows, "I guess I really worked harder than most people just because I have to do so. Twelve hours a day, eight hours at the office and then four hours trying to figure out how I was going to do tomorrow's job. A little bit of success goes a long way. It was lots of fun—especially to be involved with drilling a well from start to finish, and to follow the drilling report like it was your own well." Jack retired in July of 1992. He was more than a key man—he was a fine gentleman and a great storyteller as well.

Peter Dyck joined DeKalb in August 1964 after ten years with Gulf Oil Corporation. In 1978 Peter was made vice president of production. His expertise in the design and construction of several gas plants, including Garrington, Nevis, and Leafland, were major contributions to making these plants key profit centers for DeKalb.

In addition to his contributions to the construction and maintenance of our several plants, Peter supervised all of our drilling and completion operations. He also played an important role in the management team's decisions about what kind of deals would ultimately benefit DeKalb Petroleum Corporation.

Clive McCord, an excellent geologist, worked for a geological consulting firm and for the Cree Oil Company as a geologist before joining DeKalb in June of 1964 as our chief geologist during the exciting 1960s when most of our key plays were developed. Clive resigned in 1972 and started a geological consulting practice, working with Doyle Resources. Clive died in an airplane accident on November 22, 1988.

DEKALB'S U.S. OIL BUSINESS IN THE 1960S

In the early 1960s, Paul Pugh, our man in charge of U.S. operations, was in failing health. He became more and more frustrated by the increasing percentage of dry holes he drilled in post–World War II years, and after a significant disappointment in a play in Vernal, Utah, he decided to retire in early 1963. Paul's geological expertise was responsible for the enormously profitable discoveries made during the war in the Wasson, Slaughter, and Leveland fields in west Texas, which were still contributing 25 percent of our oil income at the time he retired and continued to be highly productive for many more years.

Art Tiddens Takes Over in the United States and Canada

When Charlie Roberts and I agreed that Art Tiddens should be put in charge of our oil businesses in both the United States and Canada, Art decided to return to the States, moving to Denver, along with petroleum engineer Cliff Heglin. We leased an apartment near our Calgary office to allow both of them to divide their time between the two cities.

Canadian versus U.S. Exploration (a Significant Issue)

I was concerned that once Art moved to Denver his interest in Canadian exploration would diminish. I acknowledged that our lower "costs of finding" in Canada were offset by the longer delays in bringing the product to market. At the same time, Charlie and I were both much concerned about the high costs and frequent dry holes in the more fully developed U.S. fields.

I believed we should put most of our exploration dollars into Canada, but Charlie favored U.S. exploration for its more advantageous political and marketing environments. Both of our arguments were well founded, so we agreed to spend half of our exploration dollars in the United States and half in Canada. That important policy decision remained unchanged until I retired as CEO.

Art's first move as he took charge of U.S. operations was to ask Cliff Heglin to visit our U.S. production locations and report on both their efficiency and their people. On May 19, 1965, the U.S. company's name was changed to Depco, Inc., to clearly differentiate it from its Canadian associate, and all of DeKalb's U.S. oil and gas assets were transferred to it.

Rebuilding the U.S. Oil & Gas Operation (Depco)

After a two-week visit to our Odessa, Texas, production office, Cliff was convinced that Carl Bizzell was "keeping that operation alive" and appointed him field superintendent. Cliff judged Monty Montgomery to be a very competent land man—a solid guy who always made sure the i's were dotted and the t's crossed in his contracts. We never had a failure on any of the leases Monty completed. In addition, Cliff sold or closed down marginal properties, losing very little production but increasing profits significantly.

In late 1964, Cliff hired geologist Bob Gross and assigned him to a Utah oil play that had been originated by Paul Pugh. It was a joint venture with a Utah utility called Mountain Fuel. Several mediocre wells were drilled before the project was abandoned, and in 1966, Gross was moved to Denver, where Art and Cliff were setting up an office to develop the International Oil & Gas properties that had been acquired jointly by Depco and Husky, with Depco serving as managing partner (see discussion below). Bob Gross was a key man until the late 1970s, when other opportunities stemming from escalating oil prices caused him to leave the company.

Bob Kenyon, an excellent geologist, was hired in the late 1960s, replacing Gross as Depco's chief geologist. Kenyon usually took a conservative approach to the excitement that developed when new plays were being considered served the company well. He often had a tempering effect on Art's sometimes overenthusiastic approach to new plays. Both Kenyon and Cliff Heglin played the necessary "conservative" role when Art became a bit carried away. They were a great team.

Charlie Crump, a very able production manager, joined the Depco staff in Denver in 1966 to take charge of all U.S. production and marketing activities. The Depco staff was completed in that year when an excellent land man named Jerry Kowalski came aboard.

DeKalb Sells Its Illinois Properties

DeKalb's Illinois oil-producing properties, which had been producing small and declining quantities of oil since their development in the late 1930s, were among the properties Cliff and Art sold in taking over management of our U.S. oil business. They sold all of them except those in a "unit" near Salem, Illinois, which was operated by Texaco.

Reflecting on that sale, Cliff commented that it was a darned good thing that we sold them during the 1960s.

DeKalb Acquires International Oil & Gas

Art's first big move in the United States was the 1966 purchase of the International Oil & Gas Company (IOG), which was owned by Buddy Fogelson (whose wife was film star Greer Garson). Art and Charlie discussed buying IOG but agreed that it was too big for DeKalb to take on alone. They would look for a partner.

Jerry Pearson, a fine oilman working for the Continental Illinois Bank, found a potential partner: the Husky Oil Company, a vertically integrated oil company headquartered in Casper, Wyoming, which had oil exploration, refining, and marketing activities in both the United States and Canada. It was publicly listed, and its CEO, Glen Nielsen, was a competent executive but, according to Art Tiddens and Charlie Roberts, he was often hard to deal with.

Gene Rourke, our oil consultant, supported Pearson's conviction that Husky would be a good partner, as long as Art, representing DeKalb as the operating partner, could handle a lot of second-guessing by his non-operating partner.

Art's interest in IOG was supported by the opinions of a leading oil consulting firm, the James A. Lewis Company. Initially, IOG had been reluctant to even let Depco bid, but Art twisted their arms, and our bid was submitted and accepted on Labor Day of 1966.

Using "ABC" Financing to Buy IOG

Thereafter, a clever financing arrangement called an ABC was arranged between the buyers, Husky and Depco, who were the A part of the ABC. Continental Bank was the B, and a charitable trust was C. In essence, A pledged most of the income from oil produced to flow through B (the bank) to C, the charitable trust, which would not have to pay taxes on that income. This made IOG a more valuable property to C than it would have been to a taxpaying lending institution.

Continental Bank made the deal at a fixed interest rate, which it tried unsuccessfully to renegotiate a few years later. B, the bank, loaned part of the money needed and farmed out the rest to C, the charitable trust, for a fee, and the A companies borrowed at a lower rate, on balance, than they would have paid if they had borrowed exclusively from taxpaying lenders.

IOG was a good deal for Depco, which invested $16 million for its half of the company. The Bell Creek field in southeastern Wyoming was discovered in 1967. It included a large oil deposit in the "Muddy" formation on acreage acquired from IOG. In 1969 we borrowed $5 million to finance development of our Muddy play and created a production payment carve-out to collateralize the loan. The loan was paid off very quickly in the mid-1970s, and so was our ABC debt when oil prices rose sharply about the same time.

Despite the success of the IOG acquisition, living with Husky was always hard for Charlie and Art, because Glen Nielsen felt that Husky should have been the operating partner and kept asking,

"What are you Roberts farm boys doing in the oil business anyway?"

Depco Purchases Williston Basin Leases

Art's imagination (and astute preparation) paid off again for Depco when he launched an aggressive lease acquisition program for the Williston Basin in North and South Dakota before the Basin turned "hot." He moved so fast that Depco became the area's second-largest leaseholder, a position that would create significant opportunities in the high-oil-price era of the 1980s.

Table 19-14
DeKalb's Oil Businesses in the U.S. and Canada, 1958–1969

	Depco (U.S.)				DeKalb Energy Canada			
Year	Oil Price (US$)	Gas Price (US$)	Ann'l Vol.	P-T Inc.	Oil Price	Gas Price	Ann'l Vol.	P-T Inc.
1959	2.82	0.13	585	n.a.	2.31	0.13	126	(921)
1960	2.74	0.14	404	n.a.	2.36	0.14	325	(925)
1961	2.73	0.15	457	n.a.	2.32	0.15	501	142
1962	2.78	0.16	344	n.a.	2.29	0.16	488	5
1963	2.77	0.15	447	n.a.	2.33	0.15	567	170
1964	2.76	0.15	466	n.a.	2.33	0.15	806	456
1965	2.75	0.16	564	n.a.	2.33	0.16	883	800
1966	2.68	0.16	542	n.a.	2.33	0.16	893	687
1967	2.72	0.19	599	n.a.	2.34	0.19	888	618
1968	2.67	0.16	853	n.a.	2.42	0.16	941	750
1969	2.73	0.17	1014	n.a.	2.62	0.17	1029	1124
Total								2906

SOURCE: DeKalb Energy Canada
Notes: Annual Volumes are in 000 bbls of oil-equivalent, gas at 6 Mcf to one barrel of oil. P-T means Pre-Tax and is expressed in U.S. $000. No U.S. income figures are available until 1972, and after that, only pre-tax figures are available.

Table 19-14 provides the best perspective available of the relative volume and profitability of DeKalb's oil and gas businesses in the 1960s: Unfortunately, income figures from Depco were not available until 1972. But the annual volumes of oil and oil-equivalent gas sold show relatively flat production from Depco between 1959 and 1967, followed by increases in 1968 and 1969. Depco showed new vigor after Art Tiddens assumed operating responsibility, and our steady growth in Canada also reflect his successful management. By the end of the decade, DeKalb was producing almost equal volumes in the United States and Canada.

Chapter 20

DeKalb Poultry Adjusts to Changing Markets 1960-1995

Ray Nelson took the next big step toward separating DeKalb's seed and chick sales forces at the June 1961 meeting of DeKalb's board with this report, taken from Leo Olson's history of DeKalb:

> The growth of the integrated poultry operation throughout the country is causing us to change our method of selling. We are having to grow more pullets, and we needed personnel more thoroughly trained in poultry. In some cases, we are making changes effective July 1 (1961) of placing district managers on the basis of either selling chicks only or selling seed only. The poultry salesmen will be given much more intensive training than in the past. Some of the responsibilities in the associate hatchery division have been reassigned, and the men who formerly handled them will now be poultry specialists who devote the major part of their time to sales under the direction of regional managers. Sales and service men are now being made poultry specialists, and each region will be assigned three to five men. (Olson, "Genetics to Genius")

By May 1963, the separation of sales responsibility between seed and chicks was completed; regional sales managers were made responsible for either seed or chick sales. With four new sales regions for chicks, individual regional managers were given their choice of product to manage whenever possible. Operations were further simplified as crosses involving "heavy" breeds were discontinued, and DeKalb committed itself solely to the highly efficient "leghorn" type of white-egg-laying bird.

The new poultry regions were manned as follows:

- *Carroll Christensen*, an up-and-coming district manager, was promoted to regional poultry sales manager in the Midwest region.
- *Orin Williams*, a solid career man in DeKalb's seed and poultry sales, was made regional poultry sales manager in the Eastern region.
- *Ralph Thomas*, a World War II colonel who marketed the eggs from DeKalb's large Illiopolis, Ill., poultry farm, was appointed manager of poultry sales in the Southeast.

- *Dixie Autry*, who had been successful selling chicks to large operations, was pointed manager of poultry sales in the Southwest.

The newly appointed chick district and regional managers were backed up by an expanded poultry pathology lab at DeKalb, operated by two of the best U.S. poultry veterinarians as well as an expanded group of poultry geneticists. They were well qualified to serve the needs of large, integrated egg producers, who would be, in increasing number, the main producers of eggs in our country and around the world.

Consistent with our policy of utilizing our financial strength to support our poultry business, funds were provided to grow ready-to-lay "started" pullets, which were in strong demand. Unfortunately, starting pullets turned out to be a lousy business because our customers would not hesitate to cancel their orders during cyclical downturns in egg prices. After several bruising years, we abandoned the started pullet business.

A more successful use of our funds was to loan money to selected associate hatcheries that needed to expand in order to better supply the large operators. However, despite our best efforts, our poultry business never really made "big bucks."

INTERNATIONAL POULTRY OPERATIONS

Some of our best poultry experts were sent abroad to contract with leading hatcheries to hatch and distribute DeKalb chicks. The birds we had entered in official random-sample tests overseas compared very favorably with competitors' birds. Shortly thereafter, leading egg producers in many countries conducted similar tests.

Our largest overseas contract was signed before 1967 with Toshoku, a Japanese trading company that dealt primarily with agricultural and food products. It liked our birds but needed the help of U.S. experts to suggest husbandry practices that would maximize the genetic potential our birds had to produce lots of eggs. Earl Jacobsgaard, who had managed a large U.S. hatchery for many years, lived close to the Toshoku farms in Japan and helped them tremendously.

Similar contracts for DeKalb parent stock were completed in the mid-1960s with hatcherymen in several European countries as well as in Central America and South America. Sales of both pullets and parent stock to overseas poultrymen expanded our markets and tended to reduce some of the cyclical demand that had characterized our North American poultry business.

DOMESTIC SALES INCREASE

Our efforts began to pay off in steady expansion of our domestic sales as well. Domestic sales by year from 1955 through 1964 are shown in Table 20-1. Sales records for the period 1965 through 1967 were destroyed, but we do know that the poultry division started making money in the late 1960s, as one would expect from the sales increases shown.

Table 20-1
Domestic Sales, 1955–1964

Year	Pullets Sold
1955	9,674,751
1956	14,176,584
1957	14,078,607
1958	19,252,194
1959	21,855,223
1960	16,044,707
1961	18,364,139
1962	21,721,818
1963	26,282,080
1964	28,796,855

SOURCE: Olson, "Genetics to Genius," p. 658.

SOURCE: Leo Olson

DeKalb Poultry Logo

Ray Nelson fought hard to reduce the volatility of his poultry earnings by expanding foreign operations and the production of started pullets. By the end of the decade, farm flocks had virtually disappeared, and DeKalb's marketing system changed dramatically to fit the realities of the "large operation" marketplace. Ray's son

Jack, his assistant general manager, helped him enormously in making the changes so necessary to the survival of our poultry operation.

Ray retired on June 30, 1967. He had faced and overcome continuing change with great success, earning the respect and affection of the entire DeKalb organization. He deserves credit, too, for the training and development of his son, Jack, who succeeded him as vice president for poultry in 1967. Ray died on August 31, 1971, and is missed by all who knew him.

SOURCE: Corporate Records, DeKalb Poultry

Lester Shick, Dixie Autry and Ray Nelson

SOURCE: Corporate Records, DeKalb Poultry

Photo of Modern Egg Production.

DeKalb Acquires the Pilch Broiler Breeding Co.

In September 1969, DeKalb acquired the Pilch broiler breeding operation for $2,275,000. Although it was a logical addition to our poultry business, the acquisition was a disaster, as I explain in later chapters. DeKalb poultry profitability varied significantly in the late 1960's as shown here.

Table 20-2
DeKalb Pre-Tax Poultry Profits and Losses, 1965–1969
($000)

Year	Domestic	Foreign	Total	In 1992$
1965	(27)	35	8	32
1966	1,080	57	1,137	4,423
1967	929	89	1,018	3,818
1968	50	4	54	195
1969	1,298	46	1,344	4,637
Total	3,330	231	3,561	4,637

SOURCE: "DeKalb Poultry Results Book," 1990, p. A27.

POULTRY EXPANSION, DISASTER, AND RECOVERY

In the early 1970s, Jack Nelson made two significant moves to broaden his poultry product line by acquiring a broiler breeding operation and a leading brown egg breeding organization. The concept of adding broiler chicks to our product line was sound. In most overseas locations our contract hatcheries hatched both egg-producing chicks and broiler chicks, and their largest customers produced both eggs and broilers. As they became sold on DeKalb's egg-producing chicks, they urged us to add broiler chicks to our product line because they wanted to serve all of their customers' needs.

Jack, therefore, was interested when he learned that the Pilch broiler breeding operation was for sale by its founder and owner, Chester Pilch. Pilch's broiler sales had increased substantially in the late 1960s, and Pilch birds performed well on many broiler farms. He did a due-diligence investigation by asking Pilch's largest and most respected customers how they liked the Pilch bird and how it compared with other leading broilers. Satisfied with their answers, Jack purchased the Pilch company in 1970 for $2,275,000 in cash; he retained Chester Pilch as a consultant and appointed Carroll Christensen, Jack's sales manager, to be the CEO of the Pilch organization.

Carroll moved fast, expanding and streamlining the organization and making improvements in both production and marketing. But soon after the acquisition was announced, previously happy Pilch customers began reporting bad experiences with their second-round purchases of Pilch breeders. After a careful internal investigation, we discovered that Chester had filled original orders with chicks that were only one generation removed from personal selection by the breeder. The second orders were all too often filled with chicks that were two generations from personal selection by the breeder. Genetic drift begins in the generation following selection, so the very good chicks Chester had introduced to the market were followed by second-generation chicks that were genetically inferior to his original offering. In fact, they were arguably no better than the customer could have collected from amongst his own Pilch flock. Jack took steps to correct the problem, but he was too late, so he sold the Pilch business, at a loss, to a competitor who wanted to sell Pilch chickens overseas (see Table 20-3).

The process of acquiring, expanding facilities and breeding stock, and then divesting the Pilch operation took four agonizing years. It was a terrible experience for Jack, but the concept had been sound, and his pre-purchase research had been careful. None of us knew that product quality had changed before the acquisition, so we all shouldered the blame and moved on.

Table 20-3
Pilch Losses, 1970–1973

Year	Pre-Tax Losses ($)
1970	(578,000)
1971	(1,975,000)
1972	(867,000)
1973	(508,000)
Total	(3,918,000)

SOURCE: DeKalb Form 10K (1974).

On July 1, 1971, Jack acquired the J. J. Warren poultry breeding operations for $1 million worth of DeKalb's Class B common stock at the current market price.

Jim Warren, an outstanding breeder of brown-egg-laying birds, agreed to continue his breeding work with DeKalb at the former Warren research facility at North Brookfield, Mass. Jim joined DeKalb a bit in doubt that he would fit well into such a "large" operation, but Jack's good sense and the support of the entire organization soon dispelled his doubts, and he became a very effective breeder and advocate.

CHANGING RESEARCH EMPHASIS

Jim Warren's entire breeding experience had been devoted to selecting strains and crossing them to take advantage of hybrid vigor in the finished product. Before the acquisition of the Warren operation, Dr. Estell Schnetzler, our poultry research director since 1944, had gradually come to realize that inbreeding, which he had used successfully to fix some desirable traits, also tended to reduce genetic variability and to limit the improvement of his strains. Therefore, he gradually eliminated inbreeding and relied on selection within strains with genetic diversity and then crossed unrelated diverse lines to utilize hybrid vigor in his finished product. Snetz's system of strain cross-breeding was similar to the one used by Jim Warren in his brown egg breeding program. This similarity of breeding systems led quickly to mutual respect and exchange of ideas, to the benefit of both breeding programs.

Snetz retired in 1971 at the age of sixty-five but agreed to serve for five more years as adviser to Dr. Dewey Harris, who succeeded him. Dewey had distinguished himself at Purdue as a population geneticist and poultry breeder and was well qualified to serve as successor to Snetz. It is next to impossible for me to adequately and succinctly describe the importance of Snetz's contributions to DeKalb's poultry operations. He was a superb breeder and deserves full credit for the development of the "DeKalb Chix," whose outstanding performance propelled DeKalb into its leading position in the egg producing industry. More than that, he trained and developed every DeKalb poultry executive in place at the time he retired. His gentle personality and thorough knowledge of the egg production business were the reasons for our success while he was director of DeKalb poultry research.

Dr. Dewey Harris

Dewey Harris was Snetz's hand-picked successor in 1972. A highly respected scientist, Dewey was skilled in the use of computers. He used that skill in conjunction with his expertise in population genetics to develop a computer-based model for selecting within segregating populations of poultry using criteria weighted in accordance with their heritability and their economic value in the finished product. However, serious differences of opinion developed between Dewey and field personnel, who observed field tests of birds in commercial operations. The differences were over the weightings given to performance criteria, and they eventually became irreconcilable. Dewey resigned in 1974 and returned to academia. We liked and respected Dewey and hated to see him go. Dr. Larry Vint, who had been his assistant, took over responsibility for our white egg breeding effort and did a marvelous job for many years, eventually taking ofet the leadership of our poultry operations. Jim Warren succeeded Dewey as director of poultry research and moved to DeKalb after his appointment.

Closing out an active 1974, Jack purchased Kimber Farms, a highly respected competitor, and added the Kimber white egg breeding stock to DeKalb's white egg germ plasm pool. The purchase price was recovered through asset sales, leaving a "zero" net cost to DeKalb for the germ plasm pool. DeKalb offered a Kimber cross for several years, but we never found a good cross between Kimber and DeKalb lines.

Operational Changes

DeKalb's poultry operations struggled in the 1970s to adjust to the rapid concentration of egg production in large operations. Most of our remaining contract hatcheries went out of business because they could not supply the large numbers of chicks that integrated operators needed on single delivery days. Jack adjusted by expanding company-owned hatcheries and by financing a few of our most respected associate hatcheries.

Our poultry sales force became smaller but far more individually effective because the survivors had been superbly trained in the expertise required to serve large operations. They were backed up by the finest available poultry veterinarians and pathologists. DeKalb had come a long way from the 1950s and 1960s, when we had become accustomed to customers sending crates of sick chickens to our lab at the home office for diagnosis!

Sales volumes increased, but profitability was under continuous heavy pressure. Large operators constantly demanded more services and reduced prices. We suffered losses in first half of the 1970s but recovered nicely in the last half of the decade.

POULTRY EARNINGS STABILIZE, 1980 - 1995

The stabilization of DeKalb poultry profitability that began in the late 1970s carried on into the 1980s. Annual profits varied with egg production cycles but averaged a bit more than $2.5 million pre-tax for the 1980–1990 period, during which sales volume increased but margins decreased. Our profit and loss performance was much better than that of the U.S. egg breeding industry, which reported operating losses in sixteen of thirty-six quarters between 1980 and 1988.

However, industry financial performance reports after 1988 suggest that the egg breeding industry has finally stabilized. This was achieved primarily by the bankruptcy of smaller breeders or by their acquisition by the larger, better-funded breeders.

In 1994 only these large operators remained in the egg breeding business:

- DeKalb, which was the only U.S.-owned primary

egg-type breeder after we acquired Warren Farms and Kimber Farms;

- Lohmann A.G. (Germany), which owns LSL, Hy-Line, and H&N;
- Institut Selection Animal (France), which owns ISA, Babcock, and Shaver; and
- British Petroleum (England), which owns Bovans and Euribred.

Table 20-4
DeKalb Poultry Profits and Losses 1970–1979
($000)

Year	U.S. Egg Type	Foreign Egg Type	Pilch Broilers	Post-Tax Earnings	Earnings in 1992 $
1970	1,669	(241)	(923)	263	868
1971	(1,093)	(18)	(3,092)	(1,134)	(3,515)
1972	(1,361)a	95	(1,635)	(1,470)	(4,410)
1973	1,427	(786)	(1,240)	(311)	(871)
1974	(188)	(511)	(282)	(491)	(1 076)
1975	(5,011)b	337	0	(2,571)	(6 170)
1976	535	(74)	0	250	550
1977	1,347	593	0	1,067	2,241
1978	2,441	774	0	1,794	3,497
1979	4,558	490	....	2,930	5,274
Total	4,324	659	(7,122)	(327)	(3,612)

SOURCE: Poultry management report entitled "DeKalb Poultry Research," p. A25.
Notes: These numbers report poultry operations only. They do not include profits or losses from other animal science operations—e.g., cattle feeding and swine research operations—which are also part of Animal Science operations reported in 10 Ks. Earnings were calculated by multiplying pre-tax earnings x corporate tax rate and subtracting the tax due from pre-tax results each year.
a. A portion of this loss is derived from forward purchase of feed grain needed for DeKalb's breeder egg production farms and its research operations. Two large commercial egg farms owned by DeKalb also experienced heavy losses from low egg prices.
b. A large part of this loss was the consequence of Marek's disease being eliminated by vaccination. Before the development of this vaccine, nearly one-third of the nation's flock had died of the disease. The success of the vaccine resulted in a huge egg surplus, low egg prices, reduced replacements and heavy losses for DeKalb and its competitors.

Lohmann, through its aggressive acquisitions and heavy investment in large company-owned breeder hatcheries, is clearly betting that integrated operators who often require delivery of 100,000 chicks in one day from a single source will prefer their services to those offered by DeKalb. Also, Lohmann-Hy-Line had two other cost-saving advantages in the early 1990s: their parent birds were more productive than DeKalb's, and they produced baby chicks that could be feather-sexed (that is, their sex could be determined by the appearance of their feathers).

DeKalb pressed hard to incorporate these two advantages into its birds, but was making only slow progress in the early 1990s. So far, it has met the competition by networking its own facilities with associate hatcheries to serve the needs of the sixty integrated customers that own 74 percent of U.S. layers. Table 20-5 shows the status of company ownership of hatcheries by the three leading breeder suppliers in the United States in 1993, according to DeKalb's poultry managers. Approximately 240 million layer-pullet chicks were hatched in the United States in 1993. In Table 20-5 "Large Hatcheries" are defined as producers of at least 10 million layer-pullet chicks per year.

Table 20-5
Large Hatchery Ownership, 1993

	Total Hatcheries	Co-Owned Hatcheries	Est. Capital ($ million)
Lohmann/Hy-Line/H&N	14	12.0	28.5
ISA/Babcock/Shaver	4	2.0	7.0
DeKalb	8	2.5	3.4

SOURCE: Corporate Records, DeKalb Poultry

Producer-owned hatcheries utilize 1,054,000 of the 2,700,000 breeders sold each year in the United States, making a total free market of 1,646,600 breeders. DeKalb supplies 37 percent of this market, partly through its own hatcheries, and partly through associates. Financially speaking, DeKalb's networking strategy has been wise: it realized an average of $2.8 million in pre-tax profits annually on a $9 million investment in net operating assets between 1978 and 1990.

Service to customers remains DeKalb's primary goal. It is, in fact, absolutely vital to long-term success, so it seems certain that more capital will be required during the next few years to modernize and enlarge the DeKalb hatcheries, which supply the needs of its large customers.

It seems to me, however, that success or failure in the future will depend on the genetic superiority of DeKalb's birds, so I was pleased to learn from the poultry management team that their product line is currently the best in its industry, thanks to Dr. Larry Vint and his outstanding "Delta" bird. It seems likely to continue to improve with the contributions of these recent additions to the poultry research staff: Dr. Dale Tindall, who is Dr. Vint's assistant, joined us in 1988; Dr. Shen Cheng, a molecular biologist whose applied research efforts are showing real promise in selection for disease resistance, joined DeKalb in 1992; and Dr. Keith Boldman, a population geneticist who joined DeKalb in 1993, is an expert on the use of super computers to assist breeders with their selection decisions.

In an industry dominated by large operators who are very alert to subtle improvements in bird performance, emphasis on research to make a better product is the surest way to success, in my opinion.

OUR BIRDS AND OUR MARKET SHARE

DeKalb's share of the world market in fiscal year 1993 was 15.6 percent, according to management estimates.

Table 20-6
DeKalb's Share of
the World Poultry Market, 1993

Country/Region	Market Share (percent)
United States	27.6
Canada	46.3
Mexico	29.6
Far East	29.7
Latin America	10.3
Western Europe	1.7
Eastern Europe	1.2
Middle East/Africa	7.0
North America	29.7
World	15.6

SOURCE: Corporate Records, DeKalb Poultry

DEKALB'S PRODUCT LINE

Sales shifted steadily toward the DeKalb Delta between 1990 and 1993. The Delta is a white-egg-laying bird that came into prominence in our domestic mix after proving popular in China and Japan. It was bred by Dr. Larry Vint, who came into his own after being appointed poultry research director when Jim Warren retired in 1992. Delta's best features are: it lays an outstanding number of eggs; its eggs are consistently large; and the shell quality of its eggs (a characteristic that is usually negatively correlated with egg numbers and size) is excellent. Its principal weakness is that day-old chicks cannot be feather-sexed. However, the breeders are working on that problem.

DeKalb Poultry Managers

During the 1980s and 1990s, the poultry management team was strengthened by these additions:

Dr. Gary Waters, an outstanding poultry veterinarian with extensive experience in the fast-changing egg production industry, came to us from Hy-Line. Gary proved to be a valuable assistant to Jack Nelson, and was named vice president and general manager for poultry operations when Jack retired in 1992.

Tom Roberts III, my son, who earned an MBA from the Harvard Business School, became chief financial officer in the mid-1980s. He did good work in evaluating the fundamental economics of sale of grandparent breeders instead of parents in some international operations. In the late 1980s he was put in charge of international sales, where he did a fine job, especially in Asian markets. Tom aspired to the top poultry job but realized that Gary Waters richly deserved it too. When Gary was selected, Tom decided not to wait twenty years for Gary to retire and quietly resigned from the company. I was disappointed, of course, but I respected his decision and was pleased that he showed such respect for Gary's qualifications.

Eugene Liu, a Chinese man who was born and educated in Okinawa, Japan, introduced both DeKalb's birds and modern poultry management systems to Chinese egg producers and did a truly outstanding job: DeKalb holds a leading 25 percent share of the Chinese market. He a close friend and supporter of both my son Tom and Gary Waters.

Earl Jacobsgaard, a knowledgeable poultry husbandryman, deserves special credit for introducing DeKalb chicks to Japan. Earl lived in Japan for more than ten years, partly as manager of DeKalb poultry facilities there and partly as adviser to his Japanese friends employed by Toshoku, a leading agricultural trading company that has the DeKalb franchise for Japan. Earl's understanding of people and Japanese business practices won him their everlasting respect. In 1993 DeKalb had 41 percent of the Japanese egg-producing poultry market.

Jack Nelson ably succeeded his father, Ray Nelson, as vice president of poultry operations during a period of revolutionary change and tough times. Jack is more responsible for today's successful DeKalb poultry division than any other individual.

A SURPRISE ANNOUNCEMENT

On April 28, 1995, the DeKalb community was surprised by the announcement that DeKalb's poultry operations had been sold to Toshoku, a Japanese trading company that for many years had been our soundest and most profitable overseas operation. The price was very fair: $12.5 million cash (as reported on page 41 of DeKalb's 1995 10K). Toshoku is a well-managed, profitable business experienced in the poultry business in the Far East. It has purchased a sound and respected poultry breeding company that should be a solid base from which it can expand its egg business in the Orient. Most employees will remain in their jobs.

Table 20-7
DeKalb Poultry Earnings,
Pre-Interest, Pre-Tax, Pre-Consolidation, 1980–1984
($000)

Year	Pre-Tax Worldwide Earnings	Pre-Tax (in 1992$)	Post-Tax Worldwide Earnings	Post-Tax (in 1992$)
1980	5,240	8,698	3,249	5,393
1981	2,325	3,511	1,442	2,177
1982	6,192	8,792	3,901	5,359
1983	91	118	59	80
1984	1,146	1,512	878	1,159
1985	2,205	2,708	1,521	1,932
1986	3,258	3,897	4,500	5,580
1987	1,906	2,189	1,029	1,235
1988	511	573	291	338
1989	1,127	1,215	721	822
1990	4,200	4,494	2562	2741
1991	2,500	2,575	1625	1674
1992	900	900	567	567
1993	1,000	970	1760	1707
1994	(300)	(285)	(210)	(195)
Total	31,101	41,867	23,895	30,959

SOURCE: DeKalb Poultry Yearbook prior to 1990; 1993 and 1994 10Ks after 1990. Post-tax earnings are pre-tax earnings less poultry's pro rata share of corporate taxes paid for the year.

Chapter 21

The Tumultuous 1970s 1970-1979

The 1970s were a tumultuous time for DeKalb's seed business. In the first half alone, the following events were noteworthy:

- DeKalb "went public" in 1970.
- Southern corn leaf blight hit the corn crop hard in the fall of 1970.
- DeKalb's business boomed, and we began to diversify, with several successes and three fiascoes.
- The Heinold Companies merged with DeKalb in 1972.
- Lubbock Swine Breeders, joined DeKalb on January 7, 1972.
- Lindsay Manufacturing Co., yet another successful acquisition, joined DeKalb in 1974.
- We began to focus on management succession.
- Pioneer began to catch up with DeKalb.

DEKALB GOES "PUBLIC"

Our realization that DeKalb's unlisted common stock was far undervalued in the local marketplace, where it usually sold at book value, which was the primary reason we decided to list it in the public marketplace. Tom, Sr., had never been interested in a public listing of common stock, because he wanted to keep the value of his estate as low as possible as long as he lived in order to minimize estate taxes. That was not a factor in a decision Charlie and I made in 1968 to study the possibility of listing our stock publicly.

Our primary motive in going public was to create value for our shareholders—especially the members of our profit-sharing plan, whom we believed were not getting full value for the stock that was held for them in our profit-sharing portfolio. We offered our retirees the option of taking the DeKalb shares "in kind" when they retired, but many preferred to take all of their retirement benefits in cash even though we advised them that our common stock (at book value) was considerably undervalued.

Given the rate of earnings growth we had experienced in the 1960s, we were convinced that the public market would value our stock well above book value, so we decided to seek the advice of investment bankers in evaluating the pros and cons of "going public."

Choosing Our Investment Banker

Charlie and I thought highly of Smith Barney & Co., with whom we had placed most of our personal funds, and all of our bankers and lawyers ranked the firm highly as well. Over a period of several months, we gave the Smith Barney analysts our financial records to study, discussed some accounting changes, and described our business to them in careful detail. They told us what they had to offer in the way of research, marketing, counseling services, and the like, and advised that it would probably take a year's time to actually make the initial public offering from the time we chose our investment banker. They recommended that each of our shareholders have an opportunity to tender up to "x" percent of their holdings.

From Smith Barney's analysts, we were primarily interested in knowing:

- what price our shares would sell for, both on and after our initial public offering (IPO);
- why we should choose them to manage the IPO and how they differed from their competitors;
- what other investment bankers would be in the selling syndicate;
- how many shares they would recommend we offer in the IPO;
- whether they could effectively limit the shares sold to one customer (we wanted many, not few, new share holders); and
- which person in their firm would specialize in our stock during and after the offering.

All of the above were important but routine questions; their answers allowed us to both evaluate and learn from them. We also asked Smith Barney to estimate, in writing, what earnings multiple we would be offered for our shares if the offering were held "next Monday." After much hemming and hawing, they replied that in their best judgment, their offer would be twenty-five times earnings.

Charlie and I agreed that their estimate was higher than either of us had expected and that this decision would be so important to our shareholders and to us that we should take the time to negotiate with two other investment bankers before choosing one of them, so we then went through the same procedure with two other respected firms. I was naive enough to believe that these firms would be very close in their estimates, and so was Charlie, but we were wrong. The three estimates were (1) approximately twenty-five times earnings, (2) twenty times earnings, and (3) fifteen times earnings.

We were shocked at the disparity between the estimates! We believed the officer who gave us the low bid was overworked and offered a bid equivalent to that of a building contractor who will take on a job only at a very high price because he is busy. In the end, we chose White-Weld, the firm that gave us the "twenty-times" estimate, for two reasons: White-Weld had a bigger sales force that was more "in touch with the market," and we thought they would be more effective in keeping the price up in the after-market. We thought Smith Barney's twenty-five-times earnings estimate was overly optimistic.

We insisted, however, that Smith Barney be given the second largest position in the offering. When we saw how well they performed in the after-market, we made them the lead underwriter in alternate future underwritings. In my opinion, Smith Barney has done a fine job of selling DeKalb stock over the years.

Having selected White-Weld (which later was acquired by Merrill-Lynch) to lead the offering, we prepared to "sell" DeKalb to the investment community. We had a good record, so I found myself enjoying preparing my pitch to analysts. We had some practice sessions, of course. I was urged to "keep it simple" because most of the people I would be addressing really didn't know the difference between sweet corn and "field" or "feed" corn, which is DeKalb's market. I tried the speech out on my four kids, who ranged in age from seven to fifteen. They could understand it—at least most of it—so I figured the city slickers would, too; and they did! Here is what Harrington (Tony) Bischoff, the White-Weld investment banker who handled our IPO, remembers about our offering and my presentation of it:

SOURCE: Tony Bischoff

Tony Bischoff

> "It was obvious to me that DeKalb's profit margins and returns on investment, plus the nascent excitement of the prospects for hybrid wheat, made the company distinct and unique. Two of the most attractive (and highest p/e [price to earnings] ratio) stock concepts at the time were (a) pharmaceutical firms with their proprietary research-based products and (b) Avon with its dedicated door-to-door sales force. DeKalb embodied both of these, and I recommended to you that we cast the story within that context. You crafted the story and it flew like a cob with wings!" (Letter to the author, Nov. 19, 1995)

Why Not Offer Non-voting Stock?

A few days before we committed our offering to White-Weld, Blair White of the law firm of Sidley & Austin (our Chicago attorneys) called our attention to the fact that several firms, including A. C. Nielsen & Co. (a leader at public opinion polling) had listed Class B non-voting shares on the market, and that they had sold at substantially the same market prices as their voting shares.

My brother-in-law Charlie and I were delighted to learn this because we had been reluctant to sell our voting shares in the public offering. We saw the opportunity to offer Class B non-voting shares as a way to participate in the public offering without having to reduce our share of the voting stock.

Therefore, we recommended to our board that we create a new, non-voting class of stock and issue it as a stock dividend to our shareholders, issuing them each one share of Class B non-voting stock, which would be added to their Class A voting shares. The public offering would, then, be in the form of Class B non-voting shares offered for sale by our shareholders, in the quantities our investment bankers felt would be advisable. The board approved our recommendation after a full discussion with our lawyers and with White-Weld.

One Big Offer

After our most important presentation to the investment community in New York City, with Harrington Bischoff of White-Weld doing a great job leading us, Morgan Guaranty offered to buy the whole offering. We declined because we wanted to distribute our shares widely, but Morgan Guaranty ended up with as many of the offered shares as anybody.

A Big Increase in the Value of DeKalb Shares

The public offering was a complete success. The stock was sold at the price we expected, a little more than twenty times earnings, and moved up a bit in the after-market, as we had hoped it would. The value of DeKalb common stock was more than tripled by the public offering. The price realized on the first day of the offering was $26.50 per share, producing an increase of 352 percent in value per share. A few years later, it rose to over $60 per share (Standard & Poor's, July 19, 1976).

Happy Shareholders

Our shareholders, most of whom were DeKalb County farmers who had held their shares since either 1917 or 1921, were surprised at the increase in value of their shares, but they were not in a rush to sell. One of our older farmer-stockholders whom we will call Oscar Decker was a little confused by the volume of literature he had received and asked our corporate secretary, Mary Pesut, to explain it to him. Knowing that at his age it would be better for him not to sell, Mary explained to him that the company had decided to offer shareholders a chance to sell some of their stock when it was first offered to the public, and that we expected the per-share price to be about $20.

Oscar took a moment to calculate that his shares would be worth more than a million dollars. Amazed by this discovery, he exclaimed: "By God, I never thought I would make it!" After a few minutes, Oscar reminded Mary of the time that his second wife had been after him to give her title to half of his farm and half of his Ag stock. He hadn't signed the stock over to her, and in Mary's office he sat back with a little grin on his face and said, "Well, she died."

THE SOUTHERN CORN LEAF BLIGHT EPIDEMIC

In the late summer of 1970, farmers and plant pathologists in our southern states reported that an unusually virulent epidemic of southern corn leaf blight (Helminthesporium maydis) had broken out, destroying many fields. It was moving northward toward the corn belt.

At first, corn belt plant pathologists were not greatly concerned; the disease had come into their fields late in other summers and had done little damage to yields. However, as reports of crop disasters became more frequent, serious damage was reported as far north as southern Wisconsin. When the season was over, the nation's corn yields had been reduced by more than 20 percent, and many fields were totally destroyed.

It became vital to quickly answer the questions: (1) Why did it happen? (2) Is it likely to happen again next year? and (3) What can we do to prevent it in the future? We and every corn pathologist in the United States worked hard to find the answers, and by harvest time we had them.

It happened because the disease struck hybrids whose female parents carried male-sterile cytoplasm and had transmitted it to their hybrid progeny. In view of the fact that a large percentage of hybrid seedcorn had been produced using male-sterile cytoplasm for the previous fifteen years without similar problems with southern corn leaf blight, it became apparent that the pathogen had mutated into a much more virulent form, to which hybrids having male-sterile cytoplasm were susceptible. The new race had spread to the north as the corn crop matured. It was therefore likely that the more virulent form of the pathogen was present on most central corn belt farms at the end of 1970, and that it posed a threat to any farmer who planted susceptible seed.

Resistant Susceptible

SOURCE: Corporate Records, DeKalb Genetics

Blight Resistant Vs Blight Susceptible Corn

Worse yet, most of the hybrid seedcorn produced in 1970 for planting in 1971 was likely to be susceptible. Only farmers who lived in the northern or western corn belt were likely to avoid damage, because their summers were shorter, cooler, and dryer.

By October, hybrid seedcorn producers were in a scramble to contract seed production in Mexico or the southern hemisphere to produce hybrids with resistant normal cytoplasm. But the supply of "normal" parent seed was far too small to produce as much resistant hybrid seed as was needed, so most of the winter production efforts were aimed at multiplying resistant seed parents to be planted in 1971, which would produce a full supply of resistant hybrid seed for 1972 planting by farmer customers. But finding resistant hybrid seed to plant in 1971 was a big problem.

DeKalb's Position

Like all hybrid seed producers, we had been aware of the advantages of using male-sterile female parents to produce hybrids. Until the new and virulent form of southern corn leaf blight came along in 1970, hybrids made with male-sterile female parents were both less costly (because they did not require detasseling) and more pure than hybrids produced by hand-detasseling. This was because youthful detasselers inevitably missed a few tassels, which contaminated the production of the hybrid to some extent. This kind of problem was manageable, however, with close inspection of seed production fields at pollinating time. However, hybrids produced on male-sterile females were also less costly, by 4 to 8 percent, so all seed producers had preferred using male-sterile female seed parents.

At DeKalb, we knew of the cost advantages of using male-sterile female seed parents, but these females parents required the use of pollen from fertility-restoring male parents in order for hybrid progeny of male-sterile seed parents to produce pollen (an absolute necessity to produce grain).

Development of fertility-restoring male parents took at least five years. Hence, when our corn breeders came up with new hybrids that were better than our competitors', we in DeKalb's management often faced a choice between (1) waiting for fertility-restoring genes to be transferred into the male parent and (2) going into large-scale production immediately, using detasselers to produce the latest and best hybrids.

Because male-sterile female lines could be developed faster than fertility-restoring males, we often produced hybrids that were blends. These were made by using the non-fertility-restoring male parent and planting half of the female acres in a seed production field to the male-sterile parent and half to the "normal" female parent, which was detasseled. The seed from the normal female parent would be capable of producing pollen and would be blended at harvest with seed from the male-sterile female parent, whose progeny would be male-sterile. The finished product would therefore contain 50 percent male-sterile plants and 50 percent pollen producers, which was enough to ensure complete pollination in customers' fields.

In 1971, DeKalb's total seed supply available for planting consisted of 13 percent fully resistant hybrid seed; 52 percent hybrids that were blends of seeds, of which half were resistant and half susceptible to the new strain of SCLB; and 35 percent fully susceptible hybrid seed (Olson, "Genetics to Genius," p. 396).

Finding Resistant Seed for 1971 Planting

Farmers in threatened areas wanted fully resistant seed, but it was usually not available in 1971, so their second choice was the blends of resistant and susceptible seed such as those DeKalb had produced in its seed production fields in 1970 and earlier. These could be planted a bit thicker than usual, which would ensure an acceptable crop if the new race of SCLB should strike again, as seemed probable.

For southern farmers, who were the most vulnerable, DeKalb imported flint hybrid seed from DeKalb Argentina, which had been produced using male-fertile (resistant) cytoplasm. We told them that the hybrids would not yield quite as well as the ones they had been planting, but that they would be resistant to the new race of SCLB.

Ways to Fight Blight

The big scramble for SCLB-resistant seed seemed to pay off in 1971; as many southern farmers whose corn crop had been destroyed in 1970 planted either resistant hybrids or none at all. Apparently this prevented the huge blight buildup in the south that had swept northward to the central corn belt in 1970, and the nation's average corn yield in 1971 returned to normal. About 6 percent less corn was planted in 1971 because farmers who could not obtain seed that was not at least partially resistant switched to other crops like soybeans, wheat, or grain sorghum. By 1972 planting time, the crisis was over. Farmers could buy resistant hybrid seed that had been produced in 1971 on seed parents that had normal (resistant) cytoplasm. The female seed parents were, of course, male fertile and were, therefore, detasseled and pollinated by pollen from nearby "male" rows. The hybrid kernels, which carried SCLB-resistant cytoplasm were harvested from the female rows, exactly as had been done before sterile (susceptible) cytoplasmic sterility was discovered.

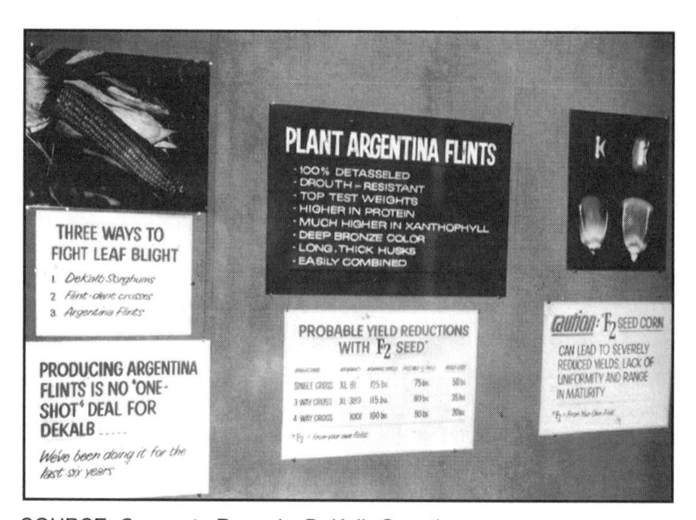

SOURCE: Corporate Records, DeKalb Genetics

DeKalb fights southern corn leaf blight epidemic

What Did the SCLB Epidemic Teach Us?

The SCLB epidemic reminded all plant breeders of these basics:

- Genetic and cytoplasmic diversity are vital because mutations occur regularly in pathogens. If everyone plants the same thing, eventually a mutant pathogen will appear that is capable of causing great damage to homogeneous hosts.

- Plant breeders must support efforts to collect and preserve diverse genetic material in "germ plasm pools" quickly accessible to everyone faced with an epidemic.
- "Early warning" plantings must be organized, planted in many locations, and carefully observed in order to detect new and potentially dangerous pathogens before they balloon into epidemic proportions.

We hired a full-time plant pathologist, Dr. David Smith, to take steps to achieve the above objectives, and to assist our corn breeders, most of whom had good plant pathology backgrounds. Since his arrival in early 1973, he has done a superb job.

Candor at Risk during the SCLB Epidemic

There were many tense moments during the six-week period in 1970 after the SCLB epidemic was discovered. Dr. Art Hooker, a distinguished plant pathologist at the University of Illinois, and his student, David Smith, spent full time in the field for many weeks, assessing the situation, trying to figure out what had happened, and guessing how much damage would be done to the nation's corn crop.

Commodity markets became alarmed and feared that as much as half of the nation's crop might be destroyed before harvest was over. When a reporter asked me how much damage might be done to the crop, I replied that no one could forecast that very well, but added that it seemed to me that 40 to 50 percent crop losses seemed highly unlikely. After my comment made the newspapers the next day, a farmer I knew and respected telephoned me to say, "I agree with your comment, but I wish you hadn't made it. Look what happened to the corn market today!" The market had dropped a bit, but it was, of course, only coincidence.

Despite the problems with southern corn leaf blight and some difficulties we had keeping up with demand (which we responded to by building two new state-of-the-art seed processing plants at Remington, Indiana, and Boone, Iowa), DeKalb U.S. seed sales grew to new highs in the first half of the 1970s, as is shown in Table 21-3 at the end of this chapter.

RASMUSEN, CFO, RECOMMENDS DIVERSIFICATION

Roger Rasmusen, Rus' son, who had done a fine job for several years as manager of international seed operations, was appointed chief financial officer in 1971. Dr. David Curtis, a knowledgeable geneticist, took Roger's former position. One of Roger's first assignments was to forecast our cash flow and compare it with the cash requirements of our operating divisions. He pointed out that we were generating much more cash than we would need in our businesses for the foreseeable future and recommended that we either substantially increase our dividends to shareholders, or consider diversifying.

Since we had recently increased our dividend and did not feel pressure to increase it further, we consulted the Boston Consulting Group about the advisability of diversifying and how best to go about it. They thought diversification would be wise and counseled us to consider buying firms close to our "base businesses" in agriculture and oil.

SOURCE: Corporate Records, DeKalb Genetics

DeKalb's Boone, Iowa Seedcorn Processing Plant.

High Spirits in 1972

A speech I delivered to our sales organization on July 19, 1972, sums up the spirit of our seed sales organization and the optimism I felt for the company's future:

> "First and more important than anything else I have to say tonight, congratulations. Congratulations to all of you men of the DeKalb sales organization. You came off a tremendous year in 1971 when we enjoyed increased market share primarily because we had blight-resistant seed when it was needed. But this year, 1972, was surely the year of the sales organization. You, and I say you advisedly, because this time the credit belongs largely to you. You have actually succeeded in holding on to those competitive gains this year, when everyone—not just Funk and DeKalb—was selling blight-resistant seed. The bump-it-up program was designed to help, and no doubt it did, but you, the men of the line sales organization, made DeKalb's combination of super products and super sales programs pro-

duce. Frankly, I never thought we would be able to do it. I have been hoping we might hang on to half or two-thirds of last year's competitive gain, but now I'm convinced we hung on to all of it. In fact, your latest estimates suggest we increased market share; but I do not really believe this is true, because we had a few more bags returned than you estimated. Nevertheless, when I consider last year's advantages, and also the setback we had in the South, I think you have scored a rather spectacular achievement and I congratulate you.

I am sure you in sales join with me in thanking the research and production men for coming on strong with the ever-improving product line that is the solid foundation behind this truly great achievement.

I've been talking entirely about corn so far, but we have performed even better in sorghum this year than with corn. Sales are down a bit, but not nearly as much as this year's 18 percent sorghum acreage reduction. We didn't have a "blight" advantage over competitors with sorghum as we did in corn. Instead, we have been making slow but steady progress with our product mix backed up by a solid sales organization that made a competitive increase possible. Again, congratulations.

I think I should leave the rest of the detail of where-it-happened, who did best, and so forth to the other speakers. Is it enough to say "Congratulations and thanks for a great job?"

The rest of my comments tonight will deal with the rest of DeKalb's business, those other departments we're counting on to keep our earnings running up in 1973, with our financial prospects, and with the acquisition criteria and new product development concepts we have developed. These new directions, together with even larger seed, oil, and poultry breeding operations will determine what DeKalb will be like five and ten years down the road.

Egg operations were extremely difficult this year, because of the length and depth of the current "down cycle" in egg prices. We have maintained market share, but our sales are off, earnings are red, many customers are close to or actually have negative net worths. But the end is in sight. Egg prices may well have bottomed out, and better, even good prices are around the corner, so better times are coming. We confidently expect a nice earnings contribution from both eggs and broilers in fiscal '73, but did not do well this year. We have made moves that should help us snap back—first we invested in the largest, sharpest, fastest growing egg producer in the business, and we expect him to use our birds. Second, and more important, we made our prices more competitive by lowering them, shifted towards a new bird, and made the necessary reductions in the sales department. Some of these good people are here tonight and will be working in seed. We're glad to have them.

Broiler operations came back this year, and are moving up as our new 88 bird is coming on, but they haven't achieved black figures yet. Nevertheless, we are confident for the new year in both eggs and broilers and expect to see improvement from poultry in the new year.

Our oil division is moving along, on track. Earnings will be up considerably this fiscal year compared to last, as we experienced some significant non-recurring exploration expenses during 1971.

Hybrid wheat, hopefully a coming star, is just getting started. We introduced the first commercial hybrid this year. It fits only a small area in central Montana, but we sold out in a hurry, and we think this is the beginning of a solid hybrid wheat business. All in all, our other divisions came through with flying colors, and we expect another increase in total corporate earnings this year, about on trend with the 20 percent rate we have enjoyed for the last twelve years.

Planning for the Future

During the last twelve to eighteen months, the management group has been taking a long look at our company and its future. We have forecast the cash needs of our existing product line, and compared those needs with the cash generation we can reasonably expect. We forecast continued growth from both seed and poultry, and we've set money aside to support that growth financially. It's rather clear that poultry and seed and oil can finance their own growth out of their own cash flows, and we expect to operate them on that principle. However, if we assume a continued modest dividend rate, we foresee considerably more cash generation than we can utilize in our existing product lines, assuming that they grow as expected. In addition, we have to recognize that we have significant unused debt capacity at the present time.

Accordingly, it's clear that we should be looking for new business opportunities. As we see it, these can be classified as internally generated and externally generated opportunities. In the internal classification, we think of diversifications that are DeKalb's traditional "bag." That is, those that are similar to our earlier diversifications into poultry or into sorghum or wheat: diversifications that are based on hybridization of a new product."

Other "New Business" Opportunities

The other general classification of new business opportunities I describe as "external" in nature, and by that I mean new and different businesses we either start from scratch or acquire. Good acquisitions don't come easily. The woods have been pretty well worked over, and if one looks at the sad statistical result of acquisitions made by others in the '60s, it's obvious that acquiring companies can be a very hazardous business.

So we've tried to carefully organize for it in the following ways:

- Our first move was delegation of seed division responsibility to Harold Noren.
- Our second move was the engagement of the Boston Consulting Group to help us with the evaluation of our own operations and the development of acquisition strategies.
- Our third move was Roger Rasmusen's appointment as financial vice president.

As we have worked with the Boston Consulting Group, we have studied a number of diverse acquisition possibilities and have developed some acquisition criteria we think appropriate to our business. These are formally stated, but they certainly are not perfect.

Our acquisition criteria are:

- We want to stay close to agribusiness, an area where we feel our judgement has more validity than in other fields.
- We prefer growing companies that are needing cash to expand their growth, and which are willing to be 100% acquired, preferably for stock. We want them to be large enough to be worth while, because we realize that there is approximately an equal amount of work envolved in buying a big company as is involved in buying a small one.
- We want companies that have good management that want to stay on with us.

We must set clear goals for ourselves, organize to achieve them, and be willing to take risks if we are going to be a growing agribusiness company. And I should make it clear that we are not going to become corporate farmers. We want to grow with agriculture as it becomes more complex, but we do not want to compete with farmers. We want to serve them"

MANAGEMENT SUCCESSION GIVEN CONSIDERATION

The Boston Consulting Group also advised that we give thought to management succession, perhaps hiring people to manage our diversification efforts who might later succeed Charlie and me as top corporate officers. Charlie and I reviewed the qualifications, abilities, strengths, and weaknesses of the people then in DeKalb's employ and regretfully concluded that there were none we would consider candidates for DeKalb's top job. We decided to begin a search for people who could be trained and developed to succeed us and sought help from the best "head hunter" we could find.

Executive Search Finds John McCarter

In early 1973 we learned of an outstanding young man named John McCarter, who was looking for work after spending four years running business affairs for the State of Illinois. His boss, the Republican governor, had not been reelected after increasing the state's income taxes. The tax increase was badly needed, but the voters had rebelled and thrown the Republicans out of office.

John had impressive credentials. He had been an honor student at Princeton, attended the London School of Economics, and earned an MBA at Harvard. From there, he had gone on to a leading consulting firm, which nominated him to serve as a Presidential Fellow under Lyndon Johnson. We hired him in March 1973 to be our manager of corporate development. He went right to work.

Heinold Companies Are Acquired

Harrington Bischoff of White-Weld, who had been an important factor in our public offering, brought us Harold Heinold, founder and president of the Heinold Companies, who was interested in either taking his company public or being acquired by another company that would finance further growth in his two businesses, hog marketing and commodity brokerage. See Chapter 23A for a complete report on the Heinold Transaction.

Lindsay Manufacturing and Arizona Feeds Are Acquired

In 1974, John McCarter acquired two unrelated companies, the Lindsay Manufacturing Company for 389,304 shares of class B common stock worth close to $17,518,680 at $45 per share, and Arizona Feeds for 16,547 class B shares worth nearly $744,615 at $45 per share. Lindsay turned out well, but Arizona Feeds did not. Both are discussed in Chapter 23, where our acquisitions are described more completely. (These were reported in our 1974 SEC Form 10K, p. 2.)

OTHER ACQUISITIONS

We purchased two small companies, United Detector Technology and Sensors (UDT), for cash, hoping that their developing product lines could be used in our seed business; but they did not fit our needs, so they were eventually resold or written off. In 1978, the company wrote off its remaining $1,029,000 investment in UDT (1978 SEC Form 10K, p. 6).

SOURCE: Corporate Records, DeKalb Genetics

Tom & Charlie Welcome John McCarter

We also purchased part interest in a 2,000-acre catfish farm near Yazoo City, Mississippi, and resold it after a few years at a small net gain.

Three Fiascoes

At the beginning of this chapter, I said that in our efforts to diversify, there were several successes and three fiascoes. The fiascoes were: (1) our broiler chicken breeding business (the Pilch acquisition); (2) our ill-timed entry into the cattle feeding business; and (3) the failure of the Nuclear Assurance Corporation, in which we had a stock interest.

The Pilch Fiasco

The Pilch acquisition is discussed in Chapter 27. It was a logical move, made by our poultry people before John McCarter joined us. Suffice it to say here that we suffered substantial losses while we owned Pilch, which we divested in 1973 (see Table 21-1).

The Cattle Feeding Fiasco

We suffered even greater losses from our cattle feeding operations in 1974, a total of $7.9 million (1976 DeKalb SEC Form 10K, p. 4).

DeKalb had entered the cattle feeding business after careful study of the economic advantages of large feed lots in the West over traditionally small Midwest farm feed yards. Our basic error was a failure to recognize that the cattle feedyard business had become overbuilt. We lost $4.9 million on our International Cattle Systems Yard, which we sold, and $3 million on Heinold Cattle Markets, which halted feeding.

Table 21-1
The Pilch Fiasco

Year of Loss ($)	
1970	538,000
1971	1,975,000
1972	857,000
1973	506,000
Total Losses	$3,876,000

SOURCE: DeKalb 1974 SEC Form 10K, p. 9.

The Nuclear Assurance Fiasco

The third fiasco also occurred in 1974, when a $1.7 million write-off of our investment was necessary after failure of the Nuclear Assurance Corporation, which had been in the business of providing spare parts for nuclear reactors. Objectors to nuclear power succeeded in halting the construction of new nuclear power plants and limited the profitability of those that were operating.

We took our failure with Nuclear Assurance as a warning not to become involved in investments that were far afield from our basic businesses.

PIONEER BEGINS TO CATCH UP

Our hybrid corn business sailed upward after we broke through with high-performing single crosses. We were aware that Pioneer, our toughest competitor, was watching, so we were not surprised when Pioneer, too, introduced several single crosses. In 1973 we began hearing that Pioneer 3780 was a pretty good hybrid. Upon hearing that, Harold Nolin made a project of observing it. He concluded that it was a darned good hybrid but did not think it would threaten our business. Our own research tests confirmed his conclusion, but it was becoming clear that Pioneer was catching up to us. Our strategy was to continue increasing our research effort.

A HARD FREEZE HITS WHEN CARRYOVER INVENTORY IS VERY SMALL

In early September of 1974, a hard freeze hit the entire corn belt, making a significant part (perhaps 30 percent) of DeKalb's seed crop unsalable because of low germination. We stretched our supplies as far as we could, but many competitors who had been forced to carry over seed as DeKalb's sales surged in 1973 and 1974 found their large carryover supplies to be in demand because their germination was still strong. The net result was a sharp decline of nearly a million units, or about 25 percent from our 1974 record sales of 4,403,000 units.

John McCarter Made Seed Vice President

Partly because we were uneasy about our seed sales, partly because we wanted to involve John heavily in our important seed business, and partly because Harold Noren, who had managed our seed business superbly for many years, would likely choose to retire soon, we appointed John McCarter vice president of our seed business in 1975, reporting to Harold Noren. One year later, as we became more and more concerned about our seedcorn sales, we replaced Carroll Christensen (seed sales vice president) with Tom Melton, who had performed well in many different jobs in our seed sales organization.

Some seed quality problems surfaced with the huge production job we faced in 1975, catching up with seed inventory needs. A seed "production research" function was established, with experienced production man Daryl Rolland in charge, reporting directly to John McCarter. Rolland did a good job, setting higher standards for the future and enforcing them.

Sales Recover, Then Fall Back

Led by hybrids like XL43, XL54, XL347 XL64, XL75, and XL81, all of which utilized inbred lines out of Program 5 (the Chase-Tsotsis breeding program), DeKalb recovered a lot of its momentum in 1976 when sales climbed to 4,186,000 units, the second highest record in our history, but competition was getting stronger and our sales slipped badly for the rest of the decade, as is shown in Table 21-5 at the end of this chapter.

Basil Tsotsis conducted a thorough evaluation of our products' declining competitiveness and reached the following conclusions:

> "Our problems originated in 1974, the year in which DeKalb registered its maximum market penetration with a volume of sales of almost 4.5 million units of seed sales and a 24% market share in the U.S. This level of success had been achieved with consistent gains made after 1964 (when the volume of our sales approached two million units, thanks to

XL45) with the aid of such hybrids as XL43, XL64 and XL81, most of which had been developed in the corn breeding program originated by Chase and carried on after his resignation by Tsotsis and Crum. In 1974 alone, sales increased by more than 700,000 units, on the heels of a series of meetings in Iowa and elsewhere in November and December of 1973. Their theme was to describe to farmers and to DeKalb sales personnel the company's corn research and the major role it had played in recent years in the unprecedented strengthening of its position.

In 1974, the major part of the corn belt was hit by what Earl Butz, the U.S. secretary of agriculture, called the "triple whammy," which was a combination of a very late planting season, followed by an unusually cool summer, and by killing frosts during the last week in August and the first week in September. That combination affected DeKalb much more severely than its competitors for the following reasons:

- The company had an inadequate seed supply for the 80 to 105 maturity series in the north because of its heavy sales in 1973 and an insufficient seed production in1973 to restore its depleted inventories. Consequently, later hybrids (primarily XL43 and XL64) were offered as substitutes and planted in areas where they were too late in normal circumstances. Because of this, the ravages of the 1974 season were more evident on such substitutes than they were on earlier maturing hybrids, and the damage inflicted upon DeKalb's product line was much heavier than it otherwise would have been.
- The 1974 season reduced DeKalb's planned seed crops by at least 40%. Therefore, the company entered the 1975 sales season at a disadvantage which it tried to overcome by offering seed with less than optimum germination, believing incorrectly, as it turned out, that the seed crop of its competitors was similarly affected. Sales dropped from approximately 4.5 million to about 3.1 million units. Competitors, and especially Pioneer, had ample seed supplies of good performing hybrids such as P3780 which was, in addition, earlier than XL43 and XL64 which we had deployed against it.
- The performance of DeKalb hybrids in 1975 was not helped when many DeKalb customers' fields were planted with weak germinating seed, a shortcoming that was not the case with Pioneer. Our weak germinating seed in combination with our seed shortages led to an understandable lowering of the morale of the company's sales force, even in districts where the frosts of the previous season had not been a serious problem. As an example,

on the East Coast the sales of XL43, which in the past outperformed P3780 and continued to do so after 1974, when good germinating seed was available, fell dramatically because of the complaints our Eastern District managers heard about that hybrid from their colleagues in the Midwest. Similar examples could be cited for other hybrids.

The result was that sales declined farther, but even more important, the entire line up of the company's hybrids was becoming, in the minds of its salespeople, obsolete for both real and for borrowed reasons. The discard in 1976 of literally millions of units of low germinating seed that could not be sold in 1975 did little to reverse the feeling that the entire lineup of company hybrids had become inferior to those offered by Pioneer and Pioneer's "look-alikes."

Under these conditions, in my [Basil's] opinion, our corn research could not have alone restored the company's market position even with hybrids of salable competitiveness, and do so in the course of one or two seasons, when millions of units of new hybrids could have become available to replace those considered obsolete. The production problems referred to here were chronic, but they were systematically addressed with the construction of new plants in 1974 and beyond." *(End of Basil's report)*

In my opinion, there is a lot of validity to Basil's analysis, but there were additional important factors in our loss of market share in the late 1970s and early 1980s, as follows:

- The excellent performance by Pioneer's research.
- The shift in demand toward shorter-season hybrids, which favored Pioneer because it enjoyed a strong, dominant position in the northern quarter of the corn belt and could move those hybrids south.
- Our overemphasis on disease resistance, at a time when improved harvesting equipment made more acceptable those hybrids that were bred for yield at the expense of the stalk weakness that goes with disease resistance.

We introduced new hybrids XL36 and XL39, which looked great in our research plots and in first-year dealer demonstrations, but both looked like different hybrids in our dealers' and our customers' fields the following year. Part of the problems with these two hybrids may have been caused by missed "nicks" between the time of pollination by the male plants and receptivity of silk by the female plants in our seed fields. However, in the case of XL36, one of our top marketers was so impressed with its appearance and its record in our tests that he ordered a large production of it before it had been adequately tested. It was a total flop, to the great embarrassment of our field people. It lost us a lot of angry customers. XL39 was similarly disappointing, but its failure more likely was due to its being a hard hybrid to produce. We introduced other new hybrids that performed well, but loss of dealer morale is hard to overcome, whether it is caused by low-priced, high-quality competitive hybrids or by disappointing new DeKalb releases.

All in all, the five years between 1977 and 1982 were years of frustration, low morale, and dismay for the whole DeKalb organization The problems and rationale presented above may seem like alibis by a man who was raised to absolutely accept the credo, "You are expected to make good, not to make excuses," but they are as close as I can come to explaining what happened to our products' competitiveness after 1976.

What did we in management do to resolve our problems? We threw money at them. We built new, more modern plants, we gave our people more training by sending them to schools, we hired more and more breeders—but one cannot expect immediate tangible products from newly hired corn breeders.

The "Look-alike" Problem

In the second half of the 1970s, many small and medium-sized seed companies began offering hybrids that "looked like" Pioneer hybrids 3780 and 3541. In the 1980s, the courts found that the "look-alikes" had been made using parent lines taken from Pioneer seed fields by one of the largest suppliers of parent seed to small and medium-sized competitors. The "look-alike" seed usually sold at prices lower than Pioneer's, so many small growers saw their market shares increase substantially until the court ruling denied their parent seed suppliers the right to supply them with parent seed developed by others.

The combination of Pioneer hybrids' faster dry-down, the availability of low-priced look-alikes, and our own seed quality problems contributed significantly to the decline in DeKalb seedcorn sales that began in the mid 1970s and continued into the 1980s.

New Assignments to Deal with Our Problems

John McCarter threw himself vigorously into his new job as seed vice president, spending time in the field with district and regional managers and corn breeders as well as dealers, many of whom expressed growing concern for our need to expedite release of new and better hybrids to meet Pioneer's increasingly strong product line. This field experience convinced John that a change in corn research management was needed.

Bruce Bickner hired

The employment of Bruce Bickner was part of our effort to develop successors for myself and Charlie Roberts who could, in the future, run the company in tandem as we had for many years. We also felt we should add another good man to our staff as an alternative candidate for the top job. Bruce had worked on DeKalb's account at Sidley & Austin, where he was a protégé of Blair White, an outstanding Sidley & Austin attorney and a DeKalb director. Bruce had done a good job of straightening out some legal vulnerabilities at Heinold Commodities and came to DeKalb with a strong endorsement from Blair and a reputation as being a very bright lawyer as well as a bit of a "street-fighter." He proved to be very competent.

An Important Research Leadership Change

By 1978, Harold Noren was close to retirement, John McCarter was training to replace him, and everyone at the top level of DeKalb was concerned about the market share gains that Pioneer was achieving with its new hybrids. Dick Holland (vice president for seed research), Harold Noren, John McCarter, and I agreed that Basil Tsotsis should concentrate his efforts on the development of hybrids for the tropics, and that we should appoint a new corn research leader for the temperate climates.

We asked Dr. Charlie Krull, who was responsible for DeKalb corn breeding in Europe, to return home to take responsibility for DeKalb's temperate corn research. Our decision was a difficult one, as we had a high regard for Basil. It was even harder for him, or course, but he accepted reassignment and plunged vigorously into his new job of breeding hybrids for tropical and subtropical areas. The substantial volume of tropical hybrids being sold today is testimony to his success there.

Dick Holland Resigns,
Is Replaced by Bruce Maunder

Dick Holland, who had performed superbly for DeKalb, first as the originator of our hybrid sorghum product line and next as seed research director, resigned for compelling personal reasons on June 24, 1978, and returned to Texas. He worked independently there for many more years on the hybridization of cotton by utilizing cytoplasmic male sterility to make sterile female lines and pollinating them with pollen from males carrying fertility-restoring genes. He seems to be a happy man farming and breeding cotton in his native Texas. We miss him and wish him well.

Dr. Bruce Maunder, a fine plant breeder who has been, in my opinion, the world's outstanding sorghum breeder for many years, replaced Dick temporarily as seed research director. Bruce performed well in his new job, but his heart was in "hands-on" plant breeding, so he decided in early 1980 to return to full-time sorghum breeding as sorghum research director, with my full support. I appreciated his willingness to fill in after Dick resigned. After he returned to sorghum breeding, Harold Noren assumed direction of seed research, with the directors of research for each product line reporting to him. When Harold retired in December 1980, John McCarter assumed that responsibility.

I SUGGEST SELLING DEKALB'S SEED BUSINESS

In February 1976, I wrote a note to my brother-in-law, Charlie Roberts, suggesting that our families advise DeKalb's board of directors that we wished to sell our seed company (the two Roberts families had exactly the same amounts of class A voting stock and in combination had the votes necessary to force a sale). My reasoning was as follows:

- I was concerned that competition from Pioneer, whose product line had improved considerably, and the Pioneer look-alikes sold at bargain prices would inevitably depress DeKalb's seedcorn sales considerably.
- We had recently been approached by a responsible potential buyer who already owned a medium-sized seed business as well as other large and successful businesses. I had declined to talk to the buyer, but he was probably still interested.
- The market value of DeKalb was probably higher than it would be again for a long time.

Charlie discussed my proposal with his wife, Mary (my sister), and their family and advised me that they did not wish to sell because they felt we had a moral obligation to the memory of our father, Tom, Sr., to continue our management of the company, primarily for the benefit of its employees. I accepted their decision and agreed not to take my proposal to DeKalb's board, even though I believed the problems we would face in the next few years would likely affect many employees more negatively than would a sale to a responsible firm that could better afford to ride out the coming storm.

KEY PERSONNEL CHANGES, 1970 THROUGH 1979

1971 Harold Noren was appointed senior vice president for seed, worldwide.
Carroll Christensen was appointed vice president for U.S. seed sales. Chris had been our appointee to manage Pilch, where we felt he had not been at fault.

1972 Roger Rasmusen was appointed chief financial officer, and Dr. David Curtis replaced Roger Rasmusen as director of international seed operations.

1973 John McCarter was hired as manager of corporate development. John Powers became his assistant.
Paul Vance, our outstanding seed production manager, died, and was replaced by Ed Uhland.

1974 John Cotton was hired as director of corporate planning, reporting to John McCarter.
Bill Schaefer was appointed corporate legal counsel.
Dr. Dewey Harris resigned and was replaced by Dr. Larry Vint as director of poultry research.
John McCarter was made a director of DeKalb.

1975 Bruce Bickner was hired and named manager of corporate development.
Jim Warren moved to DeKalb to become director of brown egg research.

1976 Dr. E. E. Schnetzler retired and was replaced by Dr. Dewey Harris as manager of white egg research.
Tom Melton was promoted to seed sales manager, replacing Carroll Christensen.
Daryl Rolland was appointed manager of production research in a move to remedy seed quality problems.

1977 Chuck Lindhart was appointed vice president for seed production.
John Cotton, corporate planner, moved to Dynapol.
Frank Bauer was appointed corporate planner.
Nate McGuire was appointed assistant production manager to Ed Uhland.
Leo Damkroger was made director of sales promotion.
Wilbur Strawn retired; he was replaced by Al Golden.
Bill Schaefer, in-house attorney, resigned.

1978 John Witmer replaced Schaefer as corporate attorney.
Dr. David Curtis was appointed vice president for international seed.
Dr. Tsotsis was appointed international corn research director.
Dr. Charlie Krull was appointed temperate corn research director.
Dick Holland resigned as seed research director and was replaced by Dr. Bruce Maunder.
Harold Wright retired and John Launer was appointed seed quality control manager.

1979 Bill Burrow was appointed western and southern regional sales manager.

CLOSING OUT THE TUMULTUOUS 1970S

DeKalb's mix of earnings from 1975 through 1979 came from:

- a seed business with flat earnings;

- a growing oil business, which doubled its earnings in five years;
- a recovery in animal science; and
- two fast-growing subsidiary businesses at Heinold Hog Markets and Heinold Commodities.

Financial Results - Part Five

OPERATING RESULTS THROUGH THE 1970s

Table 21-3
DeKalb Seed Sales Move Up in First Half of the 1970s

Year	Corn	Sorghum	Sudax	Alfalfa
1970	3,467,409	403,341	264,425	29,910
1971	3,655,616	367,745	267,000	30,803
1972	3,637,686	490,877	257,589	43,592
1973	3,875,155	462,273	219,443	63,504
1974	4,403,232*	469,472	184,308	40,833

SOURCE: Corporate Sales Records, DeKalb Genetics
* DeKalb seedcorn's best year.. Source: DeKalb sales records.

Table 21-4
Earnings by Segment, 1970–1974
($000)

Division	1970	1971	1972	1973	1974
Seed	14,518	23,973	27,284	27,183	38,907
Animal Science	852	(4,995)	(3,534)	88	(5,014)
Heinold Cos.	853	1,225	2,049	4,054	3,516
Oil and Gas	889	241	884	1,488	5,749
Others, incl. Lindsay	280	1,260	1,521	2,518	2,556
Pre-Tax Earnings	17,392	21,704	28,204	35,301	45,724
Less Tax	8,413	10,563	13,797	16,925	22,562
Net Earnings	8,979	11,141	14,407	18,376	23,072
Return on Earnings	14.1%	13.8%	16.3%	16.4%	17.2%

SOURCE: 1974 SEC Form 10K, p. 8; also 1972, 1976 10Ks for return calculations. Notes: Animal Science losses in 1974 were from cattle feeding in the amount of $4,900,000. The Heinold Companies losses from cattle feeding in 1974 were $3,000,000. Pilch losses in the Animal Science category were: $538,000 in 1970, $1,975,000 in 1971, $857,000 in 1972, and $506,000 in 1973. The 1975 Animal Science losses are attributable to extremely low egg prices, which followed the introduction of Marek's disease vaccine. The improvement in oil earnings was due primarily to increases in oil price.

Table 21-5
DeKalb Seed Sales, 1975–1979

Year	Corn	Sorghum	Sudax	Alfalfa
1975	3,464,655	642,652	201,700	27,584
1976	4,186,531	505,795	197,971	88,777
1977	3,818,677	488,067	184,200	109,950
1978	3,550,373	400,033	189,026	99,062
1979	3,225,072	unknown	unknown	72,461

SOURCE: Corporate records as reported in the Preface.

Table 21-6
DeKalb Earnings by Division, 1975–1979
($000)

Division	1975	1976	1977	1978	1979
Seed	24,252	25,815	29,281	25,238	26,733
Animal Science[a]	(5,855)	(743)	1,660	4,785	7,884
Heinold	4,566	5,076	5,127	12,523	16,874
Oil	16,418	21,956	24,199	27,619	32,552
Other[b]	3,759	8,628	6,231	(2,758)	(3,578)
Pre-Tax	43,140	60,732	66,498	67,407	77,465
Incl. Tax	19,174	28,180	29,318	16,204	22,737
Net	23,966	32,552	37,180	51,203	54,728
Return on Equity	15.4%	17.6%	17.2%	13%	13%

SOURCES: SEC Form 10K for 1975, p. 2; SEC Form 10K for 1979, p. F16, reported for 1978 & 1979; SEC Form 10K for 1977, p. 4, reported for 1975, 1976, and 1977.a. Includes chicks, swine, and Western Cattle Systems (p. 2 of 1975 SEC Form 10K).

b. Includes Lindsay, Dynapol, & Sensors, plus losses on our discontinued feed business at Arizona Feeds, which amounted to $2,660,000 in 1979.

Table 21-7
DeKalb's Stock Prices, 1970–1979
(average of high and low for each year)

Year	Price Range ($ per share)
1970	7.25–15.875
1971	15.25–27.50
1972	24.25–57.50
1973	37.50–62.50
1974	21.25–51.25
1975	29.25–45.75
1976	30.50–40.50
1977	18.75–34.50
1978	16.50–23.75
1979	23.25–34.00

SOURCES: Standard & Poor's 1979 report, which adjusts for splits through 1979.

PARENT COMPANY OPERATING RESULTS, 1958 THROUGH 1960s

Income from sales, net income, and book value are the best measures of DeKalb's success in the 1960s. Our seed business was by far the biggest contributor to book value increases during this decade of dynamic growth; our seedcorn market share nearly doubled and margins tripled. However, our oil business began contributing to profits, too, with nearly 1 million dollars of pre-tax profits in 1969.

Table 20-8
DeKalb Corporate Financial Data, 1958–1969
($ Millions)

Year	Sales	Pre-tax Income	Net Income	Total Assets	Book Value*	Book Value in 1992 $
1958	27.0	4.0	2.1	31.2	24.8	113
1959	36.2	3.4	1.7	33.8	26.9	117
1960	33.8	1.1	0.6	30.9	27.0	116
1961	32.0	1.3	0.8	31.7	27.2	115
1962	36.6	2.9	2.0	34.9	27.8	116
1963	39.2	4.8	2.4	36.6	29.6	122
1964	49.6	6.6	3.9	43.9	34.4	140
1965	54.7	6.4	3.7	49.8	37.6	150
1966	65.7	9.2	5.1	66.1	42.0	163
1967	78.2	9.6	5.2	81.8	46.5	175
1968	74.6	9.5	5.6	92.0	52.4	189
1969	80.8	13.2	6.9	104.3	59.1	204

SOURCE: DeKalb corporate records
*Book Value is stockholder equity.

Thus ends Chapter 21, in which I have presented our seed business performance and problems. The next chapters deal with the evolution of our corn research efforts and tell the stories of our other lines of business in the 1970s, a decade that started strongly and ended with increasing concern for the health of our central business: hybrid seedcorn.

Part Six

1970-1979

DeKalb's Acquisition Era
1970-1987

In the early 1970s, Dekalb was completing a 12 year era of great success. Our treasury was loaded with cash,and we believed our major operations were very adequately funded. Accordingly, we had to choose between a substantial increase in dividends and searching for new businesses. Our shareholders seemed satisfied with their dividends, so we sought advice from management consultants, and took their advice, which was to seek to acquire other businesses in agriculture, our field of knowledge.

We searched carefully, and acquired several fine companies. Not all of them turned out well, but most of them were excellent, and served us well when our seed business declined.

Their stories are told in Chapter 22.

Chapter 22A

DeKalb Acquires the Heinold Companies 1970-1987

SOURCE: "Sis" Heinold

Harold Heinold

HEINOLD HOG MARKETS

In the spring of 1972, Tony Bischoff of White Weld & Company told us that Harold Heinold wanted to talk with us about merging Heinold Hog Markets, Inc., and Heinold Commodities, Inc., with DeKalb. We had a great deal of respect for Harold, so we were very willing to talk with him.

The origin, growth, and success of Heinold Hog Markets was a classic example of the best in American capitalism. Harold Heinold, an Indiana hog farmer, was frustrated by the hog marketing system he had to cope with. His main complaint was that farmers had to ship their hogs to a central market like the Chicago Stock Yards without knowing what price they would get for them. Harold thought that was unfair and did something about it. He bought a small local market, and each day, very early in the morning, he and his men would call packers to find out what they were paying for top-quality pigs that day. They often contracted on the spot to deliver hogs to the packers at that price. Farmers liked knowing what their hogs would bring before they were shipped, and the packers liked the higher-quality pigs they bought by avoiding the weight losses and physical damage that often occurred when they were shipped through central markets.

Harold's marketing system worked because his market managers were paid a direct 30 percent of the profits they created each day. Volume of daily hog movement was another important factor in their success; each market manager could close a deal by taking smaller margins from farmers who had large numbers to sell. Heinold's willingness to set a price immediately for pigs each farmer brought to their hog markets was so successful that the antiquated central hog markets were soon out of business. These included even the famous Chicago Stock Yards—Carl Sandburg's "hog butcher for the world."

However, Harold's drive to build markets squeezed his financial resources, and some of his best market managers got tired of taking common stock in the company in lieu of cash bonuses. And his expansion into the commodities trading business required capital infusions that further strained his bank credit lines.

DeKalb had the financial resources to finance expansion in both of his fundamentally sound businesses, so it seemed to us a merger might make sense. We pulled together a group of our best people to perform a careful "due diligence" study of both companies.

A Talk with Leo Melamed

After others had carefully studied the Heinold Companies, I decided to do some of my own due diligence by seeking an interview with Leo Melamed, chief executive officer of the Chicago Mercantile Exchange (the "Merc"), which was where Heinold Commodities did most of its trading. I told Leo that DeKalb was considering a friendly acquisition of the Heinold Companies and asked him how the Merc would feel about DeKalb's acquiring Heinold Commodities and what he thought about the quality of Heinold Commodities and its people.

Leo assured me that the Merc would welcome an acquisition by DeKalb, not only because we had a good reputation but also because our financial strength would help both Heinold Commodities and the Merc. As to the quality of the people, Leo laughingly replied, "Well, I think they are very good people, but they are a lot different than most firms trading on the Merc in at least one respect. They are basically farm boys—quite different because they don't have many good city boys connected with them. However, Joel Greenberg, one of our biggest traders, works with them and likes them."

He went on to tell me that Heinold Commodities had a remarkable trading record on the Merc—that in fact, ***for the most recent year, Heinold Commodities' customers were the only customer group trading on the mercantile exchange that had, on average for the entire year, shown a profit on its trading!*** With that comment, Leo sold me on Heinold Commodities. It was a decision I never regretted.

The Purchase Transaction

We bought the Heinold Companies in September of 1972, paying 175,000 shares of DeKalb Class A stock worth $13,120,000 for Heinold Hog Markets and 164,000 shares worth $12,305,000 for Heinold Commodities, a total dollar-equivalent-cost of $25,425,000. Heinold's net earnings for 1973 were $2,056,000, so the purchase was made at a 12.36 multiple of Heinold's earnings. It was a good buy for DeKalb, since our own shares were selling for well over 20 times earnings. (There was a 2:1 stock split after we struck our deal to purchase the Heinold Companies. Our deal with the Heinold Companies was reported in SEC Form 10K for 1974, p. F10, in 2:1 post-split terms as our having exchanged 678,000 DeKalb shares for all of Heinold's shares.) As DeKalb's manager of corporate development, John McCarter was initially in charge of the interface between DeKalb and the Heinold Companies.

A CONVERSATION WITH HAROLD AND SIS HEINOLD, THE ULTIMATE ENTREPRENEURS, JUNE 22, 1993

Tom: Harold, I appreciate very much your willingness to sit down with me here in Kouts, Indiana, to tell the story of the Heinold Companies.

My understanding is that you were a farmer here who decided one day to get out of farming and go into the business of marketing your neighbors' pigs. I'd like to hear stories about your life and the formation of your company in a way that you would like it to be told to your grandchildren.

Growing Up

Harold: I think it never was planned—it just happened. Let me say, right now where we are sitting is where I was born, so you see I never went any place in life but right here in Kouts. I was born in a large farm family and thought I would be a farmer all my life. When I got out of high school I went ahead and worked for my dad because our family had a rule that you worked for your family until you were twenty-one. Anything you earned went to the family kitty.

Tom: What year did you graduate from high school?

Harold: In 1937. I started farming in 1942 and within six years I was probably the largest hog and cattle man in our county. I always did expand pretty fast. Just kind of the nature of what I was.

Tom: How many acres were you farming?

Harold: I was farming about 700 acres and had about 50 to 100 brood sows, which in those days was quite a bit; and I fed about 400 cattle every year. Anyway, our market at that time was basically the Chicago Stock Yards. We also had some sale barns we could ship animals to, but regardless of where we went, we did not have the price of our livestock in advance.

We would listen to the radio, and when the market sounded pretty good, we would order our trucks and head for the Chicago Stock Yards. We'd get there and they'd say, "Oh, you should have been here yesterday," or they'd say, "Oh, it's a bad day today with too many hogs or cattle."

I was disappointed in our commission men in Chicago at that time because they couldn't give us a price in advance. So I followed the livestock truck to Archibald, Ohio, where loads of hogs were going to and from Chicago. I asked why they couldn't give us a price for our hogs in advance, which Mr. Slugbill, head of the Archibald packing plant, was willing to do. We saved him some money because we kept our hogs fresh, kept our shrink low, kept them well protected in the truck with no bruises or nothing, so it paid him to price our hogs before shipment. These were my own hogs. And Slugbill really liked them You would get cheaper freight if you shipped 100 hogs at once, so I started sharing with some of my neighbors. Well, that went like dynamite. I mean, the neighbors loved it. I even got a call from Michigan saying, "I'm your neighbor, can I get in on your method of selling hogs?"

Harold Starts His Own Hog Marketing Business

I worked a little bit here at the local stock yard and at the time I got married, I was trying to work the market here with the gentleman who owned it. While Sis and I were on our honeymoon, he hired a couple of men and put them on the payroll. [After that] we started working on our own here at the house and on the farm. We weighed the livestock at the Valparaiso sale barn, and we kept right on going direct to the packer.

Tom: A sale barn that was competing with the local market?

Harold: Well, it wasn't that big of a sale barn. It didn't handle much, but we used their scale and facilities. Eventually, they went broke, so I went to the bank, which my uncle Matt and I were involved with rebuilding. We bought the debt that the bank had secured by the stock yard. That's how I got control of the stock yard here in Kouts. This was in 1949. Then we operated here at the Kouts stock yard and it did well.

Tom: Were you still farming then?

Harold: Oh, yes. Still farming, farming on a big scale. I got some more help, hired one man at the stock yard. We ran both operations, the farming and the hog market. I soon learned that if I could guarantee a packer who called me at 7 or 8 o'clock in the morn ing that I'd have hogs for him, I could get a better bid than if I'd tell him I'd let him know at noon that I'm going to have hogs.

I realized that I must have more volume than this little market at Kouts could supply, so I put an ad in the paper. I got several answers, but the only one that I could get without costing me anything (I didn't have any money) was in Marengo, Illinois. There was a man up there who had an old sale barn he had tried operating and couldn't make it a success. The yard had been sitting idle for about six months. I said, "Mr. Franks, I'll give you five cents a hog for every hog I run through here and if I make it, you'll make it." He said, "No, I've got to have fifty dollars a month." I said, "I can't guarantee you fifty dollars a month. I can't afford that."

And I said, "Well, Mr. Franks, write down on a piece of paper how much money you've made on this building in the last six months." Of course, I knew he hadn't been operating it and he was losing money, so I said, "I'll write down what you possibly can make in the next months and what volume I think I can do."

Well, that persuaded him, but we had to do all of our fixing up and everything. There I was, 140 miles from my home, had to give somebody my check book, scared to death, didn't have money, who do you go to? We were home for Christmas with my wife's family. Her brother Jim had just graduated from college and was working as an accountant for Texas Eastern Pipeline, so I asked Jim if he'd like to take a chance and work with me. He said, "Well, I don't want to sit in an office all my life," so Jim and I headed for Marengo on the day after Christmas. Jim got almost scared, [but] I wanted to try it if he would. So we went ahead and rebuilt the market. It took us about a month, and Jim stayed and managed it. I worked and trained him over the telephone from Kouts, Indiana, to Marengo, Illinois because he had very little experience. So that was our first start away from home, and it worked.

That's where it all started. I was doing too much, so I called my brother-in-law, Lynn, who had just gotten out of the army and married my sister, Marianne. I said, "How would you like to come out and take over the farm? I've got more than I can handle." He was real anxious to get started farming so he came out and took over. We had a sale in March 1954 and liquidated all of our machinery and turned the farm over to him.

Sis: Tom, he came home and said, "You've got three weeks to move. Find a place to live."

Harold: I told her that we were going to rent, because I did not think a house made you any money. So that's what we did and that's how we grew. We had markets in Marengo and Kouts.

I had my own theories about how a market should run and how it should be built. So in 1955 I built a market at Goodland, Indiana, designing it so that every farmer's hogs were separate, so that a farmer could bring his hogs to us and if he found anything that he was unhappy with, his hogs would be separate until that evening. All he had to do was come back and we'd give him his hogs or write his check. To build confidence with the farmers here in Kouts, I even offered to haul their hogs to the Chicago Stock Yards free if they were unhappy.

Selling To Meat Packers

My idea was to represent the farmer, and I never hesitated to tell a packer that. I would say, "Now look, we work for the farmer, we're doing his marketing, but that doesn't mean that we're going to take advantage of you. In fact, we want to be able to do something for you that's fair too." We kept the hogs in separate pens for every farmer, loaded them separate on the trucks to get away from bruises, fighting, scars.

If you've ever seen hogs when they're killed, there's an unbelievable difference between just throwing hogs together in a big bunch as compared with keeping them separate. By giving them feed and water and keeping them comfortable, we increased the yield 1 to 2 percent. A lot of people don't know what tissue shrink is, but to give you an analogy, to me the hardest-working man on a baseball team is the catcher. He is up and down on every play, backs up first base, backs up third base. Every play he's involved. You go to a double header on a 100-degree day and you'll find that he can lose five to nine pounds and never have to go to the bathroom. It's the same way with a hog.

Tom: You found out actually it's in both the packer's inter est and the farmer's interest to minimize that tissue shrink, so you found out something that both of them could benefit from.

Harold: My goal was to get the farmer the best possible price for his hogs. I didn't want what we got in the Chicago Stock Yards: one day a high market, the next a low one. We always told our packing houses we just wanted an honest good market. That's all a farmer asks. And they were very good to us.

SOURCE: Harold Heinold

Racing Pigs at the Illinois State Fair

Employing Honest, Hardworking People

Harold: All I hired was young men. I wanted them twenty-six years of age or younger, and I had kind of an unwrit ten rule that they did not have to go to college, but if they hadn't gone to college, they understood it was going to take them two or three years longer to develop themselves. I can't tell you what it is, but there's something about college that matures peo ple. You cannot move up the ladder quite as fast from eighteen years old as if you went through col lege and then come to work.

I wanted to find men who had a decent personality, who were honest and worked hard, and started doing work when they were young. I liked to find a boy that went out and made a few bucks when he was a kid. Peddled the papers or anything, no matter what it was. I always wanted to hire people who were competitors.

Tom: How did you compensate the managers of your yards?

Harold: Our goal with our employees was to make them part of the company. We prepared separate profit and loss statements for every market, and each market manager would get a percentage of the profit. If they did not produce, they were hurting.

Tom: What percentage of profit went to the market man ager?

Harold: Thirty-three percent. Generally, we paid one-third of the profits.

Tom: The manager got 33 percent of the net profit after expenses and that was his entire compensation?

Harold: Yes. None of the cost in the home office basically was in it, except that we charged him four cents a hog for advertising.

Tom: He had to buy pigs every morning from the local farmers competitively because there were other markets operating, and other alternatives for the farmers who had pigs to sell, so he had to convince the farmer that he was giving him the best price he was going to get anywhere. Your manager had to know a lot about what the packers were going to be willing to pay and what was a fair offer for each farmer's hogs.

Harold: Yes, when we first started in Kouts and Marengo, we had about four packing houses that I could call and get competitive bids. Eventually, we called about 100 packers every day. We would get bids from these packing houses, specifying what they would pay for each style of hog. The telephoning to packers was all done at the main office or at our sales division headquarters. We would pass that market information about 7:00 or 7:30 in the morning to each one of market managers in the country, telling them what they were going to get for pigs that day.

The Heinold School of Business

It's the manager's job to decide what they can pay, what they can spread. They learned real fast what their competition is that morning because every farmer would tell them. Especially, if we were lower than a competitor. I was even a fanatic for competition in hiring people. If I hired somebody, I wanted to know that he was competitive. I wanted to know, if he played in the band did he make first chair? I wanted to know, if he played in sports did he make it? I like a fighter. We were exceptionally fortunate in hiring competitive people. I've always felt confident that we had the best market managers in the business.

Tom: They certainly had incentive to do the job you wanted them to get done. Your managers made real good money, taking 33 percent of the profits. But if there were no profits in their yard, they had to quit.

Harold: We had to do the little things right, too. I'd be looking for land and someone would say, "Why do you want to be out on a highway?" You know, stock yards are usually back by the railroad track. I'd say, "Not mine. I want them right out there." And they'd say, "Why do you have to make that such a nice yard?" I'd say, "I want every market painted, washed, the neatest yard you can get, I want every board fixed up, every time."

I said, "I don't want one single employee that hasn't got pride in what he's doing. I want him proud of that market. I want him out there the minute that somebody's not in the yard to do a little painting and fixing up and grass mowed." It is all important to get that person to have self-esteem, proud to be a leader in his community.

Tom: Give me an idea of what kind of earnings a good market manager would make in a year.

Harold: It would be hard for me to say, because the year-to-year differences were great, but let me say it in this language. The top third of our men would probably make at least double, right at double, the guy running the bank in the local town. The guys in the middle would make as much as or more than anybody else in the local town. Our bottom third were the ones we worried about. If you recall, when we came with DeKalb one of our concerns was what we were paying our people.

Tom: DeKalb didn't try to change that, did it?

Harold: No way. DeKalb wanted us to make money just the same as our people wanted to make money, and we always felt good about our relationship with DeKalb One of the biggest breaks that I always thought I had with DeKalb was that when we first met, we met right there with you guys at the top.

Matrimonial Bliss, Entrepreneur Style

Harold: When we first started we had just gotten married. I really wasn't doing much at all about marketing hogs before we were married, but after the second year, I told Sis, "Get out of that garden, you're worth 100 times more than that to me working with me, doing my bookkeeping, and helping me than you'll ever make keeping a garden." She worried about what my mom and her mom would say if she didn't have a garden. But Sis would help me so much. She did bookkeeping, and at night she would often help drive a truck hauling hogs. If I couldn't keep awake she'd go with me and help keep me awake. We'd sing all the way to Chicago. Tuesday's we'd go to Cissna Park, Illinois, after working all day, put the hogs in the truck, and start on to Chicago. Wednesday was Plymouth, Indiana; Thursday was Coldwater, Michigan.

Tom: Having Sis drive into the Chicago Stock Yards with a load of hogs must have been quite a phenomenon to the yard people.

Harold: More than that. At Miller and Hart Packing Company in Chicago, you had to go in on the Ashland side, and they wouldn't allow a woman to go into the plant. So she had to sit out on the street in the truck.

Sis: I was too dumb to be afraid, I guess. We had one truck that every time we hit a bump, the back win dow fell out of it. So most of the time, the one that wasn't driving was holding the window up. Those were the good old days.

Harold: It sounds like it's so cheap and bad, but at the time it was just what it took.

Tom: No, it doesn't sound cheap and bad to me. It sounds like two real hard-working people getting the experiences that you had to have in order to really develop a fine company.

Organizing to Serve the Profit Centers

Harold: Well, getting back to the subject of developing markets, we decided we had to do all of our own book keeping, and at that time we were up to fifteen markets or so.

Tom: Fifteen markets by what time? 1960?

Harold: We had that many by 1960. I was really a fuss-budget about keeping every market separate. Every market had its own reputation and every market manager was the boss of his market, and we made separate profit and loss statements on every individual. Therefore, we had a set of checks, just one bank account, but a different set of checks for each market and a different set of numbers, and when we went to reconcile the bank accounts of fifteen different markets, it was a big job. We didn't have computers in those days, so we would lay them on our kitchen floor by number, see, so we could check at the end of the month what was outstanding at each market to balance out their checking accounts.

It would takes us three or four nights to do it and it was a big deal. When Joe Vogel came up with the idea of punching little holes in the checks and perforating them, that helped out until we got the computers.

Tom: Did you go right to computers, or did you have an IBM punch card system?

Harold: We went to National Cash Register system first, and then we went to the punch cards for quite awhile before we got the computers.

Tom: That's a similar experience to what DeKalb had in the mid-thirties when they were beginning to grow. My dad walked in one weekend afternoon and Edna Nelson, his bookkeeper, was sitting at her desk swamped with orders that were stacking up. She was trying to make records, and dollar bills were sticking out of them because we were taking a dollar a bushel deposit for the orders.

She was just overwhelmed and was in there on Saturday afternoon or Sunday working on it, so my dad hollered for help from a fellow named Flay Murphy who had his own accounting business in Chicago. Murphy suggested an IBM punch card system to him in 1937. He was so impressed with what that did for him that for a lot of years after that he had two ideas about investing his own money. One was to buy all of the DeKalb stock he could find whenever it became available, and the other one was if he had any money left over, he bought IBM.

So you had the same experience except with National Cash Register?

Sis: We started computers when we were in temporary quarters after a fire.

Harold: With National Cash it was a ledger system and I paid $6,000 for it. To me, that was a fortune at that time. That probably would have been in about 1956 or 1957 because it was before we moved uptown. We had our office in just a little brooder house attached to the building where our headquarters was.

Tom: Were you buying other people's yards?

Harold: No. Nearly all our yards were started from scratch. In 1957 we started Burlington, Wisconsin. In 1958 we were over in Gridley, Illinois. In 1959 we moved over more to Illinois; we had Henry, Galva, and Buffalo Prairie. We had a couple yards that we bought and remodeled like Buffalo Prairie, but basically we built most of them. Most of those available for sale were so junky and so bad and located wrong that they just didn't have quality. I wanted a market built so that if it had to be, one person could operate it efficiently.

When I built the first yard at Goodland, I made it so that as the hogs come off the truck the manager could look at the hogs, sort them, grade them, put them on the scale; but then I had him back them off the scale to go down the alley to where we kept them for a strict reason. He's there alone, and I didn't want the next farmer who comes in to be able to take his hogs and quick run them on the scale before that manager got to see them and sort them and check for any bad hogs and pull the wool over his eyes. The only thing then we changed after that was we used two men to a market. If you drive hogs onto a scale, it's hard to turn them around to come off that opposite direction, especially at night when you put twenty-five hogs on there and want to load the semis out. They're facing the wrong way and it's a job. So from then on we built our scales so they went on and off and off and on the other gate. [Harold then mentions building a new yard in Maple Park.]

Tom: That's a beautiful yard. When we first learned that Heinold might be interested in selling out to DeKalb, one of our directors was the president of the Farm Bureau. The Farm Bureau is very strong in DeKalb County and had its own yard. His first reaction was, "My God, that's like going to the enemy," but he said, "On the other hand, I'll have to say that that guy running that Heinold yard is doing a better job than the guy running the Farm Bureau yard, and they handle a lot more hogs than we do." He figured that you must have a pretty good system if you were beating out an organization with the strong farmer loyalty the DeKalb County Farm Bureau had.

Convincing Loyal Cooperative Members to Trade with Heinold

Harold: Tom, one of my toughest jobs was to convince Farm Bureau members to trade with us. We would always have to bid a higher price because they felt that loyalty [to the Farm Bureau]. You had to pay more to get them to break away from their own co-op. We also had the problem that the Farm Bureau Producers Co-op was in the Chicago Stock Yards, so Farm Bureau members felt they had to go there. We had to fight hard to convince them we could pay them extra money. We won that battle.

Tom: I'm amazed you were able to do that and at the same time make enough money to survive in the business by exploiting a differential that was based on your better handling of the hogs and the elimination of shrink. Evidently this was giving you enough added value to permit you to stay alive offering a better price than the Farm Bureau could pay.

Harold: Yes, that was a big item. And the other thing that I was always looking for was volume. I would rather run 15,000 hogs through a market and make four cents per hundred pounds than I would run 4,000 hogs through a market and make ten cents per hundred pounds. We really promoted this to our people. If I ran 15,000 hogs a month through a market, even though I made less margin, I took those hogs away from a competitor. Now he had to even raise his margin, see, and it worked for me, because his volume got weaker and weaker. We had people scold us because we ran them out of business, but then we ran Chicago Stock Yards out of business, too.

Sis: One thing that we could always do was promise that we had the market already at the beginning of the day. The hogs were already sold. The selling to the packer was done first thing in the morning so we knew we had a home for so many hogs when the day started.

Tom: And the manager knew what he was going to sell them for, so he could then form judgments about what he could afford to bid for them as compared to what the Producers [the organization that bought and sold hogs for the Farm Bureau Coops] were paying.

Harold: He also knew that if we committed a particular market to ship 500 hogs today to certain packers, it was his job to buy 500 hogs. That was real key to us—to deliver. As time went by, it even got more important. For instance, we got to the position that we were the only person in the whole United States that a packer could call on the phone and say, "Harold, I want to kill hogs on Saturday. Get me 4,000 hogs." Nobody else could do that in the whole United States That gave us stronger "in" with these packing houses, too. The little things like that.

If we never failed in delivering, that put us ahead of some of the people who would sell them a load of hogs and then couldn't deliver. The very first guy I ever dealt with, Sylvania Slugbell at his packing house, said, "I kill two loads of hogs a day. Don't ever call me at 1:00 in the afternoon and tell me your farmers didn't bring any hogs today. I can't do that because I had to keep my people busy. I must have them!!" We worked very closely with everybody.

Tom: I don't want to overdo comparisons with the cooperative yard, the Producers; but as I understand it, for example, the Farm Bureau yard in DeKalb would take the hogs and send them to Chicago and the commission man in Chicago would sell them, but the farmer would not know what he was going to get until the next day.

Harold: That was true in some of the cases, but Producers also got to doing like we did. They copied what we did; everybody did. Even Kenneth Murray did, even Swift's did, they all copied. As we put this program in the business, we eliminated a lot of things like the Chicago Stock Yards. Everybody now does it our way.

Eliminating the Chicago Stock Yards

Tom: You've mentioned eliminating the Chicago Stock Yards before in this conversation. You're saying you were so successful in building these yards and circumventing the Chicago Stock Yards that the hogs no longer flowed through the central market—there was no need for a Chicago assembly yard for pigs.

Harold: That's exactly right, Tom. When we were farming in the early 1940s, Chicago would get anywhere from

20,000 to 35,000 hogs a day. By the time we merged with you in 1972, I would say they were probably down to not even averaging 5,000 a day, and they just got weaker and weaker.

Tom: The marketing system that recognized what farmers wanted is what ruined the stock yards. Other people adopted it and so the function, the prime purpose of the Chicago Stock Yards, was negated. It was old fashioned, it didn't work, and you had built a better mouse trap.

Harold: Yes. That's really what it is. The packers knew they could trust us, and we trusted them, as we built a reputation that our word was as good as gold.

Dealing with Meat Packers

Harold: In those days, you could have $1 million, $2 million, $5 million worth of business and it was never in writing. All by just your promise.

Tom: And the packers nearly always kept their word. If they struck a deal to buy 1,000 hogs, they bought them.

Harold: Yup. I can give you one example of how it works if they don't. I'm not afraid to say the name. The name was Herman Clayman, ran a packing house in Philadelphia. Jim was on the selling desk and was selling him, and he was ornery, and one day he took $3,000 off of Jim's check, one load of hogs. Jim asked me, "What should I do with him?," and I said, "Give him to me." I called up Herman and we had quite a discussion. I told Herman, "You're done," and I said, "You aren't going to get another hog from Heinold's until you send that $3,000." He went into a big lecture about the hogs and all that and I said, "Herman, you have a right to reject hogs, you have a right to send hogs back, you don't have a right to ever take a dollar bill off of any of our hogs. Just don't do that." Now if we mutually agree, that's a different ball game. You just don't do like he did. We went back and forth and argued like this for maybe three or four months. He called Jim once in a while and wanted him to ship some hogs and Jim said, "You have to talk to Harold." And he'd talk to me and I'd say, I haven't got the $3,000 check, Herman. When I have the $3,000 check we'll talk to you." I kept saying to Jim, "There will come a day when he's going to cheat this guy, cheat that guy, cheat another guy, and he won't have any place to go. He's got to go back to somebody. Just wait it out."

One day he called and he used some excuse and he said, "I need hogs for kill on Saturday." I don't know what he wanted, 1,000 or 2,000 hogs or what ever it was and he said, "You got to get me this, I need hogs. I'll give you an extra fifty cents" I said, "No, Herman. You got to wire $3,000." He tried to get me into a run. Well, after a lot of bad language, he hung up, and lo and behold there came the check wired to the bank for $3,000. Then we sold him for quite a while again, and he was one of the best accounts we had because he couldn't buy from anyone else. Then, he tried it again, so we quit for a while.

Financing Growth

Harold: Our expansion was 100 percent from profits. Profits put us into position to borrow money. The banks were always extremely good to me. I can't believe in this day and age how good banks were to me. They would trust me, they would lend me money.

Tom: Nothing succeeds like success for a bank.

Harold: We were real open about everything and I'll give you an example. In 1958, I was going real strong and a packing house named Hammond Standish in Detroit went down the drain and he got us for $98,000. That was our total net worth at that time. Keep in mind that money values were different then. We had just started to build our house. We didn't know what to do. Didn't know how to go forward. Sis kept saying, "Harold you're walking around with your mouth moving and no words are coming out of it." But it was terrible and we never got one penny out of that company.

We basically started over. I immediately went to the bank, laid it on the line, everything. I had one farmer here who was almost like a father to me because to me he was such a solid person. He was a Mennonite farmer and was just an unusual person. When he heard about our problem, he came over and said, "Harold, you're doing what's right, you're the right person we want in the community. If you need a little help, I'll loan you some money for your house. You go ahead and finish building it."

Tom: He was quite a guy.

Harold: I was dedicated to that man all of my life.

Tom: Harold, are you a Mennonite?

Harold: No, we're Apostolic Christian, but our churches are very similar. When my folks moved out here from Illinois, there was no church here of our kind. There was one in Francisville, but that's thirty-five miles and at that time they had a horse and buggy. So they took the horse and buggy and went to church just every other Sunday because it was so far; and the Sunday in between the Mennonites and they met in their homes for church. So my folks went to the Mennonite homes one Sunday and down to our church in Francisville on the other Sunday. Then, of course, they started their own church here.

Tom: Getting back to the expansion of your business, you "grew" it entirely out of your earnings and the expansion of your credit lines from your local banks. I had the impression that you were trying to squeeze every last penny out of every dollar, and that you had made some of your key managers stockholders.

Harold: Yes. In 1958, after we incorporated, I would ask the guys if, instead of giving them a cash bonus, I could give them shares of stock in the company so that we would use that cash to continue to grow. I allowed them to draw on some of their commissions to buy stock in the company.

Tom: Now you say bonus for that year. Their compensation was based on this 33 percent of the profits, but besides that you would pay them bonuses?

Harold: Well, like Joe Vogel and Jim Yergler, the people in the main office here, they didn't work on percentages. And they were the first people we actually allowed to have ownership in the company. Otherwise, Sis and I owned it, and we didn't really have any outside ownership. We never offered anybody any stock but employees. And that just came gradually.

I was so worried about my reputation with the bank. To be sure they'd never lose confidence in us, we would never start a new hog market until we had the last one making money. I never just kept building without waiting until they made money. So what would we do after we got a little bigger? I built three hog markets, and then I would not expand until those three were profitable and showing a return so I could take it to the bank and show it. We always kept our books wide open. We showed the bank every market, what they were doing, what they were making, and the banks were always good to me. But we always paid them back, too.

I think one of the things that probably helped me with the finance side was when I got out of high-school, I got some scholarships. They were small ones, as I didn't get to go to college. One of them was from LaSalle Foundation. LaSalle Foundation taught business and economics. It's called Prentice Hall and people know their name now. Anyway, for two years they sent me information and I did my test work and stuff like that, but I was busy. When it ran out, I asked them if I could buy the correspondence course and continue, and I did that. I continued that, as a matter of fact, for thirty-seven years.

Tom: So, you were actually educating yourself all through this period.

Harold: All through that time. And I helped start the very first mutual fund in the state of Indiana. I also helped start an insurance company in the state of Indiana called Great Northern Life. It wasn't doing too good, and we were unhappy with our president because we thought he was putting on too much of a show; so we merged with another company, and that became the second largest insurance company in the state of Indiana. That experience helped give me a lot of background. When the bank went broke here in Kouts and my uncle and I got it back on its feet, I learned the banking business mostly at night.

Sis: Yes, your banking experience was really valuable to you when you got into commodities.

Tom: Do you own the bank in Kouts now?

Harold: No. What Uncle Matt and I did, after we got it going for a while, we distributed stock out to other businessmen in town to make them all a part of the bank. My trouble with the bank here was, Heinold's got so big that we were 85 to 90 percent of the busi ness in Kouts State Bank. The examiners came in here, the state department, and said I can't use the bank no more because I'm too big.

So, we made a deal, well, all of the directors. We went down to Indianapolis and made a deal with them that every deposit we made would get no credit for two days. We couldn't use the funds for two days because they said if my checks bounced it would wipe out the bank. So we did that for a while; then pretty soon they complained on that. Then they made us follow through every deposit until it was cleared.

Well then, when we got to where we were depositing three or four times as much every day as the total capital of the bank, then the FDIC stepped in and said that's it, you're done, get out of here.

Well, we were still running 85 to 90 percent of the bank business, and it just wiped out the bank. So we merged with a bank in Valpo and I stayed on that bank board for another twenty years.

Tom: Harold, you have done a good job of explaining how you financed your hog market growth. My impression is that by the early seventies many of your employee shareholders wanted more liquidity—that they wanted a place to sell their stock when they needed money. Also, you were beginning to develop a commodity trading business, which certainly would require a lot more capital to grow. Weren't those two good reasons why you decided to sell your business to DeKalb?

Harold: Yes. DeKalb offered us a good price [in the form of DeKalb shares] and promised to provide capital to allow us to continue to grow. And they lived up to that promise, and our shareholders got the liquidity they wanted.

Getting Started in the Futures Market

Tom: Why did Heinold Hog Markets go into the commodity futures trading business?

Harold: Well, a man who was working for Cudahy Packing Company up in Milwaukee, Wisconsin, their head hog buyer, who was buying hogs from us, called me and said that at the Merc they're going to start a new hog futures contract. They wanted him to go in there that night and figure out what the specifications for a load of hogs should be. He said to me, "You ship to a lot of packers, I only work with Cudahy. Why don't you come in there tonight?"

So I thought I would. I really didn't know anything about the Chicago Mercantile Exchange. I didn't even know there was such a place. I'd heard of the Board of Trade for years, but I never paid much attention to them, so I went in that night. The meeting turned out to be so exciting that I don't think I touched the seat of the car all the way home.

I had learned that they were going to guarantee a price for our farmers for hogs three months ahead, six months ahead. I knew that was what hog farmers wanted. It was exactly what I wanted to offer them. It was just unbelievable. So, I was really riding high. We had been working hard to get advance bids two, three, four days ahead at the maximum, so I called my guys and told them about it and said we're going to get into it.

I figured that the new hog futures contract would allow Heinold Hog Markets to serve our customers by offering them a contract that would set them a price for future delivery of hogs to our markets. About that time, I hired Jim Witmore to work at Heinold Hog Markets. His job would be to sell farmers on the idea of selling their hogs for future delivery.

Sis: He had to learn everything. He didn't know what livestock was.

Harold: We talked about barrows and gilts. He went home and got a dictionary out to look up barrows. He didn't know what a barrow was. But he was a good kid. Anyhow, that was how we started into the futures trading business. Our biggest problem was that farmers didn't trust Chicago. They weren't going to send $1,000 to Chicago whenever the exchange demanded them to do so.

Well then, one day I got disgusted and I went to Chicago; I went to Bates and Company and met this young man, Robert Rufenacht. I said, "Bob, what do you know about farming?" "Well, my grandfather's a farmer in Archibald, Ohio." So we got talking and I said, "Well, I'm going to start my own clearing firm one of these days. Are you capable of helping me?" He said, "Well, I think so. I'd sure like to do some thing on my own."

He was just a young fellow and he had such a young child face. He never did have a face as old as his age. A little later, I called him back and said, "I'm ready to start. I'm tired of this nonsense." So we went together, and I let Bob run our business in Chicago and I took care of the rest out here in Kouts."

Tom: He ran the commodity futures part of your business?

Harold: Yes. Well then, as we got going and growing, Bob wanted more stock in order to make it available to a big broker in St. Joseph, Missouri, named Freddy Hertz. I had already let my Heinold Hog Markets managers and Bob have so much stock that there just wasn't enough stock to go around for Freddy. He wanted 35 percent, and I couldn't give him that much. Well then, one day Bob just called me up and says he's going on his own. I stewed over that news Saturday and Sunday, and I left here Sunday night and went to Chicago.

Sis: We had our manager's meeting. We had our annual Hog Market manager's meeting going on and

Harold's mind was in Chicago.

Tom: It is my understanding that you had those meetings in Chicago with your market managers and various people on the Merc because you saw the hog futures contract as a way of serving your basic cus--tomers, the people who had pigs to sell and didn't know how to use the futures market. So, if a farmer came in to one of the yards and knew he was going to have 200 pigs ready for market in May, he would then ask your market manager what he'd pay for them.

Harold: Down the road three months or so.

Tom: Yes. And if he was satisfied with that price, he'd say yes and the market manager would complete a contract with him. And then what would the market manager do?

Harold: At that time, all he would do was fill out a form to open an account up in Chicago. And then he'd have to send money up as margin, and then we'd sell a "future."

Tom: This is the farmer or the manager?

Harold: The farmer. He would then give us a check, and we would send it to Chicago and hold it there as his margin money. Then he'd get more margin calls if it went against him, see. In the meantime, to get this started we would go to each local market and call meetings of farmers to come in and try to teach them how to use hedging as a part of their hog marketing programs.

Tom: You could see that this concept of selling their pigs for future delivery was a good one, but there were a lot of problems convincing farmers who didn't like the idea that they might get margin calls that would require them to pay the exchange before delivering their hogs and were therefore very skeptical of the futures market.

Tom: When did you arrive at a system where a farmer could come into your hog market and say, "I want to sell you 200 pigs for a delivery next May?"

Harold: March of 1969 is when we took over and started Heinold Commodities. Ralph Klopfenstine was with me. I went back out to the farmers—keep in mind I was going 1,000 miles an hour by this time in commodities trying to make our commodity business work.

We held a meeting in Goodland, Indiana, in the basement of Paul Schrader's house. Lois had made ham sandwiches, and we had about a dozen farmers in there. I was trying to explain how to sell their hogs forward, and all at once one of the farmers said, "Harold, we trust you. We trust Paul. We don't trust Chicago. Don't make us send $1,000 to Chicago. Let us deal with you. Let us work with you. You take care of Chicago."

That's when I devised this contract, we called it a "cash contract" where the farmer signed a contract to guarantee his hogs would be delivered to us at a future date, at a price, at certain weights, under certain conditions, based on the spec conditions of the Merc, and we agreed to buy them. Then we in turn took that same deal and sold a hog futures contract in the name of Heinold Hog Markets. So Heinold Hog Markets dealt with Chicago and the farmer dealt with us. And that just turned the whole complex around. Everybody in the United States started doing it after we were successful at it.

Tom: Basically then, if in January a farmer comes in to a Heinold Hog market and he likes the May price and he wants to sell his pigs forward (let's say the May price is $45 per hundred pounds), he would enter into a contract to deliver you pigs in May for how many dollars? If the quote is $45 that day, how much do you promise to pay the farmer for his pigs to be delivered in May?

Harold: We offered him two contracts. If it's $45, we offered him $45 based on the Merc, and then the day he got to our market whatever that discount was, that's what he got, but he had to put up some money for margin. We charged him interest if he didn't put up the margin money. Or, we offered him a cash contract and the deal on the cash contract was this: That you deliver 50 hogs or 100 hogs, whatever it was, to Goodland in May, you don't put up anything, just sign your name, and when we started out, we worked at two cents a pound below Chicago to the farmer to cover our marketing cost, expenses, and margin.

Tom: So if it was forty-five cents a pound May futures in Chicago, you would guarantee the farmer forty-three cents.

Harold: Forty-three cents and no expenses, no nothing, and they loved that.

Tom: And then you turned around and sold them in the futures market for forty-five cents.

Harold: And for that margin we got enough money to pay our trading costs, margin calls, and all that. We did a lot of learning on that because there were times we should have taken two and a half; sometimes you could have gotten by on a dollar and a half. We took some risks, but it worked out beautifully because the farmers just loved it. It just simplified everything.

Tom: It was something he could understand and didn't have to fool around with.

Harold: Right. And all he had to do was sign his name and knew what he was getting. All he had to do was sign the contract.

Sis: And then we had the hogs to market. We guaranteed the hogs to market.

Harold: We knew then in May how many hogs were going to come in May, how many were going to come in June, how many were going to come in July.

Tom: Okay, now, once you got going with this concept, what percentage of your business was of that sort?

Harold: Never big. It was very sporadic because when your production is going up, hogs get cheap. When hogs are cheap the farmer is not going to lock in. Now, when the market's going up, then he'd like to lock them in because he knows he's got a profit. Well, maybe that year he wouldn't have had to. But anyway, it was very sporadic, and I don't think we ever got over 10 or 15 percent of our hogs in a month that were strictly from the futures. That would be maximum.

Tom: What percentage of all the pigs in the United States were you handling?

Harold: We were running about 7 percent.

Tom: Seven percent of all the pigs in the United States, and about 10 percent of those were, on average, contracted for future delivery.

Harold: Ten would probably be a little on the high side as an average. There would be some months it would be, but there'd be some months they wouldn't because they'd be cheap and the farmer wouldn't sell then.

Tom: But this was a phenomenon.

Harold: Oh, it was big. Then it also put us in a position [to guarantee a packer hogs at a specific price]. So we went in reverse, too. Now if a guy in New York said, "I want 5,000 hogs in February." We would go buy the February contract so our price is locked in. This time we wouldn't sell, we'd buy; and then when the time came, we would convert our local hogs and sell those contracts and then deliver the hogs. Government orders are about the only ones where they would go ahead and buy in advance very far.

Your supermarkets don't; they're so competitive that they're lucky if they'll bid two days ahead. But a government order would. Or exporters would. There wasn't a lot of that done. Packers would because they knew that if the hogs were cheap they could make money, and for them it was worth the risk. They didn't want to mess with the futures.

I wanted to learn so bad, Tom, that the day they opened up in July 1966 I bought [a couple of hog contracts]. I had no reason to take them other than to learn. I just wanted to educate myself. It's not wise to take delivery on a contract, but what bugged me is they delivered them in Kansas City, Missouri, instead of Chicago. I was hoping they'd deliver them in Chicago. So I had to sit in Kansas City for about two weeks taking them hogs and peddling them and working out. But it was a real good education.

Being a Helping Hand Pays

Tom: The impression I got from Ralph was that Rufenacht's breaking up your partnership and going into business in competition with you turned out to be a blessing in the long term. When he had trouble you bailed him out and demonstrated that Heinold was a solid company and would treat people right rather than let them go down the drain, even if they had in the past treated you as shoddily as Rufenacht had.

Harold: Yes. Even the Board of Governors couldn't understand why I tried to help him. And even it made some new people start doing business with us, like the floor traders. I don't know why we were so lucky. I don't know why it worked like it did. Ralph and I started Heinold Commodities in March of 1969, and by May of 1973 we were the largest firm on the exchange. And then by 1976, we were the largest on the Board of Trade, except for Cargill and Continental Grain. Then, when we took some kids to New York, to COMEX, and soon we were the largest out there, in spite of opposition from a lot of New England traders. You were involved in that.

Tom: I think it was a remarkable demonstration of some thing that many people don't expect to find in a place like the Merc. You had faith in people, you turned the other cheek, you were willing to help. You didn't risk an awful lot, but you helped them when they were in deep trouble and you earned respect that your behavior was quite different than that which the administering people of the Merc had experienced in the past. It clearly enhanced your reputation and attracted branch offices you never would have gotten if you hadn't behaved as honestly and straightforwardly as you did. You might, in the back of your minds, have thought that this was the way to attract business, but you did it out of the goodness of your heart and a feeling of fair play, too. You demonstrated a willingness to go the extra mile that is seldom seen in either the Merc or the Board of Trade.

Sis: Well, let me say this for Harold and his group that went up there. They were invaders in a closed society who didn't quite know what to do with these country boys that were coming in there. That was an adjustment.

Tom: Yes. And they were innovators, so they were a threat to the system.

Harold: Tom, do you remember Andy Anderson?

Tom: Yes, sure.

Harold: All right, let me give you an example how things went. Andy Anderson was one of the best salesmen I've ever known. He was one of the original starters of some of the contracts, especially the cattle contracts. Andy started his own clearing firm called ANCO. Very successful. As a matter of fact, I would go study some of his moves, what he was doing. He got going real fast.

Tom: This was in the early 1970s?

Harold: Yes. Anyway, when Andy did this, he was a salesman, but he wasn't the best administrator. All at once his books were way out in left field, and he didn't know where he stood. I was on the clearing house committee, which determined capital requirements and had the job of watching the capital of everybody. They were going to stop Andy because his books were all mixed up, and they thought he was losing a lot of money. Andy couldn't show us any proof on his books, he couldn't get his position quite squared away. The clearing house committee called him in and tore him apart real bad. They thought he would have to close down, and some guys decided to go after his business.

Tom: They'd take the branch offices away from Andy?

Harold: They took quite a few of them. I went down to Andy and I said, "Mr. Anderson, I think your biggest problem is bookkeeping. If you want me to, you don't have to pay me nothin', I'll bring in some accountants, and we'll try to straighten your books up and see if we can do somethin' for you." I said, "Even if you want to come with us for a while to get this squared away, I'll work with you." And he said, "Oh, I'm all right. Don't worry about it."

I don't think two hours went by before I got a phone call from him and he said, "Harold, you're the first decent person in this whole deal." And we helped. We went in there, put our bookkeeping in there and he said, "Let me be your salesman. Let me be in charge of selling, let me do promotion, let me be your guy to get jobs done and you go ahead and do it." And then we took over what he had left.

When we got done with this books, he was not in financial trouble. Sure he had lost some money, but boy, the competition had been ready to eat him alive. And you know, Andy was good for us all those years. Our treatment of Andy was one of the little things that I think that really helped us.

New Marketing Alternatives for Farmers

Harold: I'm proud of having helped open the door for options. We had not in the past even been allowed to have options in agriculture. We are now allowed agriculture options. Now you got puts and calls and hogs and corn and beans and all that, which I had always argued for.

Here's a farmer. He wants to hedge his hogs. All right. The market today is $50, but the futures are only $43 because we got this big supply buildup. That's the day he should buy a put at $43. Then if it goes down, at least he's got some protection. If the market goes up, his put's worthless, but he gets the higher price. He doesn't have to have the future. See? And for our other people like our packers, we'd do it on calls for hogs. He [a packer] could buy a call then and be guaranteed his price for his hogs and if hogs were cheaper at the time, he didn't have to use his call; he'd just buy the hogs cheaper, but he'd lose his premium. And to me that was the turning point in getting futures.

Joining Hands with DeKalb

Tom: Was one of your reasons for wanting to sell your company to DeKalb, or to someone who had a publicly traded stock, to provide liquidity for those people that you'd been paying with Heinold stock? More than that, did you hope that you could find a buyer who would be willing to expand the commodity business, where huge capital inputs might suddenly be necessary to deal with sudden changes in the market?

Harold: Yes, the capital requirement was really the powerful thing behind our decision.

A friend who thought we should go with a bigger investment banker told me about White Weld. That's when I met Tony Bischoff and Tom Patrick. About that time Chicago Corp. called me up and said, "Hey, I think now's about the time to go [public]." Anyhow, I said to them, "Well, we was talking about maybe we ought to go to a bigger company [an investment banker who could handle a larger initial public offering]. "Well," he said, "that's probably a good idea."

He didn't fight me on that, so I met with Tony and Tom. Tony looked at the figures that we'd put together for Chicago Corp., and he liked them. He added that perhaps it would be better to merge with somebody else rather than going public. We had wanted to stay alone [private], and this was before we'd ever met you folks, and we'd already sent our Red Herring into the securities commissioner and all that stuff. Then I got this call; some people wanted to talk to me and they wanted to meet me at O'Hare Airport.

Tom: Now, for the benefit of our readers, the Red Herring is a financial report on Heinold that would provide the figures that would be used by the investment banker in taking the company public.

Harold: It has to be okayed by the Securities Commission first. So I met with these two gentlemen [at the airport], and they said, "We've got $7 million cash, we're listed on the American Stock Exchange. You come with us and we'll give you $7 million, plus we got another $7 million worth of land in a large city in the United States. We can sell that and that'll give you $14 million in cash [given that capital investments in oil well drilling were nearly all written off as expenses] and you run the company." And I said, "What kind of company is it?" And he said, "Well, we can't tell you until we know whether you're going to be sincere about this." Well, gosh, I didn't know what to say. I said, "Well, why do you want me?" And he says, "We're listed on the American Stock Exchange, we haven't made any money for two years, we're not making any money this year, and after three years you get delisted and we don't want to be delisted." And so I said, "Well, you know, it's kind of awkward for me not to know." And he said, "I'll give you the name of the company. It's Canal Randolph." Boy, that didn't mean a thing to me.

Tom: Doesn't me anything to me today, either.

Harold: Well, we set up another meeting. In the meantime, I checked out Canal Randolph. They owned about seven different stock yards, including Omaha, Indianapolis... And they said, "You can take it over, you can manage them, you run it and whatever you want to do on the American Stock Exchange, you can change the name to Heinold Companies rather than Canal Randolph." Well, here I am a farm kid out in the country, you know, and sure we weren't ashamed of what we had done, but...

Tom: Did you think they were trying to get you to bail them out?

Harold: Jiminy crickets, to be listed on the stock exchange that easy, that enticed me, you know. I had told Tony Bischoff one time that I wouldn't do anything like that. Well, then, the next time we met, Sis went with me, and she said they're not your kind of people. Well, they weren't. They had changed several things [in our discussion of a potential deal].

Well, Tony finds out about it and he calls me up. He said, "The two people you're talking to are nothing but lawyers. They're trying to run that outfit. They're just not your kind of people." He said, "Just stay away from them." He said, "If you are interested in merging your company, I've got your kind of people." And that's when he told me about you guys.

He set up a get-acquainted supper somewhere on the west side of Chicago. There was you and Charlie [Roberts] and Roger [Rasmusen].

Tom: I recall we liked each other immediately because we realized that our corporate objectives fit very well. DeKalb had surplus cash and wanted to invest it, and Heinold needed financial backing to grow. We soon decided the best way to merge would be to exchange stock for stock. Our stock for your stock. And what was the value? What did it cost DeKalb to buy Heinold?

Harold: Your stock was so high at the time; it was twenty-five times earnings, and I didn't have enough sense to realize either what all that meant, but I remember that 48 percent of DeKalb's investment bought

Heinold Commodities, and 52 percent went to Hog Market stockholders. In total, we got 300,000 shares of DeKalb B stock that was then selling at $75 per share, which was valued in the market at twenty-five times earnings. Total dollar value was $22.5 million.

Tom: Don't forget that DeKalb had a 2:1 stock split on December 22, 1972, only three months after you became shareholders.

Harold: That's the only thing I can remember. I do know this. When your stock got way down, there was a couple years we thought we earned, between Commodities and Hog Markets, just about what you paid for it, but it was after you put in a lot of new capital.

Tom: Yes.

Harold: You had tremendous growth in your stock. DeKalb had risen from $20 to $75 in five years or so.

Tom: That's right. So there was kind of a cushion in there. You had been trying to raise $5 million in cash and you suddenly got $22.5 million in DeKalb shares.

Harold: Well, we were talking about selling enough stock to raise $5 million in cash.

Tom: Oh, you were going to sell stock. I see.

Harold: And I think at that time it was to be one-third our equity. The public would own one-third.

Tom: Five million dollars a third. Implicitly $15 million. We bought it for $22.5 million in DeKalb shares, and then we put in...

Harold: You gave us $7 million right away.

Tom: Seven million dollars right away to expand the business.

Harold: We paid off a bunch of debts first. The cash requirement of the futures market is what killed me. In the hog market business we could make enough money to keep expanding, but in the futures business every time you got $10 million in new business, I think it was $160,000 cash we needed, you know, 'cause that capital requirement is pure cash.

Tom: This is the cash requirement of the exchange to do the volume of business that you were doing?

Harold: No assets counted.

Tom: Capital requirements were exploding.

Harold: Exploding. So you put the money in every time we got a capital call.

Tom: Yes. I remember the first time that happened. You know, I recall I got the call myself. I knew what our intention was, but the call was Friday and we had to meet it on Monday, and so we had to put up x millions of dollars without really knowing what the hell we were doing.

Harold: And it came faster than we had thought it would.

Tom: We had faith. We had to have faith.

Harold: It came faster than we had told you it would. We was growin' so bloomin' fast. Now we can sit back and wonder, how did we grow that fast?

Tom: The commodity business continued to grow both in terms of the number of brokers and in income generated, but also as I remember, there was a major change in the commodity business brought about by the establishment of negotiable commissions. In view of the fact that the commodities business had been dependent only on commissions, we were afraid of the implications of negotiated commissions to the profitability of the company. This was one of the reasons why we got involved as heavily as we did in the establishment of computer trading funds—to maintain the growth and profitability of the company. Ralph feels that we should have hung in for that. Quite a few different commodity trading funds have been established since we backed away from Heinold Commodities, and I think probably Ralph is right.

Bill Dubinsky, with his background in selling securities, was the kind of guy Ralph needed to expand commodity trading funds as commission income declined. He was very good at locating good fund managers and selling their product. He was a great salesman.

Harold: You bet he was. We never gave him enough credit, although we paid him good. There's no question that we made a lot of money for both ourselves and our customers' funds. We should have just kept on promoting them. I think part of the thing the guys were scared of, we were starting to get into so many law suits. That was scaring everybody.

Tom: The term "loose cannon" was what John Witmer used when I told him that I had had an interview with Ralph about the commodity company, and he said we still have law suits that are coming out of Texas and elsewhere. It was obvious in my conversation with him that he felt that the move to sell the commodity business was a wise one, because he was concerned about the litigation and sort of looseness as he saw it in the management of the company. It seems to me, however, that those things could have been managed if we had the courage to do it.

Now, on the other hand, in the hog market business, which you were really close with all the time, we had Iowa Beef coming into Iowa and there was difficult competition developing there. I wonder if you have anything you'd like to say about what happened in the hog market business and why we decided to sell it. Maybe we simply decided to sell the hog market business because we'd sold the commodity
business. I don't recall.

Harold: That was Bruce Bickner's impression. When he came here that day and said they'd got that offer on Heinold Commodities, and said he didn't know who it was from.
But he sounded like the price was good at that time and Heinold Commodities would probably be sold. I asked him about Heinold Hog Markets and he said, "One time, you talked about wantin' to buy it. Do you still want to? And I said, "Yes."

I suggested that we might be able to buy it through our profit-sharing plan. And then he said, "Well, you ought to study the ESOP plan [employee stock ownership plan]." And when he said that, we had to start all over on what an ESOP really was. I think he had it valued at $21 million, and I said, "All right, can we dividend $7 million back to your company first before we buy it and make it $14 million?" Well, he thought that was about in line and that was basically what we worked on, but the boys from the ESOP they had hired to help us wouldn't value it that high. That's when I got the people from Indianapolis, and they suggested that it should be $13 million and felt they could get approved at the IRS.

Tom: Do you recall how much was paid by the people that eventually did buy it?

Harold: No. I don't know exactly, but I was told $13 million for Heinold Hog Markets. I never heard anything different.

Tom: That would be after taking out most of the working capital. Do you know how much we got for Heinold Commodities?

Harold: I don't know. I was told it was valued at $108 million. But they had you keep all the memberships and a lot of assets and sell them, so that my understanding was that [in the end] it was considerably less.

Sis: I think when they sold Heinold Commodities and the buyer took it over they liquidated it. That was pretty shocking.

Harold: It sounded to me like what all they really wanted was the funds.

Tom: Yes, Ralph thought that, too.

Harold: They treated the employees terribly, took some of the good employees and practically sold them like slaves, we thought. [If somebody else wanted] one of our good accountants, they'd say yes, but you give us a percent of [his] pay.

Tom: No kidding?

Harold: That's what we were told. The employees were just sick.

Tom: Well, it was a sad ending to a very exciting period.

Table 23A-1
Heinold Hog Markets, Inc.
Annual Market Share, 1974–1987
(000s of Hogs)

Year	Total Slaughtered	Sold by HHM	Market Percentage
1974	75,234	3,758	5.00
1975	69,928	3,714	5.31
1976	64,721	3,707	5.73
1977	74,852	4,237	5.66
1978	74,614	4,595	6.16
1979	80,136	5,177	6.46
1980	91,635	5,794	6.32
1981	88,582	6,008	6.78
1982	83,402	6,410	7.69
1983	80,345	6,708	8.35
1984	84,811	7,005[a]	8.26
1985	82,642	6,731[a]	8.14
1986	78,992	6,325[a,b]	8.01
1987	75,958	4,748[a,b]	6.25

SOURCE: Harold Heinold

a. Heinold Hog Markets, Inc. financial statement; total head count adjusted to delete cattle and sheep.

b. Adjusted to delete hogs sold by the forty stock yards that were part of the Iowa Beef Packers transaction. Data supplied by Heinold Hog Markets, Inc.

Equity had tripled as sales only doubled over the same period, reflecting both the difficulties we experienced operating yards at greater distances from the home office, and trends toward hog production on large, specialized farms, which sold their pigs directly to packers. We felt this trend would accelerate, making the Heinold market system increasingly obsolete. Accordingly, when the employees offered a fair price ($11.3 million, as reported in the 1987 10K), we were willing to sell.

Table 23A-2
Financial History of the Heinold Hog Markets
($000s)

Year	Total Assets	Debts	Equity	Gross Profit	Pre-Tax	Post-Tax
1973	17,403	13,755	3,648	5,781	1,406	699
1974	15,381	12,530	2,851	3,528	(1,551)	(797)[b]
1975	17,445	13,999	3,446	6,953	1,136	595
1976	18,975	11,528	7,447	8,268	1,903	954
1977	17,955	9,760	8,195	8,403	1,637	839
1978	27,271	16,877	10,394	10,332	2,730	1,357
1979	24,707	13,377	11,330	12,317	2,849	1,681
1980	25,855	13,175	12,680	.14,271	3,102	1,743
1981	26,956	13,816	13,140	14,117	1,583	812
1982	30,844	16,018	14,826	17,510	3,386	1,500
1983	29,880	14,006	15,874	16,414	3,233	1,596
1984	28,990	12,424	16,566	16,668	2,013	886
1985	27,613	10,218	17,295	15,671	1,095	534
1986	27,747	16,418	11,329[a]	12,823	1,703	1,703
1987	28,792	14,827	13,965	12,684	2,521	1,424 (9 mos.)

SOURCE: Harold Heinold

a. Pre-tax return on equity averaged 24 percent.

b. Cattle losses in 1974 equaled ($2,259).

Source: HHM's successor company.

Chapter 22B

Heinold Commodities: A Vital Partner of Heinold Hog Markets 1970-1987

The following is the text of a conversation I had with Ralph Klopfenstine on March 9, 1993. It tells the story of the successes, problems, and opportunities of Heinold Commodities, a company that grew to be much larger than its parent, Heinold Hog Markets.

SOURCE: Ralph Klopfenstine

Ralph Klopfenstine

Tom: Ralph, when did you come to work for Heinold Commodities and what were your background and qualifications?

Ralph: I came to Heinold on April 1, 1969. Prior to that I had had several positions, including the operation of my own grain business, a country grain business in downstate Illinois, but I was at the time in Chicago working for Continental Grain Company and managing a string of elevators for them on the Illinois River. I was also a member of the Board of

Trade.

One afternoon my secretary said, "There's a man out here in front by the name of Heinold who would like to talk to you." I couldn't imagine who it was. I had only met Harold once in my life prior to that, but he apparently remembered me.

He described how he had started his commodity firm two or three years earlier with a man by the name of Bob Rufenacht. The name of the firm was Heinold-Rufenacht Commodities. It had operated successfully for three years trading Heinold's hedges and developing a growing commodity trading business when Rufenacht left him suddenly and without prior notice and took almost all of the company personnel with him.

It had been a successful company right from the start under Rufenacht and was growing and doing well, while Harold was occupied with operating and increasing the number of Heinold hog markets. He lived in Kouts, Indiana, and apparently hadn't paid much attention on a day-to-day basis to the Heinold-Rufenacht commodity firm, a practice which allowed Rufenacht to develop the loyalty of most of the people on the commodity trading side of the firm. He thought he could just leave and Harold would have no choice but to let him go and take the company with him. This was the point when Harold came to me to ask me to manage Heinold Commodities.

Tom: As I recall, Rufenacht simply called Harold and said, "I thought you ought to know that I'm taking all our people and going into business by myself." Didn't Harold check into the Bismarck Hotel [in Chicago] and stay there for six weeks, keeping his commodity trading business alive?

Ralph: Yes, that's right. The firm of Heinold Commodities still existed and operated, but Rufenacht and two other fellows in the company had formed another corporation to compete with Heinold Commodities. So this left Harold with some control. Very quickly, he asked me to leave Continental Grain and join his firm.

Tom: So the first thing he did was to call you when he learned that Rufenacht had taken over?

Ralph: Yes, I don't know how he remembered me or got my name. At any rate, I was not all that interested, to tell you the truth, as I was happy with my job at Continental Grain. Nevertheless, I talked with Catherine and told her I was doing well at

Continental Grain and really thought I'd spend the rest of my career there. I was close to forty years old. Catherine and I decided, "Well, Harold is such a nice guy, let's not say no; but let's put our price so high that he'll turn us down." So when I told him what compensation I wanted to join his firm, and he replied, "Okay, when do you want to start? I need you right now," I felt obligated to work for him because he had accepted my terms.

I gave Continental Grain two weeks' notice and then went to work for Harold, who took me over to the office that he was operating out of in the old Mercantile Exchange building. It was a small office. It couldn't have been more than twenty by twenty. At any rate, it was like starting from scratch again, but in the two weeks that I stayed at Continental there was a sharp break in the cattle market, and the new company under Rufenacht was already in trouble. Before I joined Heinold, I spent a couple of evenings with him meeting with Rufenacht and with exchange officials. The Rufenacht Company was about to go under, so Harold made a deal with Rufenacht, with the approval of the Mercantile Exchange. It involved Heinold taking over ten or twelve branch offices and some of the largest business producers who had gone over to Rufenacht only a few days earlier. They agreed to come back to Heinold and to stay with Heinold for a period of, I believe, two years before they would be free to leave and go back to Rufenacht's firm.

Also, Harold paid Rufenacht a small fee for encouraging his people to rejoin Heinold Commodities [and also made it possible for them to avoid bankruptcy]. In two years' time if they could recover the capital they needed, they could go back to Rufenacht, if they wanted to.

Tom: In the meantime, their big producers were working with Heinold Commodities.

A Strong Start

Ralph: Yes, and this arrangement gave Harold and me a shot in the arm right off of the bat, as it meant we wouldn't be starting from scratch. The business became profitable right from day one after I joined it, mainly because the commodity market had turned around. Harold was able, at least for a while, to put enough capital into the company to support the Merc's capital requirement for the amount of business they were generating.

Tom: About how many hog markets did he have at that time?

Ralph: About sixty.

Tom: That many? In 1969. So that was a pretty good business?

Ralph: Yes, oh yes. They had been in business over twenty years and had grown steadily. They were well established. At any rate, it became obvious almost right away that Heinold Commodities could be very profitable and had a real opportunity to grow. Harold and I made a good sales team. We did a lot of traveling the first year recruiting new business and opening new branch offices, and it just seemed to work like magic.

Tom: What sort of information did you make available to the people that you were putting on as branch managers? And why did they elect to come with you instead of staying with their existing operations?

Ralph: The Heinold name was good in rural areas in the Midwest. They seemed to know about the Hog Markets and about Heinold and we focused on the story of Harold rescuing a competitor in the commodity business. He was known for returning good for evil, I guess. Put it that way.

Tom: But those fellows in the long run have to get information from you about trends in the market that they can ride or not, so you must have sold them pretty effectively that you could give them better market information for their trading activities than anybody else.

Ralph: That's probably the biggest thing we were selling, but it was a fairly easy sale. Livestock futures were new at that time, as you know, and most of the big brokerage firms were not into livestock futures as yet. Heinold Commodities was doing well, was making money for its customers, and was really the only firm at that time that was putting together good comprehensive information on the cash markets for both hogs and cattle.

[A man named Howard Houk deserves recognition here for the work that he did in livestock for the Heinold firm and for the industry. Howard was one of the first livestock analysts in the U.S. and developed many of the techniques still used to analyze live stock fundamental factors. Howard's research for Heinold was read widely and used by the sales force extensively. —THR, Jr.]

Tom: When I first came to know Harold, the story was that they were successful in futures trading because of their intimate knowledge of the cash hog markets. Was that a big selling point with those people?

Ralph: That was a big selling point, yes, and Harold had the reputation of being the country boys' champion in the big city market in Chicago. Heinold Hog Markets was perceived to be a firm that would be honest and would treat its customers right, and it became an easy sell.

Also, I had been in the grain business for several years, some on my own and some with Continental, and at one time I was president of the Illinois Grain and Feed Association, too, so I knew lots of grain industry people throughout Illinois.

Tom: You knew the futures market in grain.

Ralph: Yes. It was one of our goals to do business on the Board of Trade, where grain is traded, as well as in the livestock markets that were traded at the Merc.

Tom: So really, you were an acknowledged successful professional in grains, and Harold had put together a success in his hog markets.

Ralph: Yes. We were a good team and worked very closely together the first year or two and then, well gradually, he began to devote more time to the Hog Markets, as the commodity trading firm was doing well.

Tom: Another way of saying that is that he gained confidence in you and wanted you to run the commodity trading part of his business and he felt at home with his Hog Markets.

Ralph: Yes, I suppose so, but Harold also devoted his time to the problems of raising capital to support the fast growth our commodity trading business was experiencing. This was a big problem, of course, almost from the start. Our need for capital reserves to meet margin calls and to support the volume of business we were doing was great.

It wasn't long after we got started, I'd say six to eight months, that we ran into capital problems. This would have been early 1970. At that time, Harold asked to renegotiate my employment contract with him because it was too favorable toward me. We hadn't expected the kind of growth we had experienced at all,

So, we renegotiated my contract. He gave me stock options in the company and reduced my cash bonus [so it] wouldn't scare new people from coming into the company. In some cases we had to entice them with some stock options

Tom: Was Heinold's need for capital to grow the fundamental reason you made the move to join DeKalb?

Ralph: Yes, It was one of the main reasons, but there were other motivations also. They were these:

A number of us had become stockholders in the company by that time. When it came to the point where the banks would no longer extend further credit to meet margin calls, we didn't know what to do. This was in 1970. Joel Greenberg was there at the time, and so was Lloyd Arnold. They were both big hitters and we wanted to get more big hitters, but we realized that if we took on more of them, our capital requirements could become even greater. At the time, I had already acquired some farmland in downstate Illinois and both Joel and Lloyd had assets, so the three of us pledged our assets to the bank, giving Heinold Commodities an additional line of short-term credit. In exchange for that we took more stock options. We wanted someday to cash in those options, so in 1972 when DeKalb bought out Heinold, the DeKalb stock we received provided opportunity for us to cash our options in. This was the case for Greenberg, Arnold, myself, and a few others.

But it was more than that, it was also important to the Hog Market people because they had been in business for over twenty years, and I personally knew some of the managers who had been with Harold all those years and always took their bonuses in the form of stock. Eventually, they wanted to cash in, but if all the capital just goes to continued growth, when do they ever cash in? So, Harold was looking around to go public or to make a sale to provide cash liquidity for his people.

DeKalb's Position and Its Objectives

Tom: Well, that makes sense, and it ties in with DeKalb's situation at the time. We were, as you know, doing very well in the hybrid corn business and we'd been increasing market share for twelve straight years. We were generating cash in excess of the needs of our business. We realized that we needed to either make more investments or pay out surplus cash to our shareholders, who were pressing us to increase dividends.

We were successful people looking for a place to

put money in agriculture, and you were successful people in the commodity trading and hog marketing businesses who wanted to cash in on some of your success, as well as find a source of capital to allow the Heinold companies to grow. So we made a deal with you, to exchange DeKalb stock [then trading at $75 per share, a few months before a 2:1 stock split] for all of Heinold's stock.

Ralph: That's right. The company would need more capital, and our key people needed the liquidity that owner ship of DeKalb's publicly traded stock would give them.

Tom: DeKalb's earnings multiple on its stock was fairly high, so it was a currency we wanted to exploit. A lot of things came together when DeKalb and the Heinold companies got married.

Tom: Do you recall how fast you grew after you joined DeKalb?

Ralph: Again, I don't recall specific numbers but would estimate that Heinold Commodities tripled its number of brokers during the twelve years we were owned by DeKalb. When we joined DeKalb there was a boost to the company almost immediately in terms of gross income and number of brokers and producers that joined the company.

Tom: Both of us remember some pretty traumatic times at Heinold, too—exciting times. I can remember how important Joel was to us. He reached me by telephone at a field day in Kansas a short time after DeKalb acquired Heinold, saying, "Tom, I've got a very big position in pork bellies and I'm just sure that I'm right, but I've got to hang in two or three more days. I'm asking you not to blow me out of my position because I think you have the authority to justify that." I said, "Well, I'm not sophisticated enough in this business to say yes, but let me think about it." And then I called you and asked you what to do. You sort of hedged, but we decided to carry him a few more days.

Ralph: The first time we had to call on DeKalb for additional capital was a few months after the acquisition was completed, on a Friday afternoon. We had large positions on the books in livestock and the market had gone a wrong way and we had a call from the exchange, which is unusual. Usually additional capital needs just became routine, but this was something special—urgent. [The call was] for an additional $2 million in capital, which at that time seemed like a shocking number. We called out to DeKalb that we needed the money right away. The money needed to be in the exchange by 9 o'clock Monday morning. I'm sure you were shocked, but you came through. Subsequent to that, over the years there were many times when you put additional capital in on a temporary basis for much larger amounts than that.

Tom: Well, there's nothing like the first surprise to give you an education. The Heinold Commodities and Hog Market businesses were very exciting to us and certainly were money makers. Let's see, we're talking about 1973 or 1974. In that period it seems to me that Nixon took price controls off of beef cattle. Was that our first really traumatic moment?

Ralph: Yes. I believe so.

Tom: Why don't you tell us about that.

Ralph: Well, it was coincidental, maybe, but that was in the summer and fall of 1974. We had been growing fast and working hard, and I had asked to take a month off. Sure enough, while I was gone the price controls were lifted. It had been announced several weeks before the price controls were actually lifted and, of course, markets were bumping up to the ceiling at that time, and everyone thought when the controls lifted cattle prices were going to go up, but...

Tom: Farmers had been hoarding cattle, waiting for the price controls to go off.

"Down The Limit" Seventeen Straight Days!

Ralph: Yes, and speculators were holding big "long" positions, thinking that when the price ceiling was taken off beef, the price would go sharply higher. Well, instead, the day that they took it off the price went down the limit...

Tom: And plunged down the daily limit for seventeen straight days, as I remember.

Ralph: I'm sure that we called on you for additional capital at that time, too, but several of our big traders got racked up pretty badly. Some of the names that I've already mentioned, Greenberg and the large cattle traders both in Chicago and out in branches who were in limit positions, lost $500,000 every day the market traded down the limit. It was the most severe series of down limit moves I could remember. There wasn't a lot I could do about it, you know, personally, but before my thirty-day vacation was up I went back into Chicago and tried to absorb some of the pressures there.

Tom: I remember being impressed that you had such sound experience with commodity trading that you somehow figured that the last five to seven days of those "down limit" moves, which were costing our people so much, were not justified by the fundamentals of the market. How did you figure that out?

Ralph: You're talking about the occasion, I guess, or period of time where we thought that others had access to our positions...

Tom: Yes.

A Fox in the Chicken Coop

Ralph: I figured our competitors must have found out what trouble we were in, or knew the severe losses that some of our customers were taking, and that DeKalb was probably sending in capital to help them keep from being blown out of the market.

Tom: How did you figure that competitors knew that?

Ralph: Well, something didn't seem right, and some of our traders on the floor seemed to think that our competitors knew our positions and you know...

Tom: And were squeezing us.

Ralph: That was the gossip on the floor, but what documents or orders they may have seen, I don't know. But our managers suspected that competitors knew our positions and knew that a lot of our traders were in trouble. Then one of our accountants noticed that an employee in the office (and a former employee of Rufenacht) was calling someone early every morning and giving him our positions. He'd get to the office early, get the computer sheets with the buying positions and float it over to one of our competitors. And further, this employee's wife worked at the competitor's office.

Ralph: Yes. So we had reason maybe to question his loyalty to us. I don't know what steps our accountant took, but he found out for sure that this telephoning was going on and confronted the culprit. He [the employee] admitted advising someone of our positions. He had some vague excuse for doing it—an excuse that didn't hold water with us. However, he was not a member of an exchange and was not subject to exchange rules and regulations, so there wasn't a lot that we could do with him other than let him go.

However, those on the receiving end of that

information were members of the exchange and had to know that this was coming in a way that wasn't consistent with ethical practices to say the least. So we filed charges with the exchange against them, if you recall.

Tom: Yes, I remember. We talked about it at one of our regular management meetings, and when you outlined the situation I said, "Let's sue those guys." You pointed out the procedure for doing that is to take it before the Business Conduct Committee of the Merc.

Exchange Self-Policing Falls Short

Ralph: That's right. We filed a complaint with the Business Conduct Committee charging that they had violated the Merc's ethical rules.

Tom: Didn't Harold talk with a woman who admitted reporting our traders' large and vulnerable positions?

Ralph: Yes. At any rate, you know the Business Conduct Committee had a hearing on it, and Harold and I were present along with someone from Sidley & Austin, and maybe someone from DeKalb. Anyway, it was whitewashed. I mean they just gave it no credibility to our complaint at all.

Tom: The woman denied her confession?

Ralph: Yes, yes, that's right, she came into that meeting and denied it all.

Tom: And they all acted like they had skeletons in their own closets. Our lawyers, as I remember, were really frustrated because they weren't even given the basic right of cross examination.

Ralph: That's right.

Tom: And none of the usual procedures of a court were allowed, and the jury, so to speak, the Business Conduct Committee, consisted of traders who were, apparently, afraid of establishing new precedents that might entrap some of them someday.

Ralph: Yes, besides, they themselves might have been a part of this operation that the hearing was about.

Tom: As a practical matter, our lawyers advised against taking it to court after the Business Conduct Committee's whitewash.

Ralph: We might have been able to, but I guess we thought at that point we wouldn't. It was all conducted in such a way that we all felt like asses for going in there when it was all over with.

Tom: Well, what happened to our customers who were

losing $500,000 a day for five or six extra days? Did you lose a lot of those fellows? Did they hear about the Business Conduct Committee's apparent white wash?

Ralph: Those in Chicago knew about it. Those in the country, or outside of Chicago, would be less likely to have known it, although we never tried to conceal it from anyone.

Tom: But Greenberg, for example.

Ralph: Sure. He knew, and many of our biggest brokers knew about it. I don't believe there were any fatalities there. They all survived financially, but all took heavy hits.

Tom: Yes. It's a wonder to me that they didn't say, "Well, I can't afford to work with this bunch of guys that let people get away with that. But they stuck anyway. Of course, they had made money, a lot of money.

Ralph: Yes. A lot of which they gave back—or a lot of their losses were giving back what they had previously made. Nevertheless, there had to be some who probably bought right at the top, I'm talking about the rank and file of customers across the country. And there were some debts that we never collected that we eventually had to write off. But, all in all, we came out of it pretty well. In those situations, as you know, the clearing firm, which was Heinold, has to pay up the losses the next morning at 9 o'clock, and if it's a severe loss, they can even call it by 4 o'clock on the day that it occurred. That happened several times and I'm sure we called on DeKalb to furnish capital. The clearing firm pays the losses and then collects as it can from the customers.

Tom: So the big dealers who were our customers, who were trading with us, probably were a little slow about paying us, but as they made money, over time, they gradually paid us back.

Ralph: Yes, yes. I'm sure we had to write off some, but it was not significant. I think you'll find that we remained profitable all through that period.

Tom: Well, that was certainly a traumatic moment for DeKalb and for you and the fellows who were losing money at that rate, but we survived a terrible injustice. It would be a powerful story to get before government regulatory agencies that seek ways to control markets more effectively. We made our shot through the right channel and the channel denied us justice. Has there been significant progress since that time in the direction of strengthening regulatory practices?

Heinold Commodities Leads Trading Reform

Ralph: Yes. At that time, the futures markets were under the regulatory jurisdiction of the Commodity Exchange Authority [CEA], which became the Commodity Futures Trading Commission [CFTC]. Helping with regulatory reform was one of the ways that DeKalb was a big help to us. When the CFTC was authorized, there were hearings held. The exchanges were active in the hearings, but we also did some lobbying of our own through Larry Hunt and others at Sidley & Austin. John Witmer was in Washington at that time with Sidley & Austin, and Harold and I went to Washington a number of times with our own lobbying effort, which complemented what the exchanges were doing and enhanced our position with them.

We lobbied in favor of trading using anticipatory hedges. We argued for a ruling from the CFTC authorizing anticipatory hedging. There was some opposition to our position, based on the theory that anticipatory hedges would not be true hedges.

Tom: Is DeKalb's practice of buying its seedcorn forward an anticipatory hedge?

Ralph: Yes. That was in real danger at one time.

Tom: Was it? To me that's the ultimate hedge.

Ralph: Yes, that's right. I agree, but there were those among the regulators in Washington and some at the exchanges who didn't believe that; they argued that a true hedge only exists if you have the actual commodity on hand.

Tom: Then, in DeKalb's case, we had contracted with growers to grow the seed, and we were sure that we'd be obligated for x millions of bushels. We wanted to establish what it would cost us by forward buying, so that we could then set the price of our seedcorn and turn our dealers loose to sell it.

Ralph: You and I can easily see where that's a true hedge, but some of them didn't see it that way, and we made quite an effort at that time to get that recognized as a true hedge.

Tom: You must have been successful.

Ralph: Yes, we were. And, of course, the advantage in having it recognized as a hedge is that there were no speculative limits and your needs far exceeded speculative limits of corn. They carried a reduced margin requirement, also.

Tom: Well, those are benefits, aren't they?

Ralph: You bet. There was a time when the CFTC wanted to regulate cash transactions. This disturbed Harold greatly because they made cash hog transactions every day. I recall going to Washington with Harold. Harold testified successfully before a congressional committee. DeKalb's contacts in Washington through Sidley & Austin and John Schnittker were a big help to Heinold.

Tom: Well, of course, it was probably reciprocal, too.

Ralph: I think so. We complemented one another in that regard. I also recall a CFTC authorization provision enabling the industry to regulate itself, or to form its own self-regulatory organization. That opportunity lingered for a couple of years and the industry did nothing about it, so you got the idea of using the Harvard Business School as a forum for initiating the organization of a strong self-regulatory agency. Ray Goldberg, who headed the HBS agribusiness program, understood the industry's needs for stronger self-governance and sponsored an industry meeting at Harvard Business School. Several of us attended, and most of the large firms were there.

I was the keynote speaker for the meeting. This was something I always look back on with pride. That was the beginning of the NFA—the National Futures Association, which is now the industry regulatory arm, and it is working out quite well. Harold was one of the original board members.

Tom: Tell me about Heinold's relationship with the Chicago Board of Trade.

Acceptance by the Board of Trade

Ralph: Very simply, the Chicago Board of Trade kept Heinold out of the business of clearing trades for probably two years longer than we should have been. I won't go into the details of being a clearing broker versus a nonclearing broker, but all major firms are clearing members, and Heinold ultimately became a clearing member of almost every exchange in the country as well as London But there was a great bias in the Board of Trade against members of the Merc.

Tom: Why?

Ralph: Everyone then was either a Board of Trade–based firm or a Merc-based firm, and I had been a member of the Board of Trade for several years. When I came to Heinold and got a membership in the Merc, they couldn't believe it. They asked, "Ralph, why are you going to that place?" Because its reputation was that of a group of shlock-houses that traded in butter and eggs and were not nearly as reputable as the Board of Trade.

Tom: Pork bellies and cattle and pigs...

Ralph: Yes, and until the Merc brought on cattle and hogs and some of the newer contracts and developed into a sizable operation, their bad reputation might have been partly justified.

Tom: Did Leo Melamed have quite a bit to do with bringing respectability to the Merc?

Ralph: Oh yes, a lot. His foresight and integrity and his insistence on everything being clean, well organized, and above board was a great contribution. I have respect for him. But there was an unwritten rule at the Board of Trade (and I was aware of it) that the Board of Trade would not allow Merc firms to become clearing members. So, even though we had the number of memberships required and we had the capital that was required, and met every criterion for being a clearing member, they would not let us clear; we had to clear through other firms, which meant it cost us more to handle each transaction. You will recall that John Morrison Co. was a clearing firm we did a lot of business with, and several others. But, when it became known that DeKalb owned Heinold and that additional capital was available to us, they looked at us with an altogether different attitude—a better attitude toward Heinold than they had before.

Tom: DeKalb didn't deserve the credit; Heinold should have had it on their own, but it helped.

Ralph: Well, yes. For one thing, I believe DeKalb bought a membership, so that was one more membership in the array of things that we had. But also because DeKalb is known through ag and grain marketing circles to be a respected name, they looked upon us differently. We were no longer a little Merc schlock-house; we were in it for real. And it wasn't long then until they approved us as clearing members.

The Great Potato Default

Ralph: Heinold Commodities took another precedent-setting stand at the New York Merc when we joined with our customers against a rigged market and defaulted on closing out potato futures contracts. The press called it "the Great Potato default." The problems we had there handling potato traders were similar to the earlier problems with our traders' cattle positions that suffered because of market rigging.

Tom: Hadn't the potatoes been sold forward basically by the Idaho potato growers Simplot and Tegaris? They controlled most of the Idaho potatoes, didn't they?

Ralph: Yes, the two of them controlled most of the Idaho potatoes, and the New York Mercantile Exchange traded a futures contract in Maine potatoes. There was no futures contract for Idaho potatoes. Nevertheless, New York Merc had encouraged Idaho producers—mainly Simplot and Tegaris—to hedge their production in the New York Mercantile Exchange Maine potato contract.

Tom: To sell their potatoes forward in the futures market.

Ralph: Yes, and they did hedge some pretty fair volume. Tegaris had an account with Heinold and put several hundred hedging contracts onto our books. A number of farmers also had individual accounts with us. Well, as it got near to the last day of trading in May potatoes, in 1978, it became apparent that the local traders on the New York Merc were squeezing the market on the Idaho potato hedgers. All of our potato-hedging customers wanted to buy back their long positions, as trading rules required, but the local traders in Maine and New York kept their asking price artificially high.

Tom: As a matter of fact, didn't our customers try to buy potatoes on Maine farms on handshake purchases, only to come back the next day to sign their "buy" contracts and find out that somebody else had bought them for a few cents more than had been agreed upon the day before?

Ralph: Yes. The executive vice president of the New York Mercantile Exchange called me one day asking what we were going to do about the May potatoes positions on our books! Our standard answer, which was later proven to be correct, was that these are customers' positions, and that we'd need to contact the customers to see what they wanted to do.

Tom: Usually, when an exchange called on a member trading firm asking them to force his customers to make a trading deadline, the trading firm was required to follow exchange orders, wasn't it? In this case, to buy potatoes to fulfill the "sell" contracts that our customers held.

Ralph: Yes, we would have the authority to do blow our

customers out of the market, following exchange orders, but Tegaris told us immediately that he would challenge the exchange order. He told us in no uncertain terms that if we closed out his hedge position without his permission, he would take us to court.

Tom: And, of course, we were sympathetic with him too, because he was being squeezed.

Ralph: Yes. We had evidence to that effect. Tegaris claimed that New York brokers came to Idaho every year to solicit his hedge business and wanted him to hedge his potatoes in their contract, and then two or three weeks before the end of the contract they would squeeze him. He was determined to fight such a squeeze in 1978 because it had happened to him in other years, and he simply decided to stop being squeezed.

Tom: So he chose Heinold to be his broker, having in mind that he was going to challenge the system.

Ralph: I think so. At any rate, as it got closer...Well, we were a clearing firm on the Mercantile Exchange, and the clearing firm guarantees performance in every contract. If our customer won't perform, we have to. In the end, when we got down to the last day or two of trading, we did coax Tegaris out of quite a number of his positions, but we never took a strict arbitrary action. I was on the phone with him that last day of trading and watching the market. There was very little volume of trading, with very few bids and offers, as everyone knew who was long and who was short, but I twisted his arm a little bit into getting rid of a substantial part of his positions.

Tom: Oh, I didn't realize that.

Ralph: But he still had quite a number left on which he defaulted; and at the very same time, Simplot defaulted on a much larger amount with two or three other brokerage firms.

Tom: And this made the front page of the Wall Street Journal.

Ralph: Yes. I couldn't believe it. Such an insignificant matter in terms of the overall economy, and yet it was front page in all of the papers. Well, from the last day of trading until the final delivery date is about another two weeks, and in that period of time the exchange required Heinold to deposit full value of every contract defaulted, so we put up several million dollars to guarantee performance, and performance never did occur. At some point the exchange set an arbitrary price that was somewhat concessionary to Tegaris and Simplot as a settlement price, and at that point we got quite a bit of our money back. The rest we weren't able to collect from Tegaris.

Justice at Last

Tom: Didn't we take the exchange to court?

Ralph: Oh, yes. On behalf of our clients.

Tom: And didn't Stewart Ball, a Sidley & Austin lawyer, represent us?

Ralph: Yes. He was a great man in my experience with him. Initially the exchange held hearings. We attended and made our case, but their ruling was the same old whitewash we had experienced at the Chicago Merc when our cattle trading customers were squeezed. The people who were involved on the short side of the market and who were manipulating the squeeze were the ones who were passing judgment on us and our customers.

Tom: Just like the old Merc Business Conduct Committee.

Ralph: Exactly. In this case, the New York Exchange took action against Harold because it was his membership that was registered with the firm. They fined both the firm and Harold. We paid up but challenged the action in court, which found us not guilty of anything. We got our fines back, but it cost us around $500,000 in legal fees. As an aside, Ray Goldberg [of the Harvard Business School] made a case study of that, and for several years he invited me out to be present when the case was studied. He still looks at it as a very significant case. I keep asking him, "How can you stick with this old case for so many years? A lot more exciting things have happened in the industry since then." Ray agrees, but he believes our case clearly identifies the injustice that often occurs when self-regulation is weakly handled by commodity exchange authorities. He is pleased that the NFA has been established and is operating well.

Tom: The status of Heinold Commodities must have been enhanced by their handling of this case—by "hanging in" until justice was done to those who entered into hedging contracts in good faith.

Ralph: I think so. You don't like to see your name on the front page of the Wall Street Journal in any negative context, but over a period of time, I think our reputation was enhanced. I admired Stewart Ball, the lawyer who represented us in court. He did a wonderful job at the open hearing about the default. He argued that our opponents manipulated the market by artificially rigging it. He had evidence to prove his case, and he prevailed. In a situation where I might have sat in the middle or the back, Stewart Ball stepped right to the front and sat down with Larry Hunt and me beside him. The first thing the judge asked was, "Does anyone have anything they want to say?" and he stands right up. Front row, everyone there had to see him; he started asking questions that were embarrassing to our opposition. He confronted them head-on. He's got more guts than I have, but...

Tom: That's what made him a great lawyer.

Ralph: In looking back, I could see, boy, he handled that just perfectly.

The Birth of Computerized Trading

Tom: I recall that you originated the computer trading idea and developed it into an effort to counteract the effect of negotiated commissions, which were man dated in the early '80's. This was a life-saver for us, as commissions were our only source of income.

Ralph: Yes. The concept was developed by our Peoria branch office manager, who was a computer buff. He reasoned that historical market experiences and trends could be correlated with current market conditions to predict future changes in certain com modity prices. He tried out his theories in the market and was successful, so we decided to market the best concept and the most scientifically developed computerized market management programs we could develop.

The first customers, by and large, were very well pleased, and our various additional program offerings were generally successful, but their returns trended downward as more and more competitive computer-based funds came into the market.

Tom: It seems to me that investor returns would inevitably decline as more and more investors chased computerized market forecasts.

Ralph: Yes. At the time I resigned, we had over 300 million dollars under computerized trading programs. Bill Dubinsky deserves a lot of credit for identifying good analysts and for raising money for the funds he promoted.

My interest in commodity trading funds was based simply on the theory that if mutual funds would work in security markets, they would work in commodity markets, too. Small investors could put their money in a fund and not have to worry about margin calls and not be second-guessing the pros.

A Sad Ending

Ralph: I'm very proud of my Heinold experiences because I believe we really made a difference in bringing order to a chaotic industry. In 1984, after I resigned as Heinold's president, I stayed in Chicago for a year or so on a part-time basis.

Tom: I've forgotten why you resigned.

Ralph: Well, I was asked to.

Tom: By whom?

Ralph: Bruce Bickner. I didn't contest it in any way. I was, I think, at the point where I was about to leave any way.

Tom: What were they unhappy about?

Ralph: I don't know, Tom. I just don't know. I think there were a number of points that they might have been unhappy with. We'd had some problems in the management of our London office. Bruce said I didn't act fast enough in that situation, and I think there were a couple of other situations. Mainly, he thought I didn't act fast enough. Other than that, no reason was ever given.

Tom: It strikes me that DeKalb's handling of your situation was a big mistake. Of course, I have to take a big part of the blame because I was DeKalb's CEO at the time.

Ralph: It's a tough business—the commodity business. I needed either a long vacation, or to give it up, so Bruce's action didn't bother me.

Tom: I see, and DeKalb was having its own problems, as I remember, with the culture of the business.

The Great Silver Squeeze

Ralph: I think so. I recall yet another crisis that occurred just before I left. It was the "Great Hunt Silver Squeeze."

Tom: Will you tell me about that?

Ralph: Hunt had accounts on our books. Nothing at all like they had with others, but...

Tom: I recall that at the peak of their trading, they came to you and presented you with a deal that would have put a floor on their losses and put quite a bit of risk on us. We were very proud of you for having refused it.

Ralph: Hunt's people attracted a lot of trading firms because their trades were so huge, but we limited their positions with Heinold because we felt they were "pyramiding" and heading for trouble.

Ralph: In the last days of the silver crash, we had a small amount of their positions compared to Conti-Commodities, and they'd meet their margin calls to us every day; their daily margin calls were in the neighborhood of a million to a million and a half dollars, but they were calling Conti for $20 or $30 million or more every day, and Conti had to sell assets to meet their margin calls.

Tom: We thought you managed that remarkably well.

Ralph: Well, we came out fine, but I think on the last day or two of the crash, Hunt would say, "We'll meet our margin calls at Heinold, and if there is ever a time that we can't, we'll tell you. We won't say your money's coming and it won't come; we'll tell you." So, sure enough, one morning when he said, "Sorry we can't send it, we're done." And I think they were about a million and half dollars short, and that's what Heinold Commodities was stuck for. Luckily, the market took a jump right at the opening and we got out even. It continued to plunge after that another day or two.

Tom: Do you recall any other experiences during your tour of duty with Heinold that we should report? I can throw in one here that's greatly to your credit, too, Ralph. I think this is significant, and should be reported.

Helping to Make a Man a Millionaire

Tom: At one of our regular Heinold Commodities executive meetings you reported that a fellow from Wichita, an oil man, had sold some helium wells for 2 or 3 million dollars and was investing in gold through Heinold's Wichita broker. About a month afterwards, I met him at Harbour Island in the Bahamas. As I talked to him, he came to realize that I was an officer at DeKalb, and he asked, "Are you the ones that own Heinold Commodities?"
And he said, "Well, I've got to give a lot of credit to Ralph Klopfenstine; he's the guy who runs your commodities business isn't he? Well, I put that helium money into gold futures and as the market rose, I stayed with it and that $3 million grew to $100 million. About the time it got to $30 million, I could just sense what this fellow Klopfenstine was

thinking when he talked to me on the phone—that he had to get this wild oil man at least to cash in enough so that he is assured of recovering his original $3 million. I wouldn't listen, but when the value of my gold got to $80 million, Klopfenstine hired an airplane and came down to see me."

Ralph: Yes, that's right.

Tom: Then he said, "I finally decided I would sell every thing that I could take capital gains on. As things turned out, I would have been better off to sell all of my gold, as Klopfenstine suggested, but as it was, I came out with $95 million."

Ralph: Yes, it was fantastic what he did. I remember very well my trip down there, because he was a tough guy to deal with.

Tom: What'd he do? Keep borrowing more money and enlarging his positions?

Ralph: Yes. He pyramided to the point where we got very nervous about it.

Tom: You mean he was borrowing based on his current gains.

Ralph: Yes, which can be used as margin in the markets. He always wanted to put more on than we would let him. We'd let him put up a certain amount of his unrealized profits and he always wanted to go higher than that. When I was in Wichita meeting with him, right across the desk, he says, "Are you telling me that you would rather not have any more of my business?" I said, "Yes, that's what I'm telling you. At this point, we don't want any more. If you want to trade higher, go somewhere else and scatter it out to other firms." I think that did more to gain his respect than anything. And that's the way I truly felt. He finally decided to take our advice and discontinued his pyramiding.

Tom: That's a very good example of the moment of truth in the management of commodity trading companies and is greatly to your credit.

On to a Distinguished Record In Washington

Tom: So you went on to several good years running the USDA Feed Grains Program for the Reagan and Bush administrations.

Ralph: Five years, and it was a great experience for both of us. Our children were all grown at the time and we were free to go, so we moved to Washington.

THE HEINOLD COMPANIES: MY PERSPECTIVE

The Heinold experience was both exciting and disappointing. The first decade with Heinold proved to be everything we had hoped it would be. Our capital supported expansion of Heinold's hog markets and growth in its commodity brokerage operations. Our lawyers and administrators did a good job of cleaning up the weak spots that were inevitable in a company that had grown fast in the highly volatile commodities trading business. For example, in our first year, we discovered many newly acquired commodity branch offices that weren't even registered to do business in the states where they were located. Had their customers known that, they would have had a valid basis for suing to recover speculative losses, which were, of course, inevitable in commodity trading.

This matter was corrected quickly, and Ralph Klopfenstine grew in stature as his company grew. He did not "trade" personally, to my knowledge, but he was an experienced, honest administrator who created a solid back-office organization and dealt effectively with the inevitable crises that are a part of the fast-moving commodity business. Further, he led the company into opening offices in the New York COMEX as well as in several overseas locations.

However, the bloom started to fade after a series of major crises—for example, the "squeeze" we had to battle after cattle price controls were dropped, and the unpleasant realization that self-regulation had failed us at the Merc. Ralph and Harold and Sidley & Austin did yeoman's work to set that right, but other serious problems kept popping up: the Great Potato Default, the Hunt problems, large trading losses by key people, and the cancellation of fixed commissions. All of these problems that turned off our highly educated, young, and aspiring administrators.

In 1986 we decided to divest ourselves of our commodity business for four fundamental reasons:

- We had allowed our "young lions"—the men who would soon be leading DeKalb—to fire one of the best administrators in the commodity trading business, Ralph Klopfenstine. After he left, our business was never the same.
- Earnings had declined steadily, beginning in 1982.
- We accepted the advice of Duff & Phelps, which was one of the best advisory firms in the country, to divest all but our basic businesses: hybrid products and oil exploration.
- A series of law suits from customers of both Heinold Hog Markets and Heinold Commodities broke out. In our increasingly litigious society and its seemingly unjust jury decisions, minor slip-ups by branch offices, for example, could cost DeKalb dearly.

Liquidating

Accordingly, when we got a $53.5 million offer from Con-Agra to buy Heinold Commodities, we sold out. The amount of the sale was reported in DeKalb's 1986 Annual Report, which described the transaction as follows: "On February 24, 1986, the company sold the stock of its commodity brokerage and fund businesses, after removal of certain assets (including cash and marketable securities) and liabilities."

We had initially purchased Heinold Commodities for $12,305,000 worth of DeKalb common stock, and we sold it fourteen years later for $53.5 million after accumulating pre-tax earnings of $87,762,000.

Heinold Hog Markets Is Sold to Employees

When the Heinold Hog Markets' regional managers made us a reasonable offer to buy Heinold Hog Markets, we agonized a long time over the new problems we saw coming from (1) big hog farmers selling direct to packers on a "grade and yield" basis, and (2) Iowa Beef and Missouri Beef, two successful meat packers, which were aggressively opening their own buying stations.

We decided to accept their offer, and sold Heinold Hog Markets to its employee-managers in May of 1987 for $11.3 million (as reported in the 1987 10K). Book value of the company on August 31, 1986, was $10,746,000, and pre-tax earnings totaled $24,522,000 during the period 1973 through 1985, when DeKalb owned HHM.

Table 23B-1 provides perspective and overview of DeKalb's earnings from its three most important businesses between 1972 and 1986, when the Heinold Companies were sold. The sad decline in the profitability of our basic seed business was partly offset by earnings gains from our oil business and from the Heinold companies and served as an important source of funds as we worked to improve our seed product lines. The seed writedown shown in 1986 was a consequence of our having excessive seed inventories we judged to be unsaleable but later were able to sell. They contributed to profit shortly after being written down.

DeKalb paid 150,000 shares of Class A stock worth $11.1 million for Heinold Hog Markets, which had experienced rather "flat" after-tax earnings, averaging $1.4 for the three previous years. The price we paid was eight times HHM's post-tax earnings at the time of the acquisition. We also agreed to provide funds for adding new stock yards that appeared to be good investments.

Similarly, 152,000 shares worth $11,856,000 was paid for Heinold Commodities, whose three-year average after-tax earnings were $1,810,000, making our purchase at a multiple of only 6.55 times earnings. Consistent with our wish to invest in sound business expansion, we agreed to provide them with additional capital as needed to expand the their business soundly. In my view, these prices were a marvelous bargain for DeKalb.

Heinold Divestitures

I regretted the sale of Heinold Commodities because it had been an exciting, profitable business for us. However, we needed the cash in our other businesses. Moreover, the commodities company's profitability had declined considerably, partly because of the advent of negotiated commissions, but mostly because we had lost the leadership of Ralph Klopfenstine. In my view, the sale was a sad necessity.

Similarly, although our decision to divest Heinold Hog Markets was difficult, I believe it was the right move for DeKalb because: (1) the price was fair; (2) the hog production business was shifting rapidly into the hands of large operators who could often sell directly to packers on an attractive "grade and yield" basis that Heinold Hog Markets could not match; also, the aggressiveness of meat packing companies was making inroads on Heinold's markets, especially in Iowa and Missouri; and (3) the Heinold area managers were uncomfortable with the direction the company was going and were eager to run it themselves.

Table 22B-1
Pre-Tax Profit Contributions of DeKalb's Three Largest Divisions, 1972–1986
($000)

Fiscal Year	Heinold Commodities	Seed	Oil & Gas
1973	2,056	27,083	1,488
1974	3,516	38,907	5,749
1975	4,556	24,252	16,418
1976	5,076	25,815	21,956
1977	5,127	29,281	24,199
1978	12,130	27,800	27,700
1979	16,906	29,600	30,700
1980	17,600	29,600	46,400
1981	13,417	26,800	46,500
1982	6,800	(9,600)	47,400
1983	11,700	(9,500)	51,900
1984	8,900	17,300	54,800
1985	4,200	2,800	42,800
1986	2,500	(13,700)*	(27,400)*
1987	1,500	8,500	12,900
Totals	112,2844	246,438	390,610

SOURCES: SEC 10K forms for 1974, p. F13; 1977, p. 4; 1985 Ten-Year Statistical Review, p. 10; 1986, notes; SEC 19K form for 1981, p. 21; and, generally, 10K forms for 1970–1985.

* Heinold Commodities was sold in February 1986, HHM in May 1987. Writedowns in 1986 U.S. Oil & Gas reserves: ($54,800); well servicing company: ($26,400); seed inventory: ($23,600).

Chapter 22C

Dynapol:
An Exciting Venture Capital Investment
1970-1979

In June of 1977, DeKalb completed a venture capital investment that John McCarter had been negotiating for several months with a scientist named Dr. Alex Zafferoni. Alex had been one of three co-developers of the human birth control pill and who had founded the Syntex Corporation to produce and market the product. After Syntex was well on its way toward successful introduction of "the pill," it offered Alex free use of its research facilities, within a reasonable financial limit, to pursue any new product research that interested him, provided that the product would be useful to mankind.

Alex theorized that new compounds intended to be eaten (and digested) by human beings—such as food dyes, anti-oxidant food preservatives, and sugar—were likely to be harmful because the human race had not evolved in their presence. He reasoned that if he could make these substances safe for human consumption, many people would be willing to pay a reasonable price for his product. He founded Dynapol to create these safer food additives.

Alex sought to make such products safe by chemically binding them to inert long-chain protein molecules, which would, when ingested, enhance the taste of food but would not pass through the intestinal wall because of the very large size of the "carrier" compound's molecules. Instead, the large molecule that was tied firmly to the long-chain proteins would simply pass through the gut and out of the body with the feces.

Alex's idea caught on with the investing public when he listed Dynapol on the public market. His IPO (initial public offering) raised $40 million for the developmental research, product development, and sales. When Alex came to DeKalb he was about to run out of the money he had raised in the public market and needed to develop his product to the point that it could be submitted for FDA (Food and Drug Administration) approval.

After checking out the quality and reputation of Alex's scientists, we struck a deal with him. According to John Cotton, who represented us in the negotiations, this was the deal: DeKalb agreed to pay Dynapol $15 million in three installments, in exchange for 80 percent of Dynapol for as long as it operated, or 94 percent of Dynapol's remaining funds after liquidation. DeKalb would receive all of the tax benefits, so in the worst case DeKalb's loss would be $7.5 million, as the operative tax rate was 50 percent.

DID THE PRODUCT PASS THE FDA TESTS?

The answer to that question is "almost." White rats were the test animals. They were divided into groups and fed with food that contained several different dosages of the long-chain protein molecules that were attached to red dye molecules. Each rat that died was given a post-mortem examination, primarily testing for cancer. We became more and more excited when the post-mortems showed no difference in the incidence of cancer between the "controls" that had no red dye in their feed, and the test animals that had eaten feed containing various dosages of red dye.

In the spring of 1980, after 75 percent of the rats had died, the remaining 25 percent were slaughtered, and to our dismay they showed a rate-related incidence of cancer of the colon. Evidently, the long-chain protein used to keep the dye from entering the body through the digestive system was just abrasive enough to cause colon cancer in the rats. It was a great disappointment, of course, but on the other hand, that is what the FDA tests are designed to detect. In the final analysis, DeKalb suffered a net loss of only $4,090,000 on the deal. Credit goes to Gene Baroni of Coopers & Lybrand for negotiating a deal that greatly reduced our losses. It was worth the gamble, in my opinion, because of the enormous benefit (both human and financial) that successful tests would have made possible.

We made the final decision to close down the research in November 1981, though the corporation lived until 1982. The liquidating trust closed in May of 1985. John Cotton deserves credit and thanks for representing DeKalb very capably through the entire Dynapol experience.

Chapter 22D

Pride Oil Well Services, Inc.: A Significant Acquisition 1970-1996

The last big acquisition DeKalb made was effective September 1, 1978, when we acquired Pride Oil Well Services, Inc., of Houston, Texas. Its president and founder, Ray Tolson, was and still is a likable, ambitious, able, and imaginative businessman who fits the characterization "entrepreneur" as well as any man I have ever known—except, perhaps, Tom Roberts, Sr.

SOURCE: Pride Petroleum Services

Ray Tolson, Pride's Founder & CEO

Ray had put Pride together in 1975 with the purchase of an eight-rig well servicing company for $2 million; he had added three yards and twenty-four rigs in three years, building to a total of thirty-eight rigs in 1978. DeKalb bought Pride Petroleum Services, Inc., for $10.5 million plus $2.5 million in DeKalb stock. An important part of the deal was Ray's agreement to stay on and manage Pride's growth, with a goal of making it one of the three largest firms in the industry, along with Pool and Welltech, which were then operating 240 and 143 rigs, respectively.

WHAT IS A WELL SERVICING RIG?

Well servicing companies operate with small, portable rigs that cost $250,000 to $500,000 new, which is only a fraction of the cost of the much larger oil well drilling rigs, whose function is to drill the well bore-hole, usually working at the task of drilling twenty-four hours a day. The hourly charges for drilling rigs are usually several times the hourly rates of well servicing rigs, which are also called workover rigs. When the larger drilling rig has reached "total depth," it usually moves on to drilling another well.

However, much more work must be done before a well is either completed or capped as a dry hole. For example, the pipe must be perforated, the oil sands fractured by explosives or chemicals pumped in to optimize oil recovery. These and many other "completion" functions can be done by the less expensive service rigs. This is about 20 percent of the work done by service rigs when times are good and oil prices are high. The other 80 percent of well servicing involves just what the name implies—servicing producing oil and gas wells by pulling pipe, removing paraffin from tubing, reperforating in new formations, waterflooding, and other necessary tasks.

Accordingly, when times are good in the oil business and big drilling rigs are in great demand, they move out quickly, leaving completion work for the smaller workover rigs. But when times are bad and the big rigs don't have much work to do, they tend to stay on top of the well they have just drilled, drastically reducing their hourly rates to levels low enough to persuade the owners of the well to leave them on location after drilling has been completed, to perform the completion work normally performed by a well servicing company.

The effect of the big rigs staying on location in tough times is devastating to the well servicing companies, which are left with mainly well servicing rather than completions and workovers. When business is good, it is really good, but when it is bad, it is very, very bad.

Ray's purchase of Pride in 1975 was courageous because the $7.50 per barrel price that prevailed at the time of the purchase surely looked high in comparison with the $3.00 price level that had prevailed throughout the 1960s and early 1970s. Similarly, when DeKalb acquired Pride in 1978, $8.96 per barrel seemed high to us, too. However, we had faith in both the future of oil prices and the soundness of Ray's goal of building a company that would be big enough to compete with Pool and Welltech. Table 23D-1 shows how Ray acquired companies to achieve that goal, and Table 23D-2 reports the financial results of his efforts.

Table 22D-1
Pride Acquisitions, 1978–1994

Year	Company	State/ Country	No. of Rigs	Acquisition Cost ($000)
1978	Capshaw Well Service	WY	8	3,664
1979	Elk Well Service	TX	10	2,236
1979	Acme Well Service	TX	3	2,450
1980	El Campo Well Service	TX	10	1,600
1980	Eagle Well Service	LA	13	6,950
1980	Sierra Production Service	CA	37	21,000
1980	TP Well	TX		2,040
1985—Major Oil Price Break from $25/bbl to $12/bbl				
1987	Frontier Petroleum	CA , TX	143	6,500
1989	Tubing Anchor & Packing	TX		70
1989	Alliance Well Service	TX, NM	10	350
1989	Mack Chase	NM	12	2,623
1990	Eagle Creek	CA	12	950
	Ranger Well Service	TX	23	2,500
	Snyder Well Service	TX	7	939
	CRC Source Services	TX	12	1,300
	Redding & Moore	TX	7	1,650
	Pacer Atlas	TX	2	150
	OK Well Servicing	TX	31	4,932
	Valley Hyper Clean	CA		2,384
1991	Alliance Well Service	TX	10	1,300
1992	Felix		1	120
	Guard Trucking	TX		460
	Dutschman Trucking	TX		75
	Coil Tubing Unit	CA		135
1993	Western Atlas	Argentina	22	7,715
	Perforaciones Western	Venezuela	14	5,000
1994	Hydrodrill	Argentina		41,600c/s[a]
	Offshore Rigs	LA	22	31,213c/s
	Built 2 barges	LA		42,000dbt[b]
1995	Xpert Well Serving	NM	35	10,000c/s
	McNeel Trucking	TX		400
Total Expansion Investment to Mid-1995			$167,650,000	

SOURCE: Pride Petroleum Services.

a. c/s is cash and stock. b. dbt is debt.

Notes: The currency used was cash, except as noted. Additional cash investments were made in expanding our Argentine fleet, totaling $15 million. Additional cash invested in offshore rigs was $15.6 million. Total capital invested through June 1995 was $198,250,000.

Table 22D-2
Key Performance Data for
Pride Petroleum Services, 1976–1994

Year	Oil Price ($/bbl)	No. of Major Events	Rigs Used Rigs	(%)	Net Earnings ($000)
1974	3.89				
1975	6.74	Ray buys Pride	8	95	215
1976	7.56		12	94	265
1977	8.14		16	97	480
1978	8.96	DeKalb buys Pride	38	92	1,171
1979	12.51	Ray stays as CEO	50	81	2,074
1980	21.59		86	77	4,477
1981	31.77		177	96	17,125
1982	28.52		196	57	12,330
1983	26.19		195	48	(7,913)
1984	25.88		192	59	(2,757)
1985	24.09		191	57	(757)
1986	12.51		193	37	(6,008)
1987	15.41		202	44	(1,615)
1988	12.57		230	47	12
1989	15.82	DK spins off Pride by public listing	327	49	543
1990	21.22		373	61	4,666
1991	18.97		412	54	3,518
1992	18.97		428	47	(842)
1993	15.98	Pride strategy shifts[a] to offshore and international emphasis	460	49	5,940
1994			400	50	6,214

SOURCE: All data were provided by Pride Petroleum Services, Inc., except for oil price information for 1990–1995, which came from DK Energy. a. Specifically, in 1993 Pride acquired two Argentine companies (Hydrodrill and Pride Petrotech SAMPIC) and a company called Offshore Rigs for Gulf of Mexico operations; in 1994 it bought two barge platforms for Venezuelan and Gulf operations.

A "Slow Down" Decision

In early 1981, Ray became convinced that the well servicing industry had become overbuilt, and he was doubtful, too, that the price of oil in the United States would hold at the $31/bbl. it had reached. He discussed his doubts about the immediate future of the U.S. well servicing industry with his board and agreed to cancel the order he had placed for 100 rigs, feeling that it would not be long before rigs and well servicing companies could be acquired at much lower prices. The board approved of his excellent decision, and he canceled his order in June of 1981. Prices stayed in the mid-$20s for four more years before diving as low as $12.51 in 1986, but his decision was nevertheless a very good one.

The entire well servicing industry fell into deep depression in the mid-1980s as drilling activity declined sharply. Large drilling rigs often had no place to go after completing their drilling, so they drastically reduced their hourly rates and stayed on the wells doing the well service work. This created a crisis in the servicing business, forcing the mothballing of rigs and the bankruptcy of many undercapitalized companies.

Hard Times Hit Hard

Pride took two asset writedowns, one for $10.2 million in 1982 and another for $3.2 million in 1984. Both of these were small, however, in comparison with the $26.4 million writedown in 1985, after oil prices tumbled sharply. In 1986 we closed all of our yards in Oklahoma, where over-capacity was at its worst.

We were convinced that oil prices would recover from their $15 per barrel lows, but we were concerned about Pride's future when prices and serving activities recovered, and we would have to compete with rigs that had been purchased at very low prices. Ray figured our best strategy would be to expand aggressively, buying large, reputable service companies for thirty to fifty cents on the dollars they had invested. He saw the current depression as an opportunity and made an important decision when he bought the well-respected Frontier Petroleum Services, which operated in California and West Texas. We bought its 143 rigs for about twelve cents on each dollar of replacement cost. This purchase made Pride a strong competitor for its rivals at Pool and Welltech and made it clear to our customers that Pride was determined to be a sound, nationwide factor in the well servicing business.

TAKING PRIDE PUBLIC

The 1980s were an unhappy time for DeKalb, too. Our seedcorn business was suffering, and we had had to divest many of our acquisitions in order to focus on our seed and oil exploration businesses. We cut back our staffs and decided, regretfully, that Pride would be better off as an entirely independent, publicly listed company, with its shares distributed to DeKalb shareholders, trading on the over-the-counter market, NASDAQ.

Ray accepted DeKalb's decision in good grace and kept Pride "on course" to becoming the leading worldwide oil well–servicing company, using both cash and his listed stock as currency to purchase companies that matched his goals. Bruce Bickner, Rich Ryan, and I stayed on the Pride board at his request. Both Bruce and Rich made helpful suggestions and stayed aboard for four and five more years, respectively, before resigning to devote all of their time to DeKalb's business. I stayed on the Pride board and have found it to be a highly satisfying experience.

KUWAIT

Ray's first overseas operation was both a financial success and a learning experience. In 1991, the Kuwaiti government was eager to repair its oil fields, which had been badly damaged and sabotaged by the Iraqi army during the Persian Gulf war. They had many well servicing needs, but the most urgent one was to cut off the shards of well casing that had been sabotaged in order to limit the Kuwaiti postwar oil production. Many of the wells were burning and could not be put out by oil well fire fighters until the casing could be cut off.

Our crews managed to cut off the casing shards by stretching special cables between two rigs, which used their powered driveshafts to cause the cable to move backward and forward very rapidly, sawing the extruded damaged casing off cleanly enough to allow fire-fighting equipment to clamp on to the casing and put out the fire. Our efforts were not always successful, of course, but on balance they did good work, and Pride Petroleum Services came away from Kuwait proud of its accomplishments and pleased with the $1.5 million profit their efforts produced.

RUSSIA

With the collapse of the former Soviet Union, new opportunities opened up for American exploration companies to operate in Russia and in Siberia, so Pride equipped three of its rigs for the harsh weather conditions they would encounter there. After arriving in mid-1993, they performed nearly one hundred well servicing jobs, completed a horizontal drilling contract, and for their first two years there they operated profitably. However, the political situation grew more and more difficult, and misunderstandings were inevitable; when Pride suffered small losses during 1995 and 1996, management began to consider discontinuing its activities in Russia.

INVESTING WHERE THE ACTION IS

It became clear to Ray and his board that Pride's business plan should be based on two basic premises:

- While our domestic business had little growth potential because the United States had been so completely developed, it was capable of generating steady earnings for many years because it was very competitive and well manned, and therefore had value in the United States that could be utilized if better opportunities turned up overseas.
- Pride's best growth opportunities lay in well servicing off

shore in the Gulf of Mexico and in a number of South American countries. Management and directors agreed that there was little opportunity in antagonistic areas like Nigeria or the Middle East, but decided to be willing to consider attractive investment opportunities wherever new fields were developing and political risks were not great.

At Pride's Annual Meeting on May 27, 1997, Ray Tolson summarized major changes made by Pride as follows:

> I would like to highlight a series of significant transactions which have positioned us well to be a successful drilling contractor for many years to come.
>
> - In June 1994, we acquired our first offshore operation (Offshore Rigs), which was based in Houma, Louisiana. The offshore fleet we acquired there consisted of 22 platform workover and drilling rigs operating in the Gulf of Mexico, representing 45% of the offshore platform market in the gulf.
> - In April 1996 we acquired Quitral-Co., which was the largest drilling and workover contractor in Argentina, resulting in the combination of the largest and second largest contractors in the country.
> - In February of this year [1997] we sold our entire domestic land workover operation, which was Pride's lowest margin business segment, and we sold it at a very attractive price for Pride [$136 million].
> - In March 1997 we completed the acquisition of Forasol-Foramer, an international driller with complementary operations in Latin America [for $340 million]. Forasol's major assets are mostly offshore and include two deep water semi-submersible rigs.
> - And just two weeks ago [in early May of 1997], we acquired thirteen mat-supported jack-up rigs from Noble drilling corporation. This acquisition, in combination with our offshore platform fleet, makes Pride one of the largest rig operators in the Gulf of Mexico.
>
> As a result of these transactions, our business is now more than 85% contract drilling with approximately 50% of revenues being generated by offshore operations. We have achieved strong market positions with critical mass in most of our operations.

At the same shareholders' meeting, Paul Bragg, Pride's president and chief operating officer, reported: "We have built strong market share positions and critical mass which enables us to operate with certain efficiencies otherwise not available to competitors.... We are also pleased by the contract status of our fleet, which consists of a healthy mixture of long-term contracts providing stability to cash-flows, and spot contracts in areas which are experiencing day rate escalation—particularly in the Gulf of Mexico.... And a final point here, our geographic diversity from operating in nearly 20 countries makes us less susceptible to downturns in a particular region."

Summary

In my opinion, Ray Tolson has led his company through a remarkable series of changes—moving out of a declining oil well servicing operation in the United States into strong drilling and well servicing positions in other parts of the world. In these areas, exploration is utilizing technological advances that identify oil deposits in areas that have heretofore been unknown. Those who are equipped with drilling and servicing rigs to develop those prospects seem certain to prosper. I appreciate the opportunity Ray has given to me to participate, as a director, in the growth and development of his exciting business. Here is what he and his staff have achieved in four short years

FOUR EXPANSIVE YEARS REMAKE PRIDE

The four-year period 1993 through 1995 was a time of great change for Pride, as Ray Tolson reached vigorously and successfully for well servicing opportunities in offshore operations in the Gulf of Mexico, Venezuela, and Argentina. Before the Quitral acquisition, his moves produced more that $8 million in pre-tax earnings in 1995 and changed Pride into a much more vigorous company. In short, it seems to me that Pride has moved boldly and wisely into a leading position in a prospering industry with a very bright future. Table 23D-3 shows how it happened.

DYNAMIC CHANGES IN 1996 AND EARLY 1997

Pride continued making big moves in 1996 and 1997, as Ray Tolson and Executive Vice President Paul Bragg announced the acquisition of Forasol-Foramer, a French drilling company operating mostly offshore drilling rigs around the world, for $340 million in cash and shares of Pride common stock. To finance this acquisition, Pride sold all of its U.S. well servicing business to Dawson Production Services, Inc. I believe this to be a very wise decision because it takes the company out of a declining well servicing industry in the United States and positions it to operate in more profitable overseas areas where oil is being found more easily.

Moreover, in April 1997 the company announced it had signed a definitive agreement to purchase twelve offshore "jack-up" drilling rigs from Noble Drilling Corporation for $265 million in cash, which the company will finance with a combination of debt and equity. This acquisition, in combination with its offshore platform fleet, will make Pride one of the largest rig operators in the Gulf of Mexico, with 85 percent of its business coming from offshore drilling and well servicing.

Table 22D-3
Pride Financial Comparisons, 1993–1996
($000)

Operation	1993	1994	1995	1996
U.S. Land Operations				
Pre-Tax Earnings	6,548	6,269	12,435	13,546
Assets	78,607	64,740	77,243	94,559
Pre-Tax ROA (%)	8.3	9.7	16.1	14.4
U.S. Offshore Operations				
Pre-Tax Earnings	n.a.	4,360	9,876	10,648
Assets	"	46,693	50,978	61,251
Pre-Tax ROA (%)	"	9.34	19.4	17.4
International Operations				
Pre-Tax Earnings	2,674	6,949	20,618	45,013
Assets	31,374	93,760	129,384	386,252
Pre-Tax ROA (%)	8.52	7.41	15.9	11.7
Net Earnings, All Operations	5,940	6,214	15,359	22,728

SOURCE: All of the above figures were taken from the 1995 and 1996 Annual Reports. Notes: Return on Assets was calculated by dividing pre-tax earnings by the assets reported. Returns appear low because the assets were debt-financed, and the interest was deducted from earnings while debt financing was not deducted from the asset numbers. The probability seems high that earnings from our developing offshore and international operations will grow steadily, producing excellent returns on assets.

In short, it seems to me that Pride has moved boldly and wisely into a leading position in a prospering industry. I think it has a very bright future.

People

The story of Pride has been the story of Ray Tolson. His success speaks for his drive, intelligence, and his entrepreneurial flair, so I will say no more here about the man who built Pride. Along with him, these good men helped him build his company:

Paul Bragg has been a valuable man for Pride since he joined the company in early 1993 as chief financial officer, at the beginning of Pride's international expansion. His ability to arrange financing for the acquisitions made between 1993 and 1997 has been outstanding. He was elected president and chief operating officer in 1997.

Jim Allen, senior vice president and manager of all of Pride's operations, has been a valuable member of Pride's executive group. He lived in Argentina, Venezuela, and Peru for many years before Ray Tolson persuaded him to join Pride. He was actively involved in the acquisition of Western Atlas, an Argentine well servicing firm that had been presided over by Jorge Estrada, who is now a Pride director.

Johnny Blocker, who was raised in Argentina, is president of Pride's Argentine subsidiary. We are convinced that our organization in Argentina is the most experienced in the industry. For many years YPF, a government-owned firm, had exclusive rights over all of Argentina's oil exploration and development. The industry has now been privatized and has encouraged development of the nation's oil reserves.

Dexter Polk was Ray's right-hand man for many years. He retired in late 1995 as senior vice president. He was a leader in Pride's efforts to form alliances with major oil companies, seeking ways to work together to reduce costs more effectively than either Pride or its customers could achieve on their own. Dexter was also heavily involved in enhancing the capabilities of the well servicing fleet.

Bob Randall, vice president, general counsel, and secretary, has consistently served the company well in managing the legal challenges that characterize most acquisitions. He continues to do so after the divestiture of U.S. operations.

Four Top-Notch Vice Presidents

Four men who kept Pride Oil Service businesses running smoothly while Ray and the others planned and implemented strategy were very, very important to the company, as is reflected by their titles. They were: Thad Moore, vice president, area manager; Jim Byerlotzer, vice president, area manager; Joe Elam, vice president, marketing; and Mike Furrow, vice president, area manager. All transferred to comparable jobs when Pride divested its U.S. well servicing operations. They were all good men who served Pride well, and they will be missed by all of their friends at Pride

Chapter 22E

Lindsay Manufacturing Company: A Significant Acquisition 1970-1995

DeKalb acquired the Lindsay Manufacturing Company in January 1974 for 389,304 shares of Class A common stock, or $18,490,000 at an average monthly share price of $47.50 per share. It seemed a logical acquisition because Lindsay's hill-climbing center pivots were being well received by Nebraska farmers, and the company was extending its marketing efforts into adjacent states.

Lindsay's sales grew sporadically during the next ten years. Our 1984 Annual Report announced a record sales year, with earnings exceeding the company's goal for return on capital. Nevertheless, competition was intensifying as the numbers of manufacturers producing pivots increased substantially throughout the early 1980s, putting pressure on prices and earnings. These problems were partially offset by expansion of our selling efforts into the Middle East and South Africa. Still, margins became more and more depressed in the late 1980s, and we sold the company in 1989 to key employees who subsequently listed their shares on the Nasdaq exchange.

DeKalb's divestiture of Lindsay by public offering in 1989 was its last divestiture. It turned out to be a major mistake, as the industry had endured its most difficult period, with many competitors going out of business. Lindsay's fortunes turned around, guided by the same executives who were in place at the time of the divestiture. They had told us that a long period of oversupply of pivots was at an end, and that they believed their business had a bright future. Unfortunately, we thought their optimism was not justified. Figures 23E-1 and 23E-2 show how right they were.

The Lindsay Manufacturing Company has a fifty-year history of imaginative, entrepreneurial success. These are the highlights:

- The company was started by the Zimmerer family in 1955, offering irrigation equipment towable by tractor. Their breakthrough was the invention of a leak-proof quick-connecting coupler for easy coupling before towing.
- In 1968 the company developed the first electric self-propelled center pivot irrigation system, called the "Zimmatic."
- In the 1970s, Lindsay developed a center pivot machine

that would climb hills. This was very well received by farmers in hilly eastern Nebraska, and proved to be the lowest-cost irrigation and fertilization system on both flat and rolling land.

- In 1974, Lindsay merged with DeKalb and rapidly extended its marketing efforts beyond the Great Plains into the seventeen western states, the central corn belt, and the southeastern states, and into international markets, notably into Saudi Arabia, Argentina, Brazil, Mexico, and Spain. By 1991, Lindsay had systems operating in seventy-three countries irrigating over 10 million acres and was the exporter of 62 percent of all center-pivot and lateral-move machines exported from the United States, according to the U.S. Department of Commerce.
- During the 1980s and 1990s, Lindsay continuously expanded its manufacturing facilities and made considerable investments in factory automation.

Figure 22E-1
Lindsay's Sales and Net Earnings 1986 to 1995
($ in Millions)

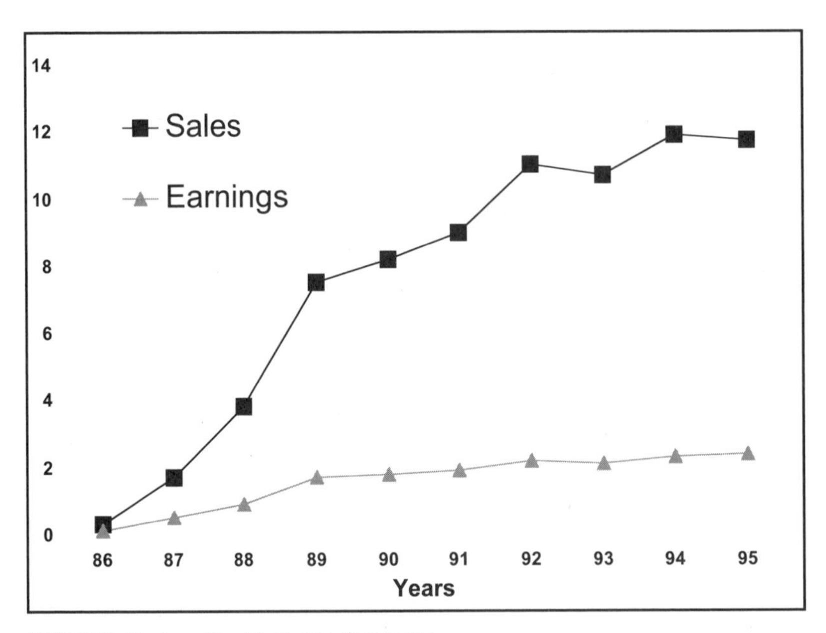

SOURCE: Lindsay Manufacturing Company

Lindsay's Product Line

Lindsay's CEO, Gary Parker, did a good job of describing his product line in this excerpt from Lindsay's 1995 Annual Report:

> We remain well positioned to continue to take advantage of what is truly a growing market, both literally and figuratively. Center pivot and lateral move irrigation equipment aids in growing crops more efficiently and can result in higher crop yields. We estimate that the market for center pivot and lateral irrigation is growing at a five-year average rate of 6 percent to 8 percent annually, largely due to the long-term demand drivers of farmers' needs to conserve water, energy, and labor and, at the same time, to stabilize or increase crop yields. There are approximately 400 million cultivated acres in the U.S., of which only 15 percent, or approximately 60 million acres, are irrigated by center pivot or lateral move irrigation systems.
>
> Lindsay's center pivot and lateral move irrigation equipment provides a more uniform distribution and timely application of water to crops, reducing water usage by as much as 40 to 60 percent compared to surface irrigation. This is an increasingly important factor, as the world moves to ensure that we carefully protect and utilize one of our most precious natural resources—water. In fact, the World Bank in a report this year warned that population growth and increasing urbanization could cause water shortages serious enough to threaten agriculture in some 80 countries.
>
> Near-term demand drivers such as the general farm economy, prevailing interest rates, and agricultural commodity prices play a variable role each year, dictating increases or decreases in North American and worldwide demand for irrigation equipment. In addition, with approximately half of the 110,000 center pivot systems in operation in North America more than 10 years old, we expect the replacement of old systems to be a contributing factor in sales growth. Today, one-fourth of our system sales are to farmers who are replacing an old or outdated center pivot with a new Zimmatic. Our customers are primarily those operating large farms, where the need to conserve water and at the same time improve efficiency and crop yields is imperative to long-term success and survival.

An Interview with Gary Parker

I interviewed Gary Parker in July 1996. In the eight years since DeKalb spun off Lindsay, he has done a terrific job of managing his company, leading it many times to investment community ratings as one of America's 100 best-managed companies. I congratulated him and asked him how he had achieved such outstanding success.

He quickly replied that he attributed the company's success to two major achievements:

- first, encouraging and supporting employee empowerment by asking hourly employees how they believed the company could enhance product quality at lower cost; and
- second, but equally important, never forgetting that his primary goal must be enhancement of shareholder value.

Gary reminded me that Lindsay's disappointing performance in the mid-1980s was due to an oversupply of center-pivot machines that stemmed mostly from the government Conservation Reserve Program to take marginal land out of production. Pivot manufacturers had built up inventories in the belief that demand would continue to grow, but that did not happen, and it took nearly five years for supply and demand to get back into balance. During that period, the number of pivot manufacturers in the United States declined from a peak of thirty-five to eight. Gary had argued to Bruce Bickner, one of our best men, that pivot supply and demand were coming back into balance, but it was hard for us to believe him, so we proceeded with plans to list the company publicly.

Gary told me we made our move at precisely the moment that supply and demand came back into balance. His record proves him to have been right.

SOURCE: Lindsay Manufacturing Company

Art Zimmerer, Lindsay CEO in 1974 - A key man who died in an automobile accident on August 13, 1978

Hourly Workers' Suggestions: A Key to Success

However, it took a lot more than a return to market equilibrium to achieve success. Gary emphasizes the importance of the role that his workers play in lowering costs at the same time that they improve quality. He insists that success at Lindsay has had a lot to do with productivity improvements resulting from the recommendations of his on-the-line hourly employees. "I happen to believe that an hourly person who's worked in a position for five or ten years has a wealth of knowledge, and if you provide the program and environment where he can contribute to improvements, he and others like him can make a difference in all operating areas," Gary says.

He listens to his hourly people and offers them financial incentives as part of his gain-sharing programs. Goals are set for safety, productivity, quality, and profit. When those goals are achieved, workers receive quarterly gain-sharing bonuses ranging from 5 percent to 7.5 percent of their hourly compensation. Gary points out that a significant proportion of the automation he has installed has been suggested by his workers, and he emphasizes that automation combined with standardization, quality at the source, and just-in-time manufacturing have all contributed to Lindsay's success.

Diversified Manufacturing Succeeds

Still, Gary had a big plant with a lot of unused capacity when he took charge in 1988. He learned that John Deere, Caterpillar, and New Holland were interested in outsourcing some of their manufacturing operations, so he sold them on Lindsay's manufacturing abilities. They started slowly but increased their orders as the quality of Lindsay products and its on-time deliveries proved to be excellent. The result of that experience has been a steady increase in orders to Lindsay that added up to over 20 percent of Lindsay's sales in 1995.

Gary doesn't forget his stockholders, either. He closed his 1995 Annual Report with this paragraph in his letter to shareholders:

> Finally, Lindsay remains committed to increasing shareholder value. We expect to continue to repurchase stock out of cash flow during 1996. We repurchased 369,250 shares in fiscal 1995, and we are authorized to repurchase up to 838,000 additional shares. Equally importantly, we will continue to seek a good fitting acquisition. We have been working diligently with a major regional investment firm, which is assisting us in finding a strategic acquisition consistent with our long-term growth objectives. While we have reviewed a number of potential acquisitions, none to date have fit our criteria of providing a proprietary product that utilizes Lindsay's

manufacturing expertise and adds value to our shareholders.

Those are demanding criteria, but given Lindsay's success since DeKalb spun them off in 1988, it seems likely that Gary's drive and the dollars flowing into his company will combine to find the acquisition he is seeking.

Chapter 22F

DeKalb Swine Breeders: A Significant Acquisition 1970-1995

In the summer of 1971, Jack Nelson and I went to west Texas to visit with Euel Liner and Roy Poage, president and executive vice president of Lubbock Swine Breeders, Inc. In ten remarkable years, Roy Poage and his father-in-law, Euel Liner, had developed one of the country's largest swine breeding operations. They had 900 sows housed in modern buildings that were specific pathogen free (SPF), because they had taken the piglets surgically from their mothers' wombs. They were then grown in total isolation from other pigs and cared for by workers who showered and dressed in clean clothing before entering the building where the pigs were housed. In that way they were assured of fast growth of SPF progeny that could be sold to pork producers as healthy animals that would perform well. Roy and Euel had a good business going but were short of the cash needed to expand it and fully exploit the potential of SPF breeding stock.

SOURCE: Roy Poage

Roy Poage of Lubbock Swine Breeders

We told Roy that DeKalb wanted to become a major breeder of quality pigs because we believed these things:

- That swine in our country could be significantly improved by competent geneticists working with minimally diseased pigs in first-class facilities.
- That American farmers would be willing to buy high-quality breeding stock, especially if its breeding took full advantage of the hybrid vigor that exists between breeds.
- That we (DeKalb), having successfully hybridized corn, sorghum, and chickens, had the financial strength necessary to fund the facilities, breeding stock, and personnel to make it a world leader in swine breeding.
- That Roy had the ability to take DeKalb to world leader ship in swine breeding. We wanted him to move to DeKalb, Illinois, to establish an SPF breeding facility—the first step toward achievement of our goals.

Roy was pleased that we wanted to create the world's best swine breeding and marketing organization. He was surprised, however, because he had been approached by other large companies who wanted to buy his swine breeding operation to use as a means of increasing their feed sales. He feared that they did not really comprehend the size of the investment that would be required to breed better pigs, and that sooner or later breeding quality pigs would play second fiddle to selling feed. He wondered the same about DeKalb.

DEKALB—ROY AND EUEL'S KIND OF PEOPLE

We invited Roy and Euel to visit us in DeKalb, where we could sit down together and plan the breeding program we would need to achieve our goals. Roy wanted to see our small swine research operation, but he emphasized that he was absolutely never going to move out of west Texas.

On arrival at O'Hare field in Chicago, they were picked up by a DeKalb driver named Wes Tolf. In the car on the way to DeKalb, Roy asked Wes what his job with the company was, and Wes replied that all he did was drive people back and forth between DeKalb and the airport. Upon hearing that, Roy whispered to Euel that if there was ever anybody who had heard everything, both good and bad, about DeKalb, it would be Wes, so he asked Wes how he felt about DeKalb. Wes replied that the biggest mistake he had made in his whole life was to farm for twenty years before taking the job with DeKalb, a job he had held for thirteen years. He told Roy that DeKalb's management was great and that they really looked after their employees.

When we got down to serious discussions, and we pointed out that there were more hogs in one county in Illinois than in the entire state of Texas, Roy lost quite a bit of his conviction that he wanted to live his whole life that far away from the center of U.S. hog production. When he saw our breeding facilities and met our key people, he began negotiations, and we assured him that we were ready to fully fund hog breeding operations. He liked what he heard and soon brought his wife to check out our community.

On January 7, 1972, DeKalb acquired Lubbock Swine Breeders, and Roy decided that he and his family should move to DeKalb. DeKalb Swine Breeders, Inc. emerged from that decision, and they developed a new logo.

SOURCE: DeKalb Swine Breeders, Inc.

DeKalb Swine Breeders logo

Getting Started

Roy jumped right in to his job, acquiring the best breeding stock he could find, taking baby pigs by cesarean section and raising them in total isolation in order to ensure that they were free of disease.

Just as important as developing minimal-disease breeding stock was Roy's need to have the facilities to house the progeny of the breeding stock he was buying. He would have to cull out the weaklings, but he also would need to multiply and house the lines he wanted to keep. He studied several locations and chose southwestern Kansas because it produced a big surplus of feed grains each year and had the dry weather necessary for waste disposal, much of which could be done by mixing solid animal waste with water and applying it to the soil as fertilizer through center pivots.In October 1973 ground was broken outside of Plains, Kansas, on the first of four farms that would constitute one of the largest swine breeding multiplication facilities in the world. As many as thirty farrowings per week (20,000 piglets per year) were planned for each farm. By 1994, the number of foundation multiplication farms had grown to thirteen, and they were located in both southwestern Kansas and the Oklahoma panhandle.

Genetic Evaluation Stations

The next step in preparation for marketing was taken in 1974 with the construction of a Genetic Evaluation Station (GES) in Mt. Olive, North Carolina. Since then, many more GES facilities have been built. All are designed to enable customers to personally select and evaluate breeding stock, both visually and from the records we kept. This customer benefit remains unmatched.

Training

As DeKalb's swine breeding program grew, Roy implemented comprehensive production and management training programs for employees, some of whom later left to produce pigs on their own farms; many are still good customers today. Employees learned production and management procedures that were detailed in manuals to ensure that our animals were raised under consistent conditions that maximized their genetic potential.

Roy worked hard to attract and select people with the potential to assist us in the production of the finest pigs in the world. Because the U.S. swine industry has been restructured by the development of large indoor swine production operations, there has been a tremendous need for highly trained swine production managers. DeKalb Swine Breeders, Inc., has responded to that need by developing an employee-customer training program that is the best in the swine industry. It is so good, in fact, that in 1995 it received the highest award given by the Association of State Councils on Vocational Education, a very distinguished achievement. DeKalb was selected over IBM, Caterpillar, and Lockheed for this award.

Here are some of the things DeKalb does to provide its customers with a high-quality product:

Breeding

DeKalb started its breeding herd with the Durocs and Hampshire breeds on the male side and Landrace and Yorkshire on the female side of our pedigrees. In 1992, Pietrain pigs were added on the male side and English and European Large Whites and English and European Landrace on the female side. All of these breeds have been selected for the quality of their meat for many, many years. In addition, Chinese breeds known for litter size, fertility, and disease resistance have been imported and successfully selected for less fatty tissue.

- DeKalb has used the Best Linear Unbiased Prediction (BLUP) in selecting pure line animals.

- Two meat scientists have been added to the DeKalb research staff to evaluate the meat quality of its selected lines and its hybrids, always selecting for leanness.
- Real-time ultrasound technology is used to measure genetic potential and select for minimum backfat.
- A biotechnology program uses molecular approaches in our genetic improvement program, through DNA marker assisted selection.
- Artificial insemination is used at all DeKalb locations to maximize use of high-quality semen from our best boars, thereby accelerating the genetic improvement of the stock it offers customers.
- Roy completed an agreement in 1992 with JSR, a leading British breeding stock company to produce and market their lines in the western hemisphere.

Organization

Here is the organization DeKalb Swine Breeders, Inc., is staking its future on:

- Roy Poage, president, still young after thirty-five years in the swine business.
- Gary Kahle, executive vice president of marketing and operations.
- Doug Jewell, vice president of production.
- Steve Roush, vice president for administration and finance.
- David Fox, Ph.D., vice president of research and development.
- Sam Buttram, Ph.D., quantitative geneticist, implemented BLUP and supervises pure line improvement.
- Albert Paszek, Ph.D., molecular and quantitative geneticist. He links quantitative and molecular genetics via linkage analysis.
- Brad Didion, Ph.D., manager of biotechnology.
- Roger Johnson, Ph.D., meat scientist.
- Jerry Cannon, Ph.D., meat scientist.

Sex—A Vital Factor in Breeding

As I started pulling my notes together and turning off the tape machine I used for my interview with Roy Poage, he commented that DeKalb is getting much better use of elite semen by diluting it, and by using a single ejaculation on more females than in the past.

I found that interesting, but even more interesting was a story Roy told about his staff's efforts to ensure that the boars selected and offered to customers have the ability to breed. His men had noticed as they collected semen that there was a lot of variation in length, girth, and hardness of the penis. This seemed very important, because we sell a lot of boars, and they must perform well when used to breed customer's sows.

Our staff realized that a soft penis would almost surely make a boar less effective, but they were uncertain about the importance of length and hardness, so they decided to collect and analyze data on these characteristics. They also knew that a boar's penis had to be very long—ten to fifteen inches—because the female's cervix is that deep in her body, and the cervix gripping the penis causes ejaculation.

Shortly after the data had been recorded, Doug Jewell's secretary, who had entered much of the data into the computer, asked Doug, "Why do you take data on length and girth of the penis? I have always understood that size didn't make any difference." How would you have answered that question?

DeKalb's swine research and development expenses were $5.8 million, $6.4 million, and $5.7 million for fiscal years 1995, 1994, and 1993, respectively, as reported in the 1995 10K.

The cyclicality of DeKalb's swine earnings has been partly the consequence of normal swings in numbers of pigs raised by farmers. They seek to maximize profits by expanding their herds when prices are high, only to create lower prices when their expanded herds are ready for sale to meat packers. This practice will likely be less prevalent in the future because large commercial producers will not go in and out of the swine production business as smaller operations have tended to do. An unusual combination of high market hog prices and low feed costs created exceptional "by-product" sales in 1987.

The term "by-product" refers to the fact that for every animal of breeding quality, there is a corresponding "sister or brother" that usually must be sold for slaughter. For example, DeKalb's pigs are selected for their superior performance as parents. The males we sell are characteristically lean, muscular, and fast growing and produce large quantities of semen. The female lines are selected for their mothering qualities, such as large litters and number of teats to feed their infant progeny. The pigs we do not offer for breeding purpose are sold to meat packers and are referred to as "by-products." By-product sales usually constitute about 40 percent of DeKalb's swine sales income.

DeKalb is firmly committed to its swine breeding programs, which grow in quality and quantity every year. At the end of 1995, DeKalb Swine owned nineteen foundation farms and ten genetic evaluation stations. Fourteen of the largest farms are located in the southwest corner of Kansas and the Oklahoma panhandle. These are areas with grain surpluses, so feed costs at the largest facilities are low relative to those in the rest of the country.

DeKalb's principal competitor is a British firm called PIC, which is currently estimated by Roy Poage to be 50 to 75 percent larger than

DeKalb in the United States, but DeKalb is driving to close that competitive gap with better products and services.

Table 23F-1
Swine and Poultry Pre-Tax Earnings, 1984–1995
($000)

Year	Swine Earnings	Poultry Earnings	Total
1984	6,200	1,100	6,300
1985	4,400	2,200	6,600
1986	3,200	3,400	6,600
1987	9,500	2,500	12,000
1988	6,200	500	6,700
1989	(300)	700	400
1990	4,500	4,200	8,700
1991	9,300	2,500	11,800
1992	4,600	900	5,500
1993	3,000	1,000	4,000
1994	5,700	(300)	5,400
1995	(900)	sold	(900)

SOURCES: 1984–87 from 1987 10K, 1988–90 from 1990 10K, and the rest are from the 1991–95 10Ks, respectively.

Chapter 23

International Seed: Patience Pays Off

DEKALB AND RAGT IN FRANCE, 1970–1992

Developing a Hybrid Seed Business in France

The rise and fall of two tremendously dominant competitive hybrids had overlapping life spans of fifteen years each, while RAGT slowly but surely built its business. Unfortunately for RAGT and DeKalb, the four-way hybrids they introduced in 1966, 1968, and 1970 were overwhelmed in the 1970s by a Limagrain three-way-cross hybrid called LG11. This was the hybrid behind the peak of 34 percent of the French market Limagrain achieved in 1978.

In my opinion, Limagrain deserves applause from the many corn breeders who, only fifteen years earlier, had believed that corn would never be a major crop in France. Thanks to LG11, heavy French government subsidies that favored corn expansion throughout the country, heavy fertilizer applications, and thick planting by smart farmers, France became a world-class corn producing country in the 1970s.

Dea—The Next Big Winner

LG11's ten years of market dominance was followed by the introduction and rapid acceptance of an outstanding single-cross hybrid by Pioneer. It was called Dea and became the major force supporting Pioneer's peak 50 percent market share in 1986, at a volume in excess of 1.5 million units of 50,000 kernels per unit. The impact of Dea on Pioneer's worldwide profits must have been profound indeed—Dea's peak sales volume in France must have been close to one-third of Pioneer's total sales in the much larger U.S. market in the mid-1980s.

Will There Be Another Big Winner?

I think it doubtful that the dominant market shares attained by Limagrain and Pioneer in 1978 and 1986, respectively, will ever be repeated. In each case the "peak" was supported primarily by a single hybrid; a phenomenon that is unlikely to recur because there are so many effective competitors in France's marketplace today. However, because the results of public tests are respected in France and contributed significantly to the quick popularity of both LG11 and Dea, an outstanding new hybrid will probably be accepted faster in France than in any other country in the world.

It could be RAGT's turn next! DK250 was introduced in 1985 and was followed by DK300 in 1988 and DK262 in 1992. These have steadily gained market share at the expense of both Limagrain and Pioneer.

Figure 23-1
28 Years of RAGT Growth on the French Seedcorn Market

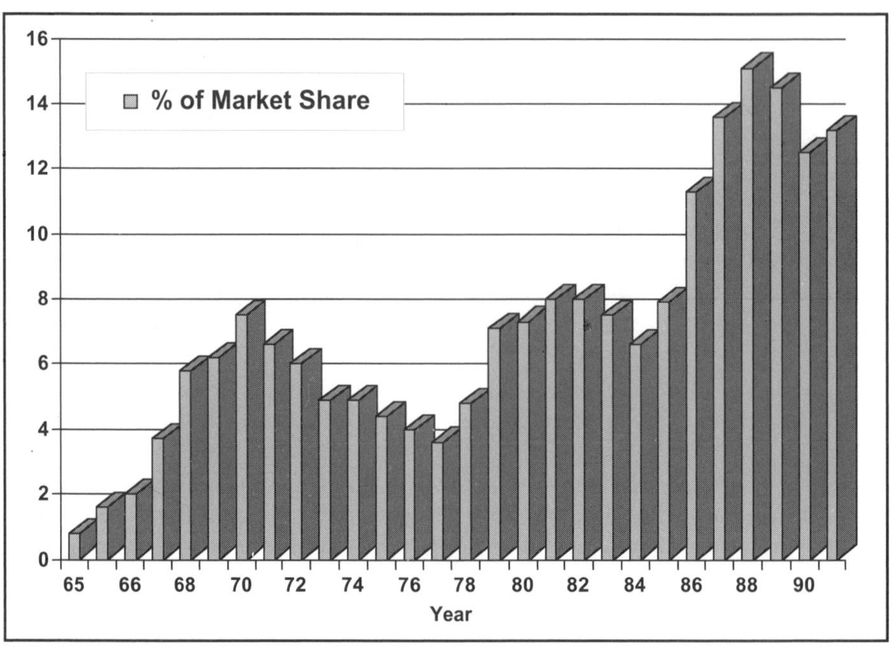

SOURCE: RAGT

Financial Returns to DeKalb from RAGT

DeKalb's financial arrangement with RAGT is a simple one. The two companies are partners in SOCKALB, in which they share costs of research, and RAGT produces and sells the products of SOCKALB's research, paying DeKalb a percentage of the wholesale price of each product.

Neither DeKalb nor RAGT has agreed to give me the RAGT financial data, but as I remember, the royalties paid to DeKalb were based on a flat percentage of revenues before 1983. At that time, the royalty calculation changed to a "semi-gross margin" system that took into consideration revenues, cost of sales, and discards. The royalty payments estimated in Table 23-2 are based on data from 1993, which indicated that DeKalb's portion of SOCKALB research costs was approximately $2 million and that it received nearly $5 million in royalty payments, for a net gain after DeKalb's share of research costs for the year of almost $3 million, or about $2.5 per 50,000 kernel units (bags) of seed sold that year. I have used that per-bag royalty figure to estimate the royalties paid to DeKalb over the years.

Table 23-2
RAGT's Growth in Northwestern Europe, 1967–1979
(Sales in U.S.$ after sharing research costs)
(These are estimates as stated above)

Year	Seed (metric tons)	Total (000 units)	DeKalb (000 units)	Royalty Due DeKalb from Research ($)[a]
1967	2,436	174	34	85,000
1968	2,478	177	47	117,500
1969	3,598	257	107	262,000
1970	5,404	386	210	525,000
1971	5,530	395	268	670,000
1972	8,386	599	434	1,085,000
1973	9,674	691	482	1,205,000
1974	9,926	709	510	1,275,000
1975	10,304	736	618	1,545,000
1976	8,372	598	528	1,320,000
1977	10,150	725	671	1,677,000
1978	7,840	560	541	1,352,500
1979	7,630	545	515	1,287,500
1980	7,700	550	532	1,330,000
1981	9,548	682	671	1,675,500
1982	11,060	790	790	1,975,500
1983	10,570	755	755	1,887,500
1984	10,688	762	762	1,905,000
1985	9,240	660	660	1,650,000
1986	8,132	581	581	1,452,000
1987	9,884	706	706	1,765,000
1988	12,964	926	926	2,315,000
1989	15,204	1,086	1,086	1,629,000
1990	16,100	1,150	1,150	2,875,000
1991	17,220	1,230	1,230	3,075,000
1992	15,400	1,100	1,100	2,750,000
1993	16,436	1,174	1,174	2,935,000

SOURCE: RAGT plus estimates of royalty payments

a. Royalty amounts are estimates, as indicated in the text. They are based on units of DeKalb seed sold (column 4) x $2.5. Most sales were in Germany and France.

Table 23-3
Corn Acreage in
RAGT Franchised Countries, 1993

Country	Acreage
France	7,500,000
Germany	3,800,000
Austria	700,000
Netherlands	450,000

SOURCE: RAGT marketing manager.

Hybrid Sunflowers

A hybrid sunflower breeding program began at RAGT in 1985, guided by Dr. Henry Shands of DeKalb and Dr. Anibal Fernandez of DeKalb Argentina, under the direction of Dr. Daniel Segonds, RAGT research manager. Its primary goal, the development of earlier-maturing sunflower hybrids, was first achieved in 1993, when an RAGT hybrid sunflower called DK3790, which was lodging-resistant and had good grain yield as well as excellent oil content, was registered in France. It drove RAGT from tenth position in the French sunflower market in 1993 to second position in 1995 and into first position soon thereafter. Figure 23-4 presents the history of RAGT in the hybrid sunflower business.

Figure 23-4
French Sunflower Hectares Planted

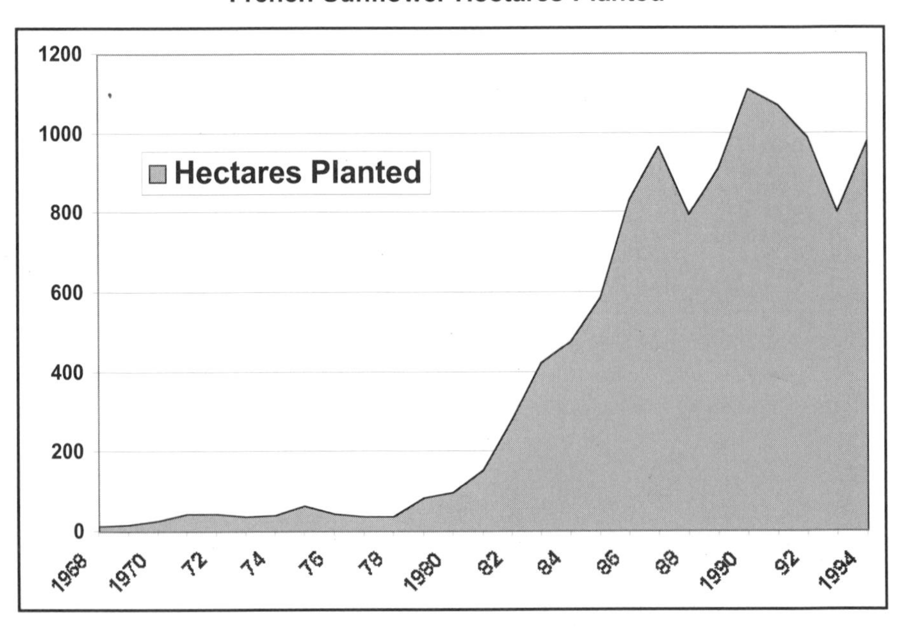

SOURCE: Charts and comments provided by RAGT

DEKALB AND DEKALB ITALIANA, 1970–1980

Dr. David Curtis assumed responsibility for DeKalb's international seed operations in 1972, succeeding Roger Rasmusen, who had been named DeKalb's chief financial officer. David had been recommended to us by three of the most distinguished plant breeders in the world, Drs. Norman Borlaug, Glen Burton, and George Sprague. David's first assignment with DeKalb was in Australia. He was transferred to the United States in 1970 to assume responsibility for our eastern hemisphere operations, and for overall international seed operations in 1972. David held a Ph.D. in plant breeding and had demonstrated his business ability while in Australia. Even more important were his strong sense of loyalty to DeKalb, his intelligence, and his extraordinary personal integrity, since he would be making important decisions for the company in many distant parts of the world. David was elected vice president for international operations in 1978.

SOURCE: DeKalb Genetics

Dr. David Curtis

David Curtis

David was a key contributor to the success of DeKalb Italiana. He was considered at various other times for other key DeKalb jobs as well, and I regret now that I did not press harder for his advancement, which I proposed several times.

The decade 1971 through 1980 was a very successful one for DeKalb Italiana. Sergio Marchetto expanded the company's sales network to cover all of Italy and hired agronomists to promote DeKalb's products and to advise farmers on good farming practices. In 1977, sales reached a peak of 7,989 thousand tons of DeKalb, which was 38 percent of the market.

New Hybrids Reflect Interest in Later Maturities

New hybrids were regularly added to DeKalb Italiana's product line. XL342, which was introduced in 1971, grew steadily in popularity and became our best seller in 1978. XL75, XL85, and XL72A were other significant additions to our product line in the mid-1970s. These were all later in maturity than the hybrids we had been selling in Italy. They reflected farmer recognition that late-maturing hybrids had more yield potential and could be grown safely in much of the Po valley if gas-fired drying equipment were used to dry the grain after harvest. During the early 1970s, natural gas was cheap, so a trend toward planting later-maturing hybrids was developing. Its growth slowed sharply in the mid-1970s, however, when world prices of hydrocarbon fuel soared, causing farmers to prefer earlier-maturing hybrids (DeKalb's strongest product line) in order to reduce drying costs. However, Pioneer's organization and product line were getting stronger, casting an ominous shadow over our future in Italy.

Responding to Fears of Southern Corn Leaf Blight

In early 1971, after southern corn leaf blight (SCLB) had hit the U.S. corn belt in the fall of 1970, killing hybrids that were made utilizing cytoplasmic male sterility, DeKalb scrambled to convert all of its parent lines to SCLB-resistant ("normal") cytoplasm, which would make its entire seedcorn product line resistant by 1972. To achieve this, we made extensive use of winter line multiplication. But we feared that our massive winter production effort might fall short of its goals, simply because we were contracting with so many southern hemisphere farmer-growers who had never before multiplied inbred lines.

Antonio Marchetto, whose hybrids had not been affected by SCLB in Italy, was understandably concerned that, sooner or later, the disease would reach his country. When he phoned me about his concerns in 1971, I told him that, although no one could be certain what would happen, I thought it was possible for it to be carried into Italy on grain corn imported from the United States. I promised him that we would give DeKalb Italiana the same priority in allocating our disease-resistant parent seed supply that we gave to our U.S. seed production plants. He accepted my assurance gratefully. Fortunately, our fears of winter production crop failures were not realized, and our winter production was successful. We had enough SCLB-resistant parent seed to fill both U.S. and Italian needs.

All in all, the 1971–1980 decade was one of steady growth and success for DeKalb Italiana (see Table 23-5). However, hard times were ahead in the 1980s.

Table 23-5
DeKalb Italiana Sales and Share of Profits, 1971–1980

Year	Sales (000 metric tons)[a]	DeKalb Income (U.S.$)[b]
1971	5,854	643,940
1972	5,044	554,840
1973	6,352	698,720
1974	6,482	713,020
1975	6,176	679,360
1976	6,684	735,240
1977	7,898[c]	868,780
1978	6,584	724,240
1979	6,401	704,110
1980	6,399	703,915

SOURCE: DeKalb Italiana
a. One metric ton = forty-four 50-lb. bags.
b. DI records of DeKalb's 50 percent of earnings were not available, so I have estimated that DeKalb's income per 50 lb. unit of seed sold in Italy would approximate the $2.5 U.S.$/unit that was the same sum per unit that I calculated we realized in France in 1993. This sum, therefore, is based on only one year's experience in an adjacent European country. Accordingly, the DeKalb profit figures shown are only estimates I believe to be reasonable.
c. DeKalb Italiana's best year, in which we estimated that we held a 38 percent market share.

DEKALB ARGENTINA, 1971-1992

Argentine farmers shifted from grazing back to farming in the 1970s, and DeKalb's steady genetic improvements in seeds helped them significantly. Here are the important factors behind their success and our growth:

- Our grain sorghum and sudax hybrids developed in the U.S. fit well in Argentina, keeping us well ahead of competitors. However, as corn harvesting equipment gradually became available, many farmers in the moist eastern portion of the pampas found corn to be both higher yielding and higher priced than grain sorghum, which outperformed corn in dryer western areas.
- Although DeKalb's development of F880 gave our hybrid seedcorn business a fast start during the late 1960s, its development only a few years after our coming to Argentina was possible only because it was a unique hybrid between flint inbred lines developed by Argentine government breeders. Their internecine rivalries caused

breeders at some experiment stations to disregard the possibility that inbred lines from other stations might make good hybrids when crossed with their own. That opportunity was not overlooked by Sherret Chase of DeKalb, who crossed and tested hybrids between inbreds from different stations and produced F880, the best flint hybrid in Argentina from 1965 through 1972.

- The success of DeKalb seedcorn hybrids introduced in the mid-1970s stemmed from our strengthening the heterosis (hybrid vigor) in our hybrids. We reinforced the yield potential of flint seed parents by crossing into them the dent germ plasm that has been the basis for our success in the United States.
- Furthermore, hybrid sunflower breeding became a major project in Argentina with the hiring of Dr. Anibal Fernandez.

SOURCE: DeKalb Argentina

Ramon Agrasar in 1975, Founder and First President of DeKalb Argentina

Hybrid seedcorn sales fell off from 12,148 metric tons in 1970 to only 3,783 in the 1974 as research progress at the INTA public experiment stations overtook our opportunistic F880, but our sales recovered to 10,759 metric tons in 1979, as our flint-dent corn breeding products came into their own and hectares of land planted to corn increased. DK4F32, an outstanding four-way flint hybrid with a lot of the dent Reid-Lancaster heterotic "kick" in its pedigree was largely responsible for our late-1970s sales resurgence. Dr. Raoul Mella, a very competent corn breeder, was hired to strengthen our corn research staff.

Recognizing the excellent growth potential in Argentina for sunflowers (which out-yield soybeans in the dry western pampas), Fabio Nider added Dr. Anibal Fernandez, an outstanding sunflower breeder to our staff in the late 1970s. Hybrids they developed would contribute significantly to our sales in the late 1980s and early 1990s.

Our sorghum sales remained remarkably steady, between 4,000 and 4,900 metric tons per year, in spite of the fact that corn was displacing grain sorghum in the eastern half of the pampas, and Sudax sales grew steadily, reaching a peak of 5,057 metric tons in 1977 before falling off to 3,452 metric tons in 1979, as cattle grazing retreated from the prime land in the east.

Corn and Sorghum Sales in the '70s

Unfortunately, profits still swung widely as inflation continued. However, even this problem appeared to be lessening in the late 70's. My confidence in the long-term success of DeKalb's business in this beautiful, fast-developing country is based on my belief in the competence of our research team, which is reflected in the following April 1995 interview I recorded with Fabio Nider, our Argentine seed research director. Fabio and I had been talking about the high drought resistance of one of his corn inbred lines, a semi-flint. He went on to tell me about it. *(A note to readers: The following interview contains technical material; those who are not interested in the specifics of plant breeding may want to skip over it to the next section.)*

SOURCE:T.H. Roberts, Jr.

Fabio Nider (on left) in an Argentine Sorghum Field

An Interview with Fabio Nider, a Great Plant Breeder

Tom: DeKalb 4F37 has been by far the most drought resistant hybrid seedcorn of all the ones tested in Rio Cuarto. Is this correct, Fabio?

Fabio: Yes, and there is another story. It is the story of what happened in the western part of our country in the Rio Cuarto area when we decided to set up a segregating nursery to select for resistance to a virus that was a devastating factor in the area. It was commonly known as the Rio Cuarto virus, which in the scientific literature is known as the maize dwarf virus. At that time, about fifteen years ago, our market share in the area was almost zero.

Tom: What were they planting?

Fabio: They were planting mostly Morgan 400 hybrid seedcorn because it performed somewhat better than most competitors' commercial hybrids but was not perfectly resistant to the virus.

Tom: Was it a pure flint?

Fabio: Yes, and it had a much higher degree of tolerance to the virus than any other commercial hybrid. So at that time our market share was very low. I would say less than 1 percent. We began a program to develop more resistance, following the suggestion of Dr. Dave Smith at DeKalb. He suggested we use the same set of segregating lines but plant on three different dates to see which planting date would be most affected by the virus. In the future we could plant on that date in order to have the highest degree of natural infection.

This virus is very peculiar because it is transmitted by a very tiny leaf hopper no more than two millimeters long. The virus grows in the guts of this leaf hopper, which is the only insect that is capable of transmitting the virus. We found that the best planting date for the occurrence of the highest natural infection was the first fortnight of November, so that is when we planted most of our segregating nurseries.

And fortunately we were able to find an area where the transmission of the virus by the leaf hopper was almost uniform throughout the nursery. Sometimes that is very difficult because the insects normally attack the plants on the edges of fields, and even within a field just in spots instead of covering the whole area. We were fortunate because the insect attacked our plants with almost the same intensity all over the nursery. How did we find out that that was true? Every few rows all across the nursery we planted what we called a susceptible check, and this susceptible check was just wiped out, melted down by the virus throughout the nursery. So, thanks to these breeding nurseries, we were able to select several inbred lines that showed a high degree of tolerance to the virus. Then, using those inbred lines as seed parents, we put together today the famous seedcorn hybrid called 4F37. That was our first hybrid developed for that area [the major corn producing area of Argentina] that had a high degree of tolerance to the virus.

Tom: And was DeKalb 4F37 [our most virus-resistant hybrid] a flint-dent hybrid?

Fabio: Yes, because most of the inbred lines that are in the pedigree of this hybrid were derived by crossing a flint and a dent and then selecting for the best-per forming inbred lines—those with a better stalk quality and more stability, for example. But I think the moral of the story is that after we introduced that hybrid in 1987, by 1994 our market share in that area was 70 percent. Fifteen years ago it was zero percent.

Tom: I didn't start making this recording until after you had said quite a few pretty important things about corn breeding, flint-dents, and so forth. Would you mind repeating some of your earlier comments?

Fabio: One of the routine trials that we run every year is called the genetic gain test. Its purpose is to monitor improvements over the long term and also whether we are making progress over a relatively short span of time—every three or five years. If we find out that we have reached a ceiling, we take steps to change the situation for the better. Last year in these trials we included all the hybrids that the company has released since 1965.

Tom: The Argentine company?

Fabio: Yes, DeKalb Argentina. DeKalb Argentina has released hybrids for sale in Argentina over the past thirty years, beginning with F880, which was our first four-way flint cross released in 1965.

Tom: F880 was a pure flint that Sherret Chase put together, wasn't it?

Fabio: Yes, using inbred lines developed by the Pergamino and Parana INTA stations. So what we found from our genetic gain trials was that over thirty years the yield of our commercial hybrids has increased by 98 percent. And concurrently, the stalk quality of our commercial hybrids has also increased dramatically. The first hybrid, F880, had an average total plant damage of 40 percent, and our newest release, DK752, had in the same trials over eight locations an average total damage of only 8 percent.

Tom: To what would you attribute your success at doubling yields in thirty years?

Fabio: I think there are several reasons. One is that in the beginning we set clear goals. Second, we took calculated risks. The standard approach is just to improve what you have little by little, and we chose to follow that, too. However, simultaneously we devoted a substantial part of our program to looking for something new, something unusual.

And what was unusual for us? Well, we considered what was available to us as genetic breeding material and found that the flints from Argentina did have unique traits regarding tolerance to drought, tolerance to heat, and stability of performance in our environment. But we also found that they had quite important weaknesses in both their yield and standability. Their yield was limited and their stalk quality very poor, so we looked around to see where we could get sources of better stalk quality and higher yield potential. We found that the germ plasm that had both yield potential and stalk quality was the germ plasm from the U.S. corn belt.

By introducing that germ plasm into our flint germ plasm we were able to increase dramatically the performance of the flint hybrids. In other words, we were able to put together the best of the two worlds: the drought tolerance and good adaptation to our environment of the flints together with the yield potential and the stalk quality of the best U.S. dent germ plasm.

When Charlie Krull joined us, under his direction we set up diallel study, crossing our best flint inbred line times with the best U.S. Reid and Lancaster lines. We found that some of our inbred lines behaved like Reid and some others behaved like Lancaster. Basically we found that the Iowa stiff stalk synthetic–derived inbred lines times Lancaster-derived inbred lines, the heterotic group that has been so important in the United States, could be also used in Argentina. So since the beginning, we decided that a selected group of elite flint inbred lines could be used as the equivalent to your Iowa stiff stalk synthetic or derived inbred lines, and on the other side of that pedigree we used another set of elite flint inbred lines that were behaving like the Lancaster types. So in a certain way what we did was to over impose the best U.S. heterotic group on our flints. We took advantage of that heterotic pattern, and since then we have kept those two groups entirely separated. Today we can say that every line that we derive from one group when crossed to the lines derived from the other group shows heterotic kick.

Tom: I remember that Chase started doing that too. He started crossing things like the male of one of our best hybrids with some flints and the female of the same hybrid with another set of flints. It's the same idea.

Fabio: Exactly right. Along the way we found that our F group was getting more and more "denty," so to speak, while our N group was getting more and more flinty. So finally, what we have today is a group of F or Reid type of flints, and another group of M or Lancaster type of flints.

Tom: They're reinforcing each other.

Fabio: Exactly. But today we find that our F or Reid lines such as Iowa stiff stalk synthetic–derived inbred lines are very denty while our Lancaster-derived lines are very, very flinty. Today every new inbred line that falls into our hands is crossed continuously to our F group and to what we call our M group to see whether it or another should be put in place. When we found an inbred line that was very flinty we also could assign that line to the M group. As a rule of thumb, when we get an inbred line that is very denty, we know that that line is going to behave like a Reid type, and when we get a line that is very flinty, we know from the beginning that the line is going to perform like a Lancaster type. Nevertheless, we were also looking to other genes from other sources of germ plasm. In the case of the tropicals we found that one of the best heterotic groups in the tropics is Tuxpeno times Eto. Tuxpeno is a very denty type of corn, either white or yellow, and we found that the Tuxpeno group could be also incorporated into the Reid type of F groups. And Eto also has either yellow or white corn, but is also flinty. We have found out that lines derived from that variety could be assimilated or incorporated into our Lancaster or M groups. We might have kept those families or races separated, but just for the sake of making everything simpler we are working with only two heterotic groups that we could call the Reid types times the Lancaster types

Tom: But at the same time you have imposed the Tuxpeno Eto heterotic pattern on top of that.

Fabio: Yes. And I think that another reason for our success was that we didn't exclude from the beginning the use of exotic sources of germ plasm. Some of them, particularly the Catetos from Brazil [Catetos is what the Brazilians and the Portuguese call the flints] were the origin of some of our best M or Lancaster lines. I think one of the keys to the success of our corn breeding program in Argentina has been the fact that we introgressed into our germ plasm a lot of exotic, but positive germ plasm. We bring into our germ plasm traits of importance like genes for yield, resistance to foliage diseases, and stalk quality.

Tom: I think there may be a parallel in Pioneer because Dr. Bill Brown [Pioneer's longtime seed research director and later its president] spent a lot of time in Jamaica many years ago working with tropicals. They've done a pretty good job with corn in general, but particularly in the southern states in the United States, they're tough.

Fabio: Yes, that's true. In other words, we could say that one of the keys to the success of our program has been that we have introgressed a great deal of genetic viability, but it was what I call positive genetic viability. We introduce into our germ plasm traits like yield and resistance to diseases that were contributing to the performance of our existing germ plasm. We were after new things, and we didn't take the classical approach of trying to improve the existing inbred line by crossing. We believe in transgressive segregation. We just cross best times best, and then we self it out looking for better combinations of two complementary parents. We have taken chances because some times you might find that there is no significant transgression segregation and that you are not making progress. So far, and I knock on wood, we have been able to make steady progress.

Tom: This is somewhat comparable to what we call population breeding versus line breeding. Isn't it?

Fabio: Yes, it is, but the concept of population in this case is different, because some breeders think that a population ought to be a line race or another pollinate, and we found that in most of the line races or open-pollinated varieties there is a line of value once out of maybe two thousand lines. So it takes a lot of time to be able to find one decent inbred line. What we call population breeding is just the segregating generation of a cross of an elite line times another elite line or times another line that was contributing a trait that was lacking or was not very strong in the first one. So our concept of population is more narrow. The reason is that our resources were limited and we couldn't undertake the effort of crossing breeding material that has a high percent age of junk in it.

Over the last thirty years, while we were doubling the yield of the first hybrids, we were also able to reduce the stalk lodging and root lodging and ear droppage from a total of 40 percent to 8 percent. We were able to do that without increasing the moisture of the grain at harvesting.

Tom: Without going for a later maturity.

Fabio: Exactly. That is the most common way many other breeders increase the yield potential of the hybrid. Going to later hybrids. But not all of our moves were roses. We also found some thorns in this process, and we paid the cost. The cost was that by introgressing more and more dent blood, we lost some things of value. Our new hybrids do have a significantly lower test weight than the original flint. Nevertheless, their test weight is within the range that is accepted by the trade.

Tom: Isn't flint corn in general heavier in test weight than dent corn?

Fabio: Definitely. And also it has a higher percentage of protein and higher percentage of xanthophyl and carotinoid pigments. So it has some nutritional values that are better than the dents.

Tom: I've always thought that the higher protein of the flints was a reflection of their lower yield.

Fabio: You are right. Because the percentage of starch of the flint kernel is much less than what you find in a dent hybrid, the weight of the embryo is heavier and so is the protein of the embryo—the one that makes the corn more protein-rich than the dent corn.

Tom: So you've given up a little bit of test weight, but on the other hand you've doubled your yield. You want total nutrients.

Fabio: Exactly. There were also some very important morphological changes that have taken place over the last thirty years and some of them didn't happen by serendipity. They happened because from the beginning we decided to select for them. In 1963 when we started testing the hybrids, it was forbidden by the National Seed Commission to use any fertilizer because they wanted tests to reflect what the farmer could really expect from those hybrids. From the beginning, Ramon [founder and first president of DeKalb Argentina] and I have believed that sooner or later this country, which was a cereal-producing country in the past, should go back to the right track. And we decided...

Tom: To use fertilizer?

Fabio: Not only that. Also common sense. That is some thing that has been lacking over the last forty or fifty years. Since the beginning, we have used a rather heavy weight of nitrogen and phosphorus in our nurseries for selecting inbred lines that will be responsive to more farm inputs. Also, we tested our hybrids at the higher plant populations because we thought that sooner or later the farmer would start planting more plants per hectare because that was the trend in the modern countries like the U.S.

Tom: Almost everywhere in the world, to get higher yield you go to heavier populations.

Fabio: Yes. And then we also went to a relatively high rate of fertilizers in our yield trials. Simultaneously, we became convinced that the new hybrid should tolerate or have the ability to tolerate a higher plant population, so since the inception of our breeding program in Argentina, we selected our inbred lines at the plant population of 70,000 plants per hectare. All of our nurseries were planted at that density. At that time most of the commercial fields in the country were planted at 40,000 plants per hectare. Contrary to what the many corn breeders at that time did, we prohibited the segregating nurseries from cutting back silks because we were convinced that the corn plant that has a good floral synchrony is the one that has better tolerance to drought and heat. Floral synchrony shows that the plant has the ability to buffer the stresses originated by heat and drought. Remember that the sexes in the corn plant are separated; the tassel is the masculine gender or sex, and the silks represent the feminine sex; and in the normal plant of corn the tassels start shedding, falling normally a couple of days before the silks come out. But under stress, this lack of floral synchrony can widen to seven or ten days. This is another important fact that was found by Dr.

Fernando Endrally, the renowned corn plant physiologist who is working at the Balcarci with the College of Agronomy of the University of Mar del Plata. This fellow is a graduate in plant physiology from Iowa State University, a distinguished student of Dr. Richard Schible. We gave him a set of the hybrids that were developed over the last thirty years, and he told me recently that he found that the floral synchrony or our DKF880 was under stress.

Tom: That was our first hybrid?

Fabio: Yes. Under stress it did have a very poor floral synchrony, but he told me that our newest one, DK752, under stress had no floral synchrony. That means that the silks and the pollen came out simultaneously. So that was an important change that took place over thirty years.

Tom: Well, it reflects what you were looking for. Who is Dr. Schible, and what are the objectives of his work?

Fabio: He is a corn physiologist at Iowa State University. He is studying the physiology of the corn plant and is very much interested in trying to find out what major physiological and morphological changes have taken place over the last thirty years in Argentina. One of the most important physiological changes was the floral synchrony, or timing differences, in the emergence of silk and pollen. We believe this is important, so we are selecting hybrids which have stable floral under very difficult growing conditions.

Tom: Do you know if our breeders of dent corn in the United States take that into consideration?

Fabio: I think that most of them do. The way they do is just by not cutting back silks in their segregating nurseries. But also, since the beginning it was our intention to select not only for a better stalk quality corn plant, but also for higher plant populations. One of the best ways to do this is to select for inbred lines and hybrids that have the "upright" trait. Most of our commercial hybrids are very upright.

Tom: The same thing applies to the dents in the United States these days. You see lots of upright leaves.

Fabio: Right. We did the same here, and I think that's a trait that allows you to grow more plants per square meter or per hectare. Concurrently, we also selected for yield components. How can you maximize the yield per hectare or acre? Well, there is only one way. You need to produce more kernels or more grains per hectare or acre. How can you do that?

One way is to select longer ears that can carry more kernels. Another one is to select for higher row number because more rows will also give you more kernels per hectare.

Tom: More kernels per ear or per hectare?

Fabio: Yeah. Let's say more kernels per plant. And then by increasing the number of plants, you can also increase the total number of kernels per hectare. There is also another way of increasing the total number per plant—by selecting plants that have the ability to put up two ears per stalk. But when you go to a very high plant population, there is no hybrid that puts up two ears. When you go up to, let's say, 70 or 80 or 90,000 plants per hectare, most of the plants will have one ear. But it was found many years ago, by Dr. Russell from Iowa State University, that the prolific inbred line and the prolific hybrids when grown under high plant population did have the ability to put up at least one ear per plant. In other words,...

Tom: They would not go barren.

Fabio: Exactly right. So we selected for prolifics. We also selected for high row number, and I told you before that as an average the flint hybrids like F880 do not have more than fourteen rows per ear, while the new ones have an average of twenty rows per ear. That was a dramatic change. Simultaneously, with the introgression of a more dent germ plasm, we increased the depth of the kernels, so the kernels of the modern flint are way, way more deep than the kernels of the old flints. Another way of increasing the number of kernels produced per hectare is by increasing the plant population. We found today that under top husbandry—that means with high fertility, very good in-soil insect control, very good weed control, and the right genetics—with supplemental irrigation up to 90,000 plants per hectare can be planted without going barren and without lodging.

Tom: That's terrific. I think that all these things explain the success of your breeding program. But what is even more exciting is that right now you have identified new families that are out-yielding your best hybrid, what we call the flagship of our product line, DK752, by 10 percent. What did you do to make those families so much better?

Fabio: I think it was a stroke of good luck. We crossed our best Reid, or what you call synthetic inbred lines, with one of the very best DeKalb USA "southern" programs, the one that is located at Mount Olive in North Carolina. The lines derived from that cross are the ones that are performing so well. During the summer, we went through our trials and immediately spotted these very distinctive attractive hybrids. When we checked to see how these hybrids were doing at other locations, we found that they were consistent across locations. Then we went to Rio Cuarto and found that those inbred lines in the seg regating nurseries had a very good level of resistance to the virus. Then we checked also the trials planted where the virus is a limiting factor and found that those hybrids were outstanding.

Tom: So you decided to take a calculated risk. What was this risk?

Fabio: We decided that at least fifteen of the best-looking hybrids from those outstanding families should be increased in our winter nursery in Hawaii to make sure that the next season will have enough seed to include those hybrids in our APTs [advanced performance tests], and simultaneously the fifteen best inbred lines are being increased right now in our winter—your summer—in Hawaii. When we have all of the data processed from eight screening locations, we can decide which two or three out of those fifteen inbred lines will be planted the coming spring in Argentina for pilot-producing seed of these new exciting hybrids. In 1996 we will have those hybrids in our FACT trials [field analysis comparison trials] and again in our APTs, and simultaneously we will increase the foundation seed of those inbred lines so that by 1997, at the time when we expect peak volume of our new single crosses, this one will be introduced into the market in small quantities, and by 1998 in large quantities. So by the time the current single crosses start going down their growth curve, the new ones will overlap and take over.

Tom: You said your hot new lines were influenced by crossing the early-maturing dents from the middle corn belt with the later-maturing dents from the southern corn belt in the United States. Do the breeders in the United States know about that success?

Fabio: Yes, they know. In fact, we are using directly one of the lines that was derived by Dr. Bill Woodruff in Marshall, Missouri, who toured our testing sites and our segregating nursery just a month ago. During the winter we plan to have some of our breeders visit his program in Missouri. I think this is one of the strengths of the company, that we have established a routine way of exchanging new hybrids and new inbred lines. But simultaneously we are also exchanging people and ideas, so we are not only hybridizing inbred lines, but also we are hybridizing ideas about our methods of plant breeding.

Tom: Which direction did you take the lines that you derived from those earlier dents times later southern dents? Were they intermediate in maturity between those, or did you select for earliers?

Fabio: We have a standard. The standard is our inbred line that is worth perhaps $10 million because it has been so important in our new single crosses.

Tom: What do you call your best inbred line?

Fabio: AEB3-2. That inbred line really is doing very well. It performs very well in Argentina, and I have learned that the Mexican program is releasing a new white inbred line that has 50 percent of the germ plasm of our AEB3-2, so our germ plasm is being used more widely now than it was in the past, which is very gratifying. That inbred line is our standard for maturity, though in the past we didn't use it very much. We are establishing a cut-off date for pollination because it is our belief that the farmers are more and more willing to use hybrids that are earlier to ripen, early to mature, without giving up yield. They don't want to give up yield, but if they have the choice, they will go for earlier hybrids. What happened ten years ago in the United States is beginning to happen here. The farmers are also after shorter-cycle or faster dry-down hybrids, so we are also looking for those.

Tom: How do you distinguish between healthy, fast dry-down hybrids and hybrids that dry faster because they are susceptible to more diseases?

Fabio: We look during the pollination season to see whether these hybrids have healthy leaves or not. That's very important. Second, we look for stalk quality. Some of the hybrids that have a fast dry-down in (in many cases they could be also called "fast die-down") are carrying softer stalks. So the dry-down that we like the most is when you see the husk of the ears turning brown and then yellow, while the rest of the plant is still green, particularly the leaves and the stalk. But sometimes you have to accept a trade-off. Our goal to select hybrids that have dry husks and dry kernels while the leaves are still green and while the stalk is also healthy and green.

Tom: That's what American farmers have wanted for a long time.

Fabio: Yes. I think our organization was the first to go 100 percent to mechanical planting and also the first to go 100 percent to mechanical harvesting. Today we have only one operator on each combine, and the combine can capture electronically the weight of each plant, plus the moisture and the test weight. This information is stored in a small computer that has a data pack. At the end of the day we can pull out the data pack and take it to the office, where the information is unloaded in a few seconds; and in a few minutes we have the printout with all of the analysis of the trials harvested that day. The system is very efficient and very fast and very well organized. We can do the same thing for sorghum, soy beans, and sunflowers.

Tom: Tell me about your breeding stations. Your principal one for corn is at Salto and for sunflowers at Brigado.

Fabio: Brigado. That's for the central area of the country. And for the southern area of the country, where early sunflower hybrid is needed and grown, we have the station at Camit...

Tom: Which is Mar del Plata.

Fabio: Exactly.

Tom: And the sorghum is also at Brigado?

Fabio: No. The sorghum is at Salto. But keep in mind that today the sorghum program is much smaller than it used to be; fifteen years ago the sorghum acreage in Argentina was around 3 million hectares. Today it has dropped to 500,000 hectares.

Tom: That's a big drop. Is that because the corn hybrids have out-yielded the sorghum hybrids?

Fabio: Yes, and also because the sunflower hybrids have improved dramatically over the last twenty years. And concurrently there is competition from the soy beans, so in most of our growing areas, the farmers have the luxury to choose to grow sorghum, wheat, other small grain crops, corn, sunflowers, or soy beans. They can choose which crop to grow each year, and normally they're pretty smart. They opt for the crops that are the most profitable. Unfortunately, the sorghum crop over the last year has been the least profitable, partly because it commands a lower price, and also because the genetic gains realized in corn and sunflowers have been more dramatic. So today in most of the growing areas of our country the sunflower and the corn are more profitable to the farmer.

Tom: What is the approximate acreage planted to corn now in Argentina?

Fabio: This last season [1995] or this current season the farmers planted, according to the figures from our Department of Agriculture, 2.9 million hectares to corn, approximately .5 million hectares to grain sorghum, and 2.4 million hectares to sunflowers.

Tom: Gee, that's a lot more sunflowers than used to be there.

Fabio: Yes, sir. And approximately 4.7 million to wheat and 5.5 million to soybeans. So this season for the first time, the soybean is the most important crop in Argentina, not only because of the hectarage planted to it, but also because of the volume. Traditionally, wheat has been the largest crop planted in Argentina.

Tom: Well, that's very interesting. And especially so for Ramon, because I think he's the father of soybeans in Argentina.

Fabio: Yes. That's true.

Tom: You have mentioned some fundamental changes that are occurring in Argentina and their implications for the DeKalb sales organization in the future. You made the point that farms were getting bigger but that instead of the estancieros doing the farming, mostly they have sharecropped or rented their land to people who are really good farmers and have large machinery. Do you want to elaborate on that?

Fabio: According to recent statistics, Argentina has 450,000 land owners but only 150,000 producers. So what these figures tell us is that already important structural changes in farm production are taking place. I would say that two out of three owners are leaving their land to a more efficient and more entrepreneurial farmer. That is, they are either leasing the land for cash or sharecropping. Most of the farm economists and farm analysts think that this is an irresistible trend, to the point that perhaps in the next ten years we will see a producing force of 150,000 producers shrink to approximately 20,000. This is going to have a major impact on the way we sell seed. With a much smaller farmer or client base, I think direct sales will become almost imperative. If you can put in your database all the pertinent information regarding these farmers, you will be able to monitor their purchases throughout the season. In the future we might see a dramatic reduction in the number of dealers each organization has because most of them will not be able to make a living out of selling seed unless they, like the traditional U.S. corn belt dealer, take the seed dealership as a part-time rather than a full-time job. So I foresee that our marketing structure in the future will have to adapt to the new structure of our farming sector.

Tom; Well, if there are only 20,000 people farming most of the country, those individuals are going to be pretty intelligent, and they will also be buying large quantities of seed.

Fabio: You are exactly right.

Tom: So your representatives won't have as many people to call on as they do now, maybe only 20 percent as many.

Fabio: But the key to success in the future will be to give service to these clients. This client will be also way more demanding than most of the clients we are dealing with today. They will be more powerful in the sense that if the local agroncmist cannot meet their expectations, they will have enough economic resources just to hire the best consultant available in the country. This bigger operator will not be farming 100 or 200 hectares. Some probably will be farming 4,000 or 5,000 hectares. Also, those guys will require much more sophisticated service than they get today. Unless tomorrow's dealers are properly trained or seek advice from agronomists, they will not be able to meet the challenges that will be put to them by the new crop of customers.

Tom: It would seem to me that this evolution will occur fairly fast, but right now most of our seed is sold by dealers, and they have varying degrees of sophisti cation themselves. As our customers demand more service, we are going to have to be able to provide it, maybe first to the dealers to help them sell the farmer, but gradually the dealer system may become obsolete, so DeKalb Argentina may have to have more and more highly trained direct salesmen calling on these much larger farmers.

Fabio: That is my opinion. I think that this is going to be a stepwise process, and I think that the most important step right at this moment is to get our sales force and our dealers very knowledgeable about the product that we sell. One of the most important services we can provide our clients or farmers is accurate information about the strengths and weaknesses of our product. They don't know our product very well, and they want to know more.. They want to know to what extent they can stretch the capability of our product. This is something you have observed in the United States. The life span of the hybrid in the past was ten or twelve years, but it is no longer that. Now a hybrid is almost finished after six years. So the farmers really cannot learn all about the hybrid through trial and error.

Tom: Incidentally, we just passed some tractors that were pulling specialized wagons. You said they were people harvesting seed for delivery to our plant or to somebody else's plant. We also just passed a big Pioneer plant that appeared to be all finished with the harvest this year. It seems to me that that implies that Pioneer is either more mechanized than most of their competitors or has a plant too large for the demand for their seed. Probably DeKalb is a close second, but am I correct in thinking when we still see people harvesting seed after the Pioneer plant is shut down that they are more mechanized than most of their competition right now?

Fabio: No, you are not correct. The facts are as follows. We have a 40 percent market share in Argentina, and Pioneer has a 15 percent market share. DeKalb Argentina and Pioneer's ear corn drying capacity is equal at least for this season, but we are selling more seed. I think that now we are realizing that we need more ear corn drying capacity. That's why we are still harvesting when Pioneer has finished—because our crop is much larger, not because Pioneer is more mechanized.

Tom: But they are more mechanized relative to their size of the sales.

Fabio: Correct. They have more ear corn drying capacity relative to their market share. So this also supports our current request for expansion of our ear corn drying capacity.

Tom: Yes. If you don't keep up and have the kind of equipment that gives you the best possible quality product, Pioneer's going to be the winner.

Fabio: Unfortunately, in this case I cannot challenge your opinion. You're absolutely right. You cannot afford to lose market opportunity and give competitive advantages to Pioneer, because they are really good.

Tom: And you know that they are going to be willing to

invest the money to keep their products good.

Fabio: Yes. Because that's their track record. It's what they have been doing for thirty years.

Tom: Just as DeKalb has been doing. It seems to me that farmers have benefited greatly from the competition between the two companies. Tell me about the best hybrids you have developed.

Fabio: Well, DK4F37 was registered and introduced into the Argentine market in 1987, and in 1992 it reached its peak. That year we sold the equivalent of half a million units of corn, and 4F37 was the most widely grown corn hybrid in our whole organization.

Tom: And in the whole country, too.

Fabio: Yes, but I mean it was the hybrid that had the most volume in the entire DeKalb Genetics company. So that was kind of a landmark. In 1992 we sold 10,000 metric tons of that hybrid.

Tom: Let's see. 10,000 metric tons, 45 units per ton—that equals 450,000 units.

Fabio: Yes.

Tom: Congratulations!

How can one be anything but confident in the future of DeKalb Argentina when its research is led by a man as knowledgeable about his country, his product, and his research as Fabio Nider?

DeKalb Argentina Wheat Breeding

Dr. Charlie Krull, an outstanding wheat breeder and colleague of Dr. Norman Borlaug, who was awarded the Nobel Peace Prize for his "green revolution" wheats, took charge of DeKalb Argentina's research program in 1967 and immediately started a wheat breeding program. Charlie's objectives were to develop better wheat varieties for Argentina, to develop a hybrid sunflower breeding program, and to support DeKalb Argentina's existing corn and sorghum research.

Great New Wheat Varieties

In 1973, two of Charlie Krull's wheat varieties, Lapacho and Tala, met all of the Argentine government's quality and yield requirements and were registered for sale in Argentina. Yields of the two short, beautiful wheats were outstanding, so our small supply of 3,858 tons sold out very fast.

At the time of our development and registration of Lapacho and Tala, Argentine law granted the breeder rights to royalties from farmers for the first three years after varietal introduction. The rights to royalties were designed to be incentives to private investment in wheat breeding, but the performance of Lapacho and Tala was so outstanding that government authorities decided to suspend our royalty rights! We believe that such specific suspensions of the law are a betrayal of both farmers and wheat breeders and will deter private wheat breeding as well as slow down wheat breeding efforts.

In hopes that royalty rights would be restored, we continued breeding wheat for five more years, introducing Urunday, Quebracho, and Chanar. These were also well accepted by farmers, but the Argentine government refused to renew our three-year royalty rights, so we closed down our wheat breeding program, which had produced the five most widely grown wheat varieties in the country. There was no way we could recover our breeding expenses in the absence of the royalties or some other form of "breeders' rights" legislation. We were forced, therefore, to conclude that hybrid seeds, which farmers must buy each year from the breeder, were the only seeds we could develop that would produce enough income to cover our developmental research costs and produce profits.

As I think Fabio Nider made clear in the interview above, our success in Argentina has depended heavily on the performance of the products derived from our research.

Over the long term, however, a lot of good people and a lot of financial support pulled DeKalb through the political and economic problems that prevailed there from 1960 to 1995. The following paragraphs present some of the problems we faced in the 1970s.

Troubles in Argentina
Economic and Legislative Hurdles

During the 1970s Argentina passed a law requiring 51 percent Argentine control of all businesses. We simply ignored that law, because it would have forced us to sell control of our business at ridiculously low prices. The law was finally repealed, but the combination of inflation, price controls, governmental discrimination against foreign companies, operating losses, and a nervous board of directors forced us to seriously consider discontinuing operations in Argentina.

Recalling those dark days, Ramon Agrasar credits my personal intervention with saving the company by providing the working capital necessary for survival. The decision to do so was difficult, but my faith in the basic soundness of Argentine agriculture, combined with my confidence in our Argentine people and the promise of our research, were the main criteria behind my decision to fund their continuing operations. Stubborn determination was a factor, too.

Argentine Banks Run Out of Money!

As the banks in Argentina ran out of money to lend, even for seasonal needs, DeKalb in the United States had to finance all of D-A's seasonal needs by guaranteeing loans from U.S. banks. We did this on letters of credit, which gave us full rights to repatriate after six months. D-A always had sufficient financial strength to make the repayment, but in a time of great economic stress an Argentine financial adviser told us that the country was in such bad financial shape that we could not expect to stay in business there if we made the repayment.

The solution to our problem lay in the purchase of "Bonex" bonds, which were dollar denominated, Argentine government guaranteed, and carried a very high interest rate. No Latin American country had ever reneged on a Bonex bond. We had no choice, so we accepted the Bonex bonds in lieu of returning dollars to the United States. Ironically, it was such a good deal that for the period that we held Bonex bonds, the interest they paid us made 1980 the most profitable year we ever had in Argentina, as we earned slightly more than $7 million!

Terrorism

Moreover, the 1970s were a period of real danger for both our Argentine employees and the Americans who visited them. Kidnappings, torture, and ransom were almost commonplace. Several of Ramon's friends from college days were kidnapped and held for ransoms that were in direct proportion to the profitability of their businesses. They concluded that some of their employees had betrayed them and warned Ramon that the same thing might happen to him. When he was not kidnapped, he wryly told me that maybe DeKalb Argentina's poor financial results during the period of terrorism were the reason! Another factor may have been the terrorists' realization that good yields resulting from our research were good for all Argentinians.

Table 23-6
DeKalb Argentina Sales and Earnings, 1970–1979

	Sales in Metric Tons				
Fiscal Year	Corn	Sorghum	Sudax	Wheat	Profits (000 US$)
1970	12,148	4,418	1,080	0	464
1971	10,307	4,108	886	0	41
1972	3,149	4,448	2,831	0	240
1973	4,297	4,674	4,023	3,858	(1,287)
1974	3,783	2,492	4,948	4,599	(823)
1975	4,458	4,017	3,513	7,405	3,618
1976	unk.	unk.	unk.	unk.	233
1977	3,950	4,893	5,057	9,054	1,210
1978	5,466	4,205	4,720	2,789	3,671
1979	10,759	3,819	3,452	3,705	1,586
Totals	58,317	37,074	30,510	31,410	8,953

SOURCE: Pre-tax information supplied by DeKalb Argentina.

Both the Peronistas and their conservative (military) foes awarded medals to Ramon and, indirectly, to DeKalb for the contributions our high-yielding products had made to their country's economy. So, everything was not against us, and we hung on in their beautiful country. We didn't have much choice, but we honestly believed the company had a solid future. Table 23-6(previous page) summarizes DeKalb Argentina's performance in the 1970s.

Cargill Challenges DeKalb Argentina in the 1970s

As Table 25-4 shows, the 1970s were difficult for DeKalb Argentina, both operationally and financially. Seedcorn sales declined sharply in the middle of the decade as F880 became an "old" hybrid that was swept away by Cargill's new "120" before our seedcorn research program produced new and better hybrids. The introduction of Sudax (a sudan grass–sorghum hybrid) helped sorghum sales grow, and the short-lived introduction of outstanding varietal wheat varieties (which farmers could reproduce for seed) helped produce badly needed income, but inflation and price controls made profitability very hard to achieve.

BUILDING A BUSINESS IN BRAZIL, 1968–1995

A good seed business for DeKalb started in an unusual way in 1968 when a man who represented DeKalb's Brazilian poultry division consulted with a distinguished Brazilian professor of agricultural genetics named Dr. Ernesto Paterniani. The DeKalb man asked Dr. Paterniani to recommend someone to build and manage a poultry farm in Brazil for DeKalb. He recommended Amauri Dimarzio.

Amauri Dimarzio's Career with DeKalb, 1968–1980

Amauri's college curriculum had trained him primarily for the hybrid seed business, so he was at first reluctant to accept the challenge of introducing DeKalb chicks in Brazil, but Dr. Paterniani knew that DeKalb and Pioneer were leaders in the development of both hybrid chickens and hybrid corn and urged that he accept DeKalb's offer, even though it paid less than half of several other offers.

His first five years with DeKalb were very difficult for Amauri; the poultry business grew more slowly than he had hoped, and he was unable to manage as he wished. For reasons he could not understand, his Latin American boss refused to adjust his salary for Brazilian inflation for three years, apparently in hopes that he could force Amauri to resign. His pay was so low that he had to sell his car and his house and move into his father-in-law's home. After Amauri's fifth year on the job, Ron Myers, who was manager of DeKalb's international poultry operations, made changes in the administration of our South American poultry operations, and Amauri's difficult boss left the company. Ron then recognized Amauri's ability as well as his honesty by placing him in charge of most of the company's poultry operations in South America.

The company was losing money on its poultry operations throughout the area when Amauri took over, but within four years all past losses had been offset. Our Brazilian poultry operation, which provided parent stock for other South American countries, was the most profitable of all. By 1978 it was earning an after-tax profit of more than $300,000, plus $150,000 it paid annually for the grandparent breeding stock it imported from the United States. DeKalb had become the most profitable distributor of poultry breeding stock in Brazil, and Amauri's compensation had increased very substantially.

DeKalb Seed Comes to Brazil

In 1976, at the peak of his success with DeKalb poultry, Amauri feared that his dream of managing both hybrid seed and poultry would never come to pass when we hired a Swedish Brazilian named Bengt Naas to begin our seedcorn business. Nevertheless, Amauri did everything he could to further the fledgling seed business. He helped Naas resolve problems with regulatory red tape and assisted David Curtis (our director of international seed operations) and Naas in hiring a talented young corn breeder named Dr. Walter Trevisan to lead our corn breeding efforts in Brazil.

In 1978, when David Curtis learned of Amauri's interest in hybrid corn as well as his success in establishing our poultry business in Brazil, he recommended that Amauri be made general manager of DeKalb's Brazilian operations in both seed and poultry. Ron Myers concurred, and so did Jack Nelson and I. Amauri was fulfilling his destiny, but the storm clouds of both inflation and poultry product performance were building on the horizon.

SOURCE: Amauri Di Marzio

Amauri Di Marzio, President DeKalb-Brasil

Problems

Runaway inflation and interest costs became so severe between 1979 and 1982 that the U.S. parent company became reluctant to invest more dollars there. Simultaneously, our poultry business became less profitable in the face of increased competition. Although the problems with our breeding program were eventually corrected, costs in Brazil were skyrocketing, and Amauri was finally forced to discontinue poultry operations in 1989.

Amauri survived while waiting for his corn research team to develop good new corn hybrids by keeping operating costs low and by selling our poultry farm in 1980 for $1 million in cash. This sale netted a large profit because the farm had become surrounded by industrial development. He reinvested part of his capital gains in a much less costly poultry farm at Conchal, fifty miles northwest of Campinas, and in a corn research farm at Barretos, one hundred miles north of Campinas in the state of Sao Paulo. By 1990, the poultry buildings had been converted to broiler production, which is operating profitably. Corn research testing is also carried on there.

Twenty-seven years later, I can say with deep conviction that Amauri's decision to join DeKalb was a very important one for our future in Brazil. I believe he has grown in stature and ability every day that he has worked for the company. In March of 1995, when I met with him for probably the last time, I began thinking about what a valuable colleague he has been in building DeKalb's seed business in Brazil, often overcoming nearly impossible obstacles. I consider Amauri to be one of DeKalb's most honest and able representatives. His dedication and entrepreneurial ability rank him among DeKalb's best men. I am certain that he would also have been respected by my father, our company's founder. Indeed, I believe his achievements are comparable to those of key people like David Curtis, Emile Singla, Ramon Agrasar, and Antonio Marchetto.

DEKALB IN MEXICO, 1960-1995

DeKalb's seed business in Mexico started slowly in the 1960s, in large part because the Mexican government owned and operated a well-established monopoly over the production and sale of hybrid seedcorn. We were aware that Mexican farmers living near the U.S.-Mexican border often bought seedcorn in the United States and planted it in Mexico, but we did not attempt to produce and sell seedcorn there because it was against the law. But the monopoly did not apply to sorghum seed, and we knew that our hybrid sorghum seed would produce just as well across the border as it did on the American side of the Rio Grande. In fact, many of our south Texas sorghum dealers had been selling nonhybrid sorghum seed into Mexico for many years. We did not encourage them to establish seed stores there, however, because we thought that, in the long run, Mexican-owned and -operated seed stores and/or farmer-dealers would make more sales than Texas based dealers would. Accordingly, we signed up Mexican dealers to sell DeKalb hybrid sorghum and in 1961 established a DeKalb sorghum seed company in Mexico.

Table 23-7
Estimate of Latin American Market Size, 1995

	Sorghum			Corn		
Country	Hybrids Planted (000 units)	DeKalb (000 units)	DeKalb Share (%)	Hybrids Planted (000 units)	DeKalb (000 units)	DeKalb Share (%)
Brazil	110	12	11	4,850	445	9
Argentina	162	48	30	1,788	673	38
Mexico	748	224	30	2,000	340	17

SOURCES: DeKalb managers in each country.
Note: One unit = fifty pounds.

Hybrid Grain Sorghum Finds a Niche in Mexico

In Mexico, white corn is widely used for human consumption and is generally planted by farmers living on small farms who prefer non-hybrid seed, primarily because yields on their farms are low and the cost of hybrid seedcorn is high relative to the 20 percent yield increase they could get from planting hybrids. This is not always the case, but it is a big factor in their agriculture, because only 15 percent of their corn is produced from hybrid seed.

Grain sorghum and yellow corn are used for animal feed and are generally produced on larger farms, where better tillage practices make lower seeding rates practical, and together with fertilizer and some degree of irrigation produce yields high enough to make hybrid seed an economical proposition. Often grain sorghum is preferred over corn because it survives dry spells and minimum irrigation better than corn, and its grain sells for nearly as much as corn when used for animal feed. Also its seed costs are lower than hybrid seedcorn costs. Net-net, Mexico is the largest market for hybrid sorghum seed in all of Latin America; it will plant about 17,000 metric tons (or nearly 850,000 fifty-pound bags) of hybrid sorghum seed in 1996. Thirty percent of that will be DeKalb.

Building Facilities to Meet Demand

Before 1967, DeKalb produced seed in the United States to supply Mexican farmers who ordered their hybrid sorghum seed from their local seed stores and dealers. By 1967, our sales of hybrid sorghum seed in Mexico had increased enough to justify organizing a seed production area and a seed processing plant in Mexico. We chose a good farming area near Los Mochis in Sinaloa province in the northwestern part of the country. It was a good place to grow, process, and distribute hybrid grain sorghum seed. DeKalb still operates there.

A second hybrid sorghum growing and processing area was established in Matamoros, Tamaulipas, in northeastern Mexico. It served us well for many years but is currently "mothballed" because we can produce better quality seed in the drier, more irrigated western area.

DeKalb Mexican Seedcorn Research Begins in 1967

By 1967, we were confident that the Mexican government would soon remove the monopoly its national seed company had on research, production, and sale of hybrid seedcorn in Mexico, so we applied for and were given official government permission to establish our own private hybrid corn research program in Mexico. The new company was named Semillas Hibridas de Mexico, S. de R.L., and was the first private organization granted the right to conduct hybrid seed research in Mexico.

We manned it with very competent Mexican corn breeders, headed by Oscar Cota, who also managed sorghum production at Los Mochis. Basil Tsotsis reports that research in Mexico was supported by DeKalb's research stations at Leesburg, Georgia, and Homestead, Florida, both of which were well located for subtropical corn breeding.

After 1969, when Dr. Marv Lindsay, who had for many years been improving tropical corn varieties and hybrids in Africa, joined DeKalb, he coordinated all subtropical and tropical corn breeding in Mexico and the United States, with participation by Dr. Tsotsis. Dr. Luis Costa Rodrigues, a talented U.S.-trained Portuguese corn breeder, also was a significant participant in the development of the subtropical germ plasm "pools" our breeders needed to be successful.

It would be several years before we could expect their research efforts to develop hybrids uniquely adapted to the diverse growing areas of their very large country, but we fully funded the project and located the center of our Mexican research near Guadalajara, from which we could easily visit the many test fields we would need. Later, in 1977, we built a large seedcorn processing facility near Nextipac, just outside of Guadalajara.

A U.S.-Mexican Joint Venture

In 1973, with enough research experience in Mexico behind us to give us confidence that we could produce outstanding corn hybrids, we were still uneasy about reports that the Mexican government would soon require Mexican control of hybrid seedcorn producers. That never came to pass, but we were nevertheless pleased to welcome the Bours group to our side as 51 percent owners in Semillas

Hibridas, S.A. de C.V. The Bours were recommended to us by a highly regarded research foundation with years of experience working in Mexico, and we have never regretted our decision to establish a partnership with people who knew their country much better than we ever would.

To be certain of our control over our products, DeKalb fully funds and has absolute rights to the control of the products of its own research, which is done by Semillas Hibridas de Mexico, S. de R.L.. Two other jointly owned companies complete our Mexican organization. They are a holding company called Grupo Agrogen, S.A. de C.V., and a management firm called Semillas Hibridas Internacionales, S. de R.L.

Research Accelerates

In 1978, DeKalb moved to strengthen its research efforts by appointing Dr. Basil Tsotsis vice president of tropical corn research. Basil initiated an effort to collect diverse corn germ plasm having resistance to the many corn diseases found in tropical and subtropical areas. One of the most important corn diseases we faced in these areas was "downy mildew." This disease could devastate all known varieties of corn, but its attacks tended to be so erratic that selection for resistance in segregating germ plasm was difficult. Scientists had not succeeded in isolating and multiplying the organism in their labs for later inoculation into diverse corn germ plasm, looking for resistance.

Dr. Tsotsis found out, when he visited DeKalb's corn research programs in Thailand, that it was the one place in the world where downy mildew was always present. He then realized that the best way to select for downy mildew resistance would be to have breeders ship seed of diverse and segregating germ plasm every year to DeKalb's Thai research fields, where susceptible segregates would die, leaving only those plants that carried genes for resistance. The survivors would be turned over to all DeKalb plant breeders, and they would cross and backcross it into their best parent lines, sending the outcrosses and backcrosses back each year to Thailand, where plants susceptible to downy mildew would be eliminated, with resistant seed being returned each year to DeKalb corn breeders. In this way, DeKalb breeders for the first time could be sure that their selections retained downy mildew resistance—a very important characteristic when the disease suddenly struck.

Another difficult disease to fight was called "head smut." Until Basil worked out a way to inoculate for this disease in his research plots, nearly every hybrid in subtropical and tropical areas was susceptible. It did not attack often, but with just the wrong heat and humidity, head smut could devastate whole fields. No one had yet been able to breed for resistance, and nearly all varieties and hybrids were susceptible. In the late 1970s, a small field of DeKalb's best and most widely grown hybrid (666) was devastated by head smut. Our competitors, convinced government authorities that 666 should be removed from the market. With a large supply of this fine hybrid in our warehouses, we were forced (unwisely, we think) to destroy all of our inventory and take a very big loss.

That bad experience had a long-term happy ending, however, as Basil and DeKalb breeders in all tropical areas concentrated on finding resistance to head smut and incorporating it into many of our hybrids. Our competitors have apparently not yet done that, so they are vulnerable to the same problems we experienced with 666.

Unfortunately, Dr. Tsotsis resigned in 1985. He left DeKalb a valuable collection that was extremely diverse—and much needed for the full maximization of genetic diversity (hybrid vigor) in future hybrids.

By 1995, our research company had these facilities and personnel in Mexico:

- Corn research locations are located at Nextipac, Jalisco, and San Juan de Abajo, Nayarit (near Puerto Vallarta). These are directed by Dr. Fernando Gonzalez, a very capable scientist who succeeded Dr. Ramon Godoy, who has contributed significantly to our Mexican product line. Unfortunately, Ramon died shortly after he left the company. He was a good breeder and a fine man.
  Dr. Gonzalez's basic improvement effort focuses on disease resistance in combination with hybrid vigor enhancement by introducing the greatest genetic diversity that exists today—that which exists in dent corn hybrids. This is the diversity that creates hybrid vigor and higher and higher yields when crossed into the relatively narrow diversity that has characterized many tropical hybrids in the past. The breeder's challenge is to maintain the disease, insect, and heat tolerance of tropical germ plasm while increasing its genetic diversity.
- A sorghum research station is located at Irapuato, Guanajuato, in the Bahio area, which is one of the highest-yielding sorghum areas in the world and is at an altitude over 6,000 feet above sea level.
- Most of our seed processing plants are at Nextipac, where both sorghum and corn are processed. Their state-of-the-art 10,000 metric ton corn "husk-on" processing facility is the best in Mexico. It cost $4.5 million and is used for harvesting drying, and conditioning of seed.
- At Los Nochis, a sorghum seed processing plant has a capacity of 4,000 to 5,000 metric tons.

Sales and Management

Jose Luis Gonzales is the company's general manager and has been in his position since 1993. His education was in agronomy, and he had extensive experience in seed production and quality control before his current appointment.

Sales and distribution are handled by more than a hundred dealers, who are organized into seven geographic regions across Mexico; most of them sell both corn and sorghum seed. Before Mexico's financial crisis in 1993–94, DeKalb had the lead in Mexico in corn and sorghum sales, but is now close behind Pioneer and Asgrow, both of which offered more liberal credit terms and are thought to be having difficulty collecting from farmers who are still unable to pay. In the end, we expect quality of product to determine the market position of these three competitive leaders.

DEKALB'S TROPICAL CORN RESEARCH PROGRAMS

DeKalb carries on tropical corn research program in the 1990s at these locations:

1. In Mexico:
   - at Nextipac, Jalisco, their main research loca tion.
   - at San Juan de Abajo, Nayarit, near Puerto Vallarta.
2. In Brazil:
   - tropical corn research at Baretos in the State of Sao Paulo.
   - subtropical research at Passo Fundo in Rio Grande del Sol.
3. In Thailand:
   - tropical research at Solongpan, 250 kilometers north of Bangkok.
   - subtropical research at Kampanphat, 400 kilo meters north of Bangkok.
   - tropical and high-humidity research at Silakampoon.
4. In Java
5. In South Africa

NEGOTIATIONS IN THE SOVIET UNION

A Conversation with a Soviet Farm Leader

In the spring of 1972, Dr. John Schnittker, an agricultural economist who had been our economic adviser after retiring as the top USDA economist, suggested that we take a group of five farm leaders to the Soviet Union to ask planners if they were likely to continue their recent huge purchases of American corn, soybeans, and soybean oil meal. He believed that key Soviet economists, who considered his rank in the USDA equivalent to that of a "minister" in the Soviet economic hierarchy, would be willing to talk with us openly and frankly.

It was not hard to find five good men to travel to Moscow with John. In addition to John Schnittker and myself, our group included Howard Mullins, DeKalb director and County Farm Bureau President; "Win" Wallin, who was soon to become Pillsbury's CEO; and a leading commodity trader who was invited by John Schnittker.

We were all delighted when Dr. Demetri Martinov, one of his country's leading agricultural economists, invited us to visit with him and his staff. Our talks lasted between two and three hours, and went like this:

DM: (Martinov) Welcome. We are pleased to meet you. What would you like to discuss?

JS: (Schnittker) All U.S. farmers were very pleased earlier this year when you bought much larger supplies of our feed grains than you had in the past. We need to plan our future seed production and want to know if your country is likely to maintain your future purchases of our grains at or close to the large amounts you ordered last year.

DM: That depends on the size of our own harvests, of course, but I think it is likely that we will be buying similar large quantities of imported grain for several more years.

JS: Demetri, even though my friends here are primarily interested in grain shipments, I believe that the best buy you can make for your ruble will be the purchase of soybean oil meal, because it contains 44 percent protein, and that is what you need most, because most of your animals are fed only grain which contains only 10 percent protein, and your livestock need 16 percent protein to grow fast and efficiently.

DM: (becoming friendlier as he realizes we are honest men he can be frank with) "Yes, we are aware of that, and are already using soybean oilmeal, with good results.

TR: (Tom Roberts) Dr. Martinov, what is your job, and how do you go about it?

DM: I am responsible for creating and implementing my country's five-year plans for agricultural production. I am sad to say that I don't go about it in the way it should be done.

JS: Why do you believe you are not planning as you should?

DM: Because such plans should originate with our state farm managers, who know very well what crops they can best grow and what kind of animals they should feed, but in our society, we too often do not reward merit. Instead, we punish failure. Therefore, we get very little response from our farm managers when we ask for their recommendations because they know they have a lot to lose if they don't make the goals they have set for themselves. In the end, they often do not cooperate with us, and we have to make plans here in Moscow. In my opinion, this is a basic weakness in our system.
More than that, I am very much concerned that our leaders' policy of allocating our nation's financial resources to heavy industry at the expense of minimizing consumer goods production is becoming an enormous disincentive for our workers to work, because we have very few consumer goods to spend their rubles on. Because of that, most workers are asking themselves why they should work hard when there is nothing to buy with their wages. Hence, many are simply not working hard, and this creates tremendous problems for our economy.

We were sympathetic with him, of course, and even assured him that we would cooperate fully with him whenever he wished to send his people to the United States to study our agricultural systems. That conversation led to Dr. Martinov and his chief assistant participating several times in the agribusiness seminars Dr. Ray Goldberg conducts each January at the Harvard Business School. I visited Dr. Martinov in 1978 and again in 1987, and was pleased to learn that he had advanced to even more important positions within his country. He was clearly a very competent, patriotic, dedicated man. Needless to say, however, we decided not to try to do business in the Soviet Union until their farm sector became much better organized.

On my 1987 visit I regretted having to tell Dr. Martinov that I could not accept his invitation to invest in the construction of a hybrid seed processing plant in the Soviet Union. I believed its success would depend fundamentally on selling to farmers who could pay us a fair price for our seedcorn, and I did not think that the desperately poor economic position of most Soviet farmers would make that possible.

Chapter 24

DeKalb's Oil and Mining Businesses Grow Steadily 1970-1979

CANADA

Charlie Roberts and I felt good about DeKalb's business in early 1970. Our seed business had grown fast in the 1960s, our oil business had prospered under Art Tiddens's leadership, and we were planning to take the company public. We were optimistic about the future and had a great deal of respect for Art's business ability as well as for his imagination and his broad knowledge of geology. Accordingly, we accepted his recommendation that we start a quiet, modest, "hard rock" exploration activity.

The first promising mining play came to us in late 1971 or early 1972 through International Minerals (IMC), which was one of the world's largest miners of potash and rock phosphate, in Saskatchewan and Florida. I had been a director of IMC since 1967 and was aware that its management had retained an outstanding geologist–mining engineer named Merv Upham to identify mining opportunities.

SOURCE: DeKalb Genetics

Charlie Roberts, Executive V.P. For Oil & Administration

Hard Rock Mining Operations

IMC proposed forming a joint venture with DeKalb in the Highland Valley area of British Columbia. The company wanted to jointly reopen an abandoned underground mine located between two huge and successful open-pit copper mines. The underground deposit was thought to be the mother lode for the nearby open-pit mines, and Merv Upham believed that copper could be mined profitably at 1971 copper prices utilizing modern underground mining techniques. We set up budgets of $100,000 for the first year and $200,000 for the second year—enough, we thought, to pay the salary and expenses of a mining engineer whose job would be to verify our hopes that we could return the mine to profitability. We hired an experienced miner named Don Pringle, who recommended that we develop the mine using a fully equipped ore concentrator and mining building that was available in Hanson Lake, Saskatchewan, at an attractive price. IMC and DeKalb put up the cash in 1972 to bring the mine back into production.

Unfortunately, the mine had problems from the first day that it went into production. The quantities of ore we produced each day were less than expected, and the price of copper failed to reach the level we needed for profitable operations, even if we succeeded in raising ore production. Faced with these problems, we mothballed the mine in 1973, and our man Ron Buckley worked with Merv Upham of IMC on reserve studies and improved extraction procedures. In 1980 we reopened the mine, encouraged by rising copper prices, but closed it within a year, discouraged once again by dropping copper prices.

We brought the mine back into production a second time after negotiating with a 50 percent nonoperating partner to settle for a carried interest, and buying out IMC's interest. We carried on alone, even making three shipments to a Japanese smelter, but our costs were about a dollar a pound, and the price of copper fell to 75 or 80 cents a pound. Our ore body was worthless, so we closed down the operation permanently. Our loss was $20 million pre-tax, but we managed to reduce that substantially using Canadian law, which allowed mining losses to be written off for tax purposes against oil profits. That helped, of course.

As he reflected on our abortive mining venture, Charlie Roberts commented that we had been willing to accept its inherent risk because our seed business was doing so well. He believes (and I agree) that we were also influenced by the book *The Limits of Growth*, which argued that we were consuming more natural resources than we were discovering, and that the profits of those who own the remaining resources were likely to increase substantially. That prophecy may yet come true, but we clearly bet $20 million on the wrong resource when we ventured into copper mining.

Oil and Gas Prices Take Off

The most significant event in the oil and gas business in the 1970s was a sharp rise in prices, which was due primarily to OPEC supply restrictions as shown in Table 24-1. Oil and gas exploration boomed, and many investors jumped on the oil exploration bandwagon. Many will argue, correctly, that higher prices were long overdue, but the boom was moving toward an inevitable correction because of the oversupply of oil that was developing. When the bubble burst in the 1980s, many people and many institutions were hurt.

Table 24-1
Oil & Gas in Canada, 1970–1979

Year	Oil ($ per bbl.)	Gas ($ per mcf)	Annual Volume (BOE)	Pre-Tax Income ($000)
1970	2.67	0.13	1,541	943
1971	2.80	0.15	1,508	1,173
1972	2.69	0.16	1,448	1,106
1973	3.05	0.16	1,467	1,421
1974	4.75	0.19	1,447	2,690
1975	6.76	0.42	1,274	4,303
1976	7.97	1.03	1,306	6,713
1977	8.88	1.23	1,335	7,509
1978	9.84	1.50	1,454	10,115
1979	10.33	1.46	1,443	9,777
Total				45,754

SOURCE: Company records provided by DeKalb Energy, Canada.
Notes: BOE means barrels of oil-equivalent; mcf means 1,000 cubic feet.

In 1972 Bob Johnson, an exceptionally able geologist, was placed in charge of our Canadian exploration, replacing Clive McCord, who had resigned. Bob continued the development of the plays he inherited, but his most significant contribution to our Canadian exploration was his advocacy and development of very large, shallow, blanket sands in the Nevis area of Alberta in the Belly River and Bear Paw formations. Developmental drilling continued in the Nevis area for years, and it became an important key play (see figures for this and other oil fields in Chapter 19) Bob was appointed vice president in November 1979.

Bob also initiated exploration and development in the Blueberry Mountain, Garrington glauconite, Leafland glauconite, and South Bingley areas of Alberta. At Blueberry Mountain, we developed gas reserves equivalent to 2,280,000 barrels of oil, where our costs of

$0.47 per equivalent barrel were very acceptable (DeKalb Energy, Canada, summary, Dec. 31, 1989). Bob's next exploration and development program was in the Williston Green area of Alberta. He had some success there, developing small but profitable acreages.

SOURCE: DeKalb Energy Canada

A BIG Pumper in Canada

Garrington Glauconite Gas—A Big Winner

Bob Johnson had an important success in developing gas production in the Garrington field, which was also originally a shallow cardium oil play that held deeper horizons for later development. After selling Garrington's cardium production for $800,000 (U.S.) in 1971, our exploration of the deeper, gas-bearing glauconite horizon in 1974 qualified it for classification as a "key play."

In 1975 we were the operating partner in the Garrington glauconite gas plant and gathering system, which went on stream in September, with gas sales commencing on October 12, 1975. This was the first gas plant that DeKalb operated, and it was a significant financial success. We continued with exploration and development in the Garrington glauconite field in 1975, and purchased more Garrington properties from an American oilman named Edwin L. Cox for $2.6 million. In the 1980s, Bob Johnson led another successful exploitation of deeper horizons in zones held by earlier cardium oil producing properties.

Kaybob

Exploration in the Kaybob area of Alberta had begun in 1970, two years before Bob Johnson joined DeKalb. It was a gas play with an oil-equivalent potential in excess of 1 million barrels, but we were never successful in producing gas at high rates and so assigned it a reserve potential of 158 years, which certainly qualified it as a geological success but an economic failure.

DeKalb-Nicor Exploration Agreement Completed

In 1974 and 1975, Charlie Roberts was alarmed by the sharp rise in oil prices and OPEC's semi-monopoly. Higher prices worked in our favor to the extent that we had oil to sell, but they had been followed by higher costs for prospective oil properties and cost increases for drilling and well servicing. Furthermore, on July 1, 1971, the Alberta government changed the terms of oil and gas leases from ten years to five years. This was a good move for the government because it encouraged more rapid development of its oil and gas reserves, but it tended to accelerate drilling at a time when rising prices were already encouraging drilling increases.

An oil "gold rush" was in the making, and we were reluctant to allow our costs to skyrocket, because we did not want to be stuck with high-cost facilities when prices inevitably began to fall. Accordingly, Charlie recommended that we seek a drilling partner who would be willing to pay a premium to join us. On November 1, 1976, he found such a partner in Nicor, an Illinois public utility. According to our agreement, DeKalb would continue as managing partner and receive 50 percent of future oil and gas development made by the partnership, and Nicor would absorb 60 percent of our costs.

Charlie Roberts and Art Tiddens had searched hard in the United States and in Europe for a partner willing to accept our terms. In the end, Nicor (formerly known as the Northern Illinois Gas Company) was in our own backyard. Its headquarters was only thirty miles from DeKalb. However, in late 1983, after seven years of partnership, Nicor and DeKalb reached an amicable agreement to split up. DeKalb bought out Nicor's interest in the partnership for about U.S.$25 million, a price we considered to be very fair.

A Tax Windfall, Thanks to Alert Accountants

The Nicor buyout became a very good deal a bit later, when Gene Baroni, our tax adviser found that under Canadian tax rules DeKalb qualified for $57 million (canadian) in future tax benefits, which could be applied to the earnings realized by the properties previously owned by Nicor. Further, we learned that Canadian foreign investment rules did not require a nonresident company to seek approval from Canadian regulators to buy the shares of another nonresident company with a Canadian branch operation, which Nicor had.

Our Experience with Trudeau's Anti-Americanism

On December 28, 1978, after learning a week earlier that

McCullough Exploration, Ltd., an American-owned oil and gas exploration firm wished to sell its Canadian properties if the sale could be completed before the end of the year, DeKalb Petroleum (Canada) contracted to buy McCullough's Canadian properties for $50 million, subject to approval by the Canada's Foreign Investment Review Authority (FIRA), which operated under the liberal government of Prime Minister Pierre Trudeau. We were eager to close the deal both because it was a fair price for McCullough's producing properties and because we thought there might be deeper exploration opportunities. We believed that FIRA would approve the sale of one American company to another because the Trudeau government had not earlier threatened to force American companies to sell to Canadians.

SOURCE: DeKalb Energy Canada

John Leteta, Financial Officer

But in 1979, FIRA rejected our request for approval of the sale, giving us a reasonable period of time to find a Canadian buyer. We quickly sold the properties for $53.5 million, which left DeKalb and Nicor with a $3.5 million profit on the deal, and a bitter taste in our mouths for what we considered an unfair intrusion of a federal government into the private business of two American companies. After all, the western province's oil resources would have certainly been developed much more slowly, and the people of Canada would have had to wait many years for exploration funds if Americans had been denied rights to explore in Canada, as the Trudeau government seemed coming close to doing.

On the other hand, we had made a tidy profit on the McCullough deal, so we could rightfully have been accused of crying all the way to the bank if we had made our views public. Nevertheless, the Trudeau government's anti-Americanism, coupled with its courtship of capital from socialist countries caused many American oilmen like McCullough to sell their properties and leave Canada, fearing that if they stayed their oil properties might be expropriated. In the long run, however, in my opinion, small to medium-sized American companies like DeKalb did not suffer serious discrimination by either the provincial or the federal government of Canada.

DEKALB'S U.S. OIL AND GAS BUSINESS

The DeKalb Petroleum Company (Depco) was established on May 19,1965, and all U.S. oil properties were assigned to it. Art Tiddens was named president; Cliff Heglin and Bob Kenyon were named vice presidents in 1970. DeKalb's decision to go public in 1970 added a new dimension to its oil "team." Our oil business had clearly become an important part of the company, and investment bankers were eager to assess its significance.

The Development of Williston Basin Properties

Art Tiddens and his staff, convinced that oil or gas would be found in the western Dakotas, proceeded with the development of the extensive leases Art had purchased in North and South Dakota. They first entered into a joint exploration agreement with Hanover Petroleum and Texas Petroleum, both of whom also had large leasehold positions. This joint effort continued through the 1970s in parts of both Dakotas, where all three partners had leases near each other. Although we were encouraged by small successes, we were too often disappointed by the failure of further developmental drilling.

Depco's first discovery in the Red River formation in 1970 was named the Axel Felt #1. It was not a big well, but its discovery led to the establishment of the South Lone Tree field in Ward County, North Dakota. Next, we discovered oil in the Nesham #1 location, which established the Lake Darling field in Renville County, North Dakota.

In 1971, Depco completed the Federal 22-32 well in the Red River formation in Harding County, South Dakota, which was our first profitable oil discovery in South Dakota and led to our entering into an agreement with Amerada Hess to develop properties each company held in Harding County. This discovery excited us and our partners and led to further development drilling. Unfortunately, too often our efforts turned up dry holes, as the oil we discovered was trapped in small fields. But when we put more emphasis on seismic indications of larger deposits we continued to be discouraged by disappointing developmental drilling in this area through the 1970s.

Depco's Participation in an Oil Boom

The same increase in oil prices that started Canada's boom after 1973 ignited the oil boom in the United States. They were the basis for a lot of decisions, both good and bad, in the 1970s and 1980s, so it is important to keep them in mind (see Table 26- at the end of the chapter)..

The significant product price increases made American explorers more willing to drill to depths as deep as 20,000 feet, to drill "infield" wells (wells drilled between established wells in order to deplete the field fast while prices are high), and to scramble to hire drilling rigs at much higher drilling fees than they had been willing to pay in the 1960s. An oil well drilling boom was on, with all that such booms imply to salaries, rig rentals, prospect prices, and explorer egos.

Overall, it seems to me that Art and his staffs in Denver and Calgary responded sensibly to the surging oil prices of the 1970s and early 1980s. They saw it as an opportunity, of course, and organized to take advantage of it. These are some of the moves they made in the 1970s, as they sought to capitalize on their expertise and to grow their U.S. business:

1972	Opened a district office in Houston, Texas.
1973	Organized exploration in the Caribbean and Aegean Seas.
1974	Opened a district office in New Orleans. Opened Alaska district with Evergreen, Colorado, office. Entered into exploration with Mountain Fuel Supply to explore Wyoming's Wind River Basin. Entered joint exploration agreement with Florida Gas to explore Louisiana's Wilcox Trend area.
1975	Entered into agreement with Dow Chemical and began joint exploration in Yolo and Sutter Counties in California.
1976	Opened an Oklahoma City office. Agreed to explore Tenneco farm-in acreage in Canadian County, Oklahoma. Drilled numerous shallow gas wells in the Blackleaf formation in Glacier and Pondera Counties, Montana.
1977	Began California drilling, completed Brandt 12-27, the first oil well for Depco in the San Joaquin basin, Kern County. Found hydrocarbons in Brentwood Field, Contra Costa County, California. Opened Bakersfield, California, office. Drilled Rough Rider discovery with Belco in McKenzie County, North Dakota.

1979 Drilled a dry hole on Ventosa Unit #41-13 in Elko County, Nevada.
Had significant discoveries in Pennzoil area of mutual interest at Bull Moose and Flattop Butte areas in McKenzie County, North Dakota.

The most important of the discoveries were those in California and North Dakota. The source of this list is a Depco corporate historical document.

Depco Explores in the Caribbean and Aegean Seas

Full of confidence, but concerned about Trudeau's discouragement of large American oil investment in Canada, Art Tiddens recommended that we seek oil farther afield. With support from the DeKalb board, he formed Depco Trinidad and joined with Phillips Petroleum in drilling offshore wildcat dry holes in the Caribbean near Trinidad. He also formed Depco Aegean and drilled another dry hole with Conoco in the Aegean Sea off Greece. That was enough for Art, who never again proposed wildcatting outside of North America. Table 24-2 summarizes the key statistics for Depco (U.S.A.) and DeKalb Petroleum (Canada) for the ten-year period between 1970 and 1979.

Table 24-2
DeKalb's Oil Businesses, 1970–1979

	Depco (U.S.A.)				DeKalb Energy (Canada)			
Year	Oil Price/ Bbl.	Gas Price/ mcf.	Annual Vol. (BOE)	Pre-Tax Income ($000)	Oil Price/ Bbl.	Gas Price/ mcf.	Annual Vol. (BOE)	Pre-Tax Income ($000)
1970	2.95	0.12	1,240	82	2.67	0.13	1,541	945
1971	2.95	0.10	1,497	100	2.89	0.15	1,508	1,173
1972	3.10	0.14	1,596	106	2.69	0.16	1,448	1,106
1973	3.31	0.19	1,743	296	3.05	0.16	1,467	1,421
1974	6.56	0.27	1,701	5,071	4.75	0.19	1,447	2,690
1975	9.00	0.39	1,903	12,438	6.76	0.42	1,274	4,305
1976	9.91	0.65	3,038	15,483	7.97	1.03	1,306	6,713
1977	10.26	1.01	3,104	16,933	8.88	1.23	1,335	7,509
1978	10.95	1.22	3,229	17,377	9.84	1.50	1,454	10,115
1979	12.34	1.53	3,279	20,938	10.33	1.46	1,443	9,777
Total pre-tax net income				88,824				45,754

SOURCE: Company records provided by DeKalb Energy, Canada.
Note: BOE means barrels of oil-equivalent; mcf means 1,000 cubic feet.

Figure 24-3
DeKalb Oil & Gas Prices (U.S. dollars)
(Per barrel of Oil and 000 cubic feet of gas)

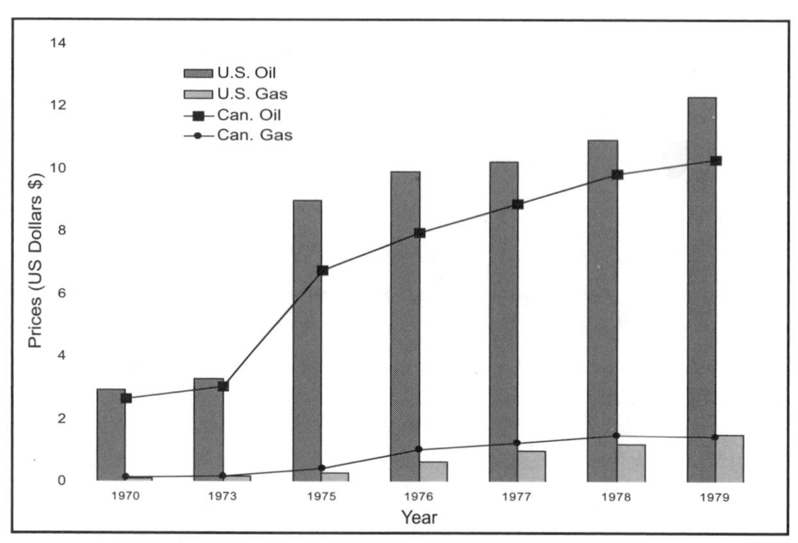

SOURCE: Depco/DPC record

A SUMMARY OF THE 1970S

In closing out Part 6, on the turbulent 1970s, I present the following summaries to give the reader perspective on the decade, as I have done for prior decades. This one differs, however, because DeKalb had a public market for its stock during the 1970s, in contrast to prior decades when our only measure of progress was "book value." Table 24-3 shows our steady growth in book value and wide swings in market value, expressed in both reported dollars and constant 1992 dollars. It clearly demonstrates the tremendous growth expectations the stock market had for DeKalb in the early 1970s and the disillusionment of investors after the disappointing results of our seedcorn business in the last half of the 1970s. It tells a story of lost opportunity.

Financial Results - Part Six

OPERATING RESULTS IN THE 1970S

Table 24-4
DeKalb' s Book and Market Values in the 1970s
($000)

	Year-End Book Value		Year-End Market Value		Yearly Net	
	Reported	in 1992 $	Post-Splits	in 1992 $	Income	Return on Equity
Year	($ Million)	($ Million)	($ Million)	($ Million)	($ Mil.)	(%)
1970	64	200	156	510	8.4	15.2
1971	74	221	264	823	10.4	15.9
1972	86	257	505	1,509	16.7	19.4
1973	108	304	617	1,740	23.1	21.4
1974	134	348	451	1,173	24.0	17.9
1975	156	349	467	1,107	32.6	20.9
1976	185	414	439	983	37.2	20.1
1977	216	456	329	694	29.9	13.8
1978	238	466	248	486	39.1	16.4
1979	266	482	356	644	43.6	16.4

SOURCE: 1970 through 1979 10Ks; 1982 S&P reports.
Notes: Book Value (common equity) is as reported by 1979 and 1981 S&P reports. MarketValue = 12,500,000 average shares outstanding after splits x average price per share. Return on Equity = Net Income (from 1981 S&P) divided by reported shareholder equity (book value). Adjustment to 1992$ for both the Book Value and Market Value columns was calculated by dividing the 1992 GNP by the GNP for each year between 1970 and 1979 and multiplying the product for each year by each year's book and market values, respectively.

Table 24-5
DeKalb Share and Price Information, 1970–1979

Year	Year-End Shares Outstanding (000)	Price Range per Share after 1970s Splits	Earnings per Share ($)	Earnings Multiple
1970	4,833	7.25–15.875	0.71	117.7 x
1971	5,510	15.25–27.50	0.91	23.5 x
1972	5,536	24.25–57.50	1.18	34.7 x
1973	12,434	37.50–62.50	1.50	33.3 x
1974	12,308	21.25–51.25	1.88	19.3 x
1975	12,336	29.50–45.75	1.94	18.8 x
1976	12,352	30.50–40.50	2.64	13.4 x
1977	12,343	18.75–34.50	3.01	8.8 x
1978	12,333	16.50–23.75	2.43	8.3 x
1979	12,201	23.25–34.00	3.53	8.2 x

SOURCE: 10Ks for each year for Earnings per Share (EPS). The 1979 10K shows shares outstanding at year end for 1975 through 1979 on page 6. 10Ks for 1971, 1972, and 1974 report shares outstanding 1970 through 1974. Year-end stock prices are from Standard & Poor's reports 8/3/88 and 8/10/79. The Earnings Multiple was calculated by dividing average stock price by EPS.

Table 24-6
Earnings by Division, 1970–1979
(U.S.$000)

Year	Animal Science	Heinold Cos.	Seed	Oil and Gas	Other	Post-Tax Earnings	In $1992
1970	852	853	14,518	889	280	8,979	29,351
1971	(4,995)	1,225	23,973	241	1,260	11,141	34,759
1972	(3,534)	2,049	27,284	884	1,521	14,407	43,076
1973	88	4.054	27,183	1,488	2,518	18,376	51,820
1974	(5,014)	3,516	38,907	5,749	2,566	23,072	60,449
1975	(5,855)	4,566	24,252	16,418	3,759	24,644	58,406
1976	(746)	5,076	25,815	21,956	8,628	33,860	75,846
1977	1,660	5,127	29,281	24,199	6,231	38,945	82,179
1978	4,785	12,523	27,800	27,700	(2,750)	31,567	61,871
1979	2,994	16,874	26,733	27,993	(3,578)	43,020	77,866

SOURCE: DeKalb 10Ks for 1972, 1974, 1976, and 1979 showed five-year net earnings by division. The last column expresses post-tax returns in 1992 dollars.

Part Seven

1980-1995

Chapter 25

Changing the Company 1980-1995

The 1980s started poignantly for DeKalb when Charles L. Gunn passed away on July 2, 1980. He was 95 years old and loved by all who knew him. When Charlie joined DeKalb in the spring of 1917, he went right to work breeding open-pollinated varieties of seedcorn adapted to DeKalb County and finding sources of the top-quality seeds for the county's farmers. Charlie's contributions to the growth and development of DeKalb have been reported throughout this book, so I will not list them again here, but he was clearly the man who made DeKalb hybrid seedcorn possible, the breeder whose hybrids made our name a familiar and respected one for northern corn belt farmers from 1935 through 1960.

SOURCE: DeKalb Genetics

Charlie Gunn in Front of His Favorite Sign

"A man with integrity" is, in my view, an apt description of Charlie Gunn. His integrity showed itself in everything he did, and it was immediately clear to people meeting him for the first time. Ramon Agrasar, for example, who was to found DeKalb in Argentina, came to our office in 1959 to get acquainted with my dad and Charlie Gunn and told me later that it was the obvious honesty of those two men that convinced him he was joining a company led by people he knew he could always count on. Charlie Gunn was the finest of men, a model for all of us.

CHARLIE ROBERTS AND I FACE TROUBLES TOGETHER

By 1980, it was clear that our seed business was in trouble, so Charlie Roberts and I realized that working together as a team was more important than ever. We had worked together for nearly twenty years. During that time, both of us had made mistakes, of course, but on balance, I thought we had been an effective management team, and I think he did, too. But with our vitally important seed business in trouble, we realized that we must work together effectively under greater stress than we had experienced in the past. I needed his help more than ever, and he was always ready to consult closely.

DEKALB'S SEEDCORN BUSINESS IN THE 1980S

Our seedcorn business was in bad shape in the early 1980s, as our sales continued their downward spiral.

Figure 25-1
DeKalb Seedcorn Sales, 1975–1993
(in bushel-equivalent units)

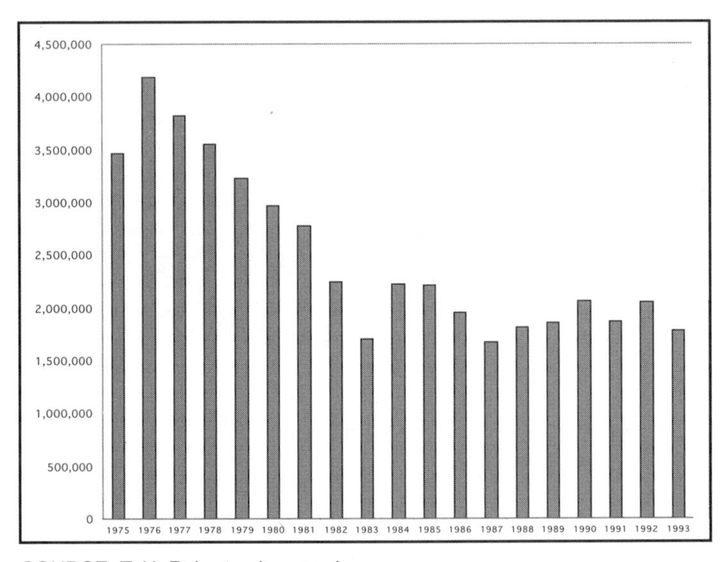

SOURCE: T. H. Roberts, Jr. records.

These were our primary problems:

- Our important hybrid seedcorn sales dropped by more than 1.2 million units between 1980 and 1983, with 1982 and 1983 showing pre-tax losses of $9.5 million and $9.6 million respectively. These losses were in part attributable to corn acreage reductions brought about by our government's Conservation Reserve Program (CRP);
- large seed inventory write-offs were caused by smaller markets that were the consequence of the CRP, but our 800,000-unit decline in seedcorn sales between 1980 and 1985 was also partially the consequence of our reduced market share.

Pfizer Shows Interest in Divesting Its Seed Business

In 1982, therefore, we were understandably interested upon learning that the Pfizer pharmaceutical company was willing to divest its eight-year-old hybrid seed business. This was our reasoning:

- Pfizer had an experienced, respected corn research director in Dr. Forrest Troyer, who had spent many years breeding hybrids for Pioneer. At Pfizer, he had formed a sound young research team of twelve corn breeders, most of whom had Ph.D. degrees. They had recently released T1100, a promising hybrid that would fit very well in the central corn belt area where we needed to improve our product line.
- Pfizer's breeders seemed to us to be on the verge of offering a series of new and promising hybrids. In short, if they joined our research group, we would have a reasonable chance of matching or besting Pioneer's research effort with a sustainable flow of new and more competitive hybrids.
- Pfizer had been researching genetically engineered hybrid seedcorn that might have breakthrough potential. Corn research leaders (both public and private) were very interested in the potential benefits of genetic engineering, but warned that its potential benefits would not likely be achieved before the late 1990s, if ever. We were convinced that merging Pfizer's team of bio-geneticists with ours could be important to us sometime in the future. We could not afford to allow ourselves to fall behind our competition in genetic research if it turned out to be successful.
- Pfizer had also improved soybean seed, and it was

> being well received by farmers. Soybeans cannot be hybridized, and farmers can save and replant their own seed if the asking price from seed producers is judged to be too high, so we knew that there was not a great deal of profit potential there. However, careful harvesting and seed treatment are needed to achieve optimum yield, so many farmers prefer to buy seed rather than plant the previous year's grain. I had resisted adding soybean seed to DeKalb's product line because its profit margins were small, and I wanted our dealers to put their effort behind our more profitable hybrid seedcorn. But when we started losing seedcorn customers in the late 1970s I realized that adding soybean seed to our product line might keep at least some DeKalb seed on farms.

After discussing the Pfizer opportunity with our corn research people, sales managers, and other DeKalb executives, including Charlie Krull, Harold Noren, John McCarter, and Charlie Roberts, I met with Ed Pratt, Pfizer's CEO, about DeKalb's either buying Pfizer's seedcorn business or forming a joint venture with the company. Ed asked Dr. Jerry Laubach to join in our discussion, which was the first of a series of confidential meetings between the key people of Pfizer and DeKalb.

It soon became apparent that both parties preferred a joint venture, so we worked out the terms of a five-year alliance and a buy-sell agreement at the end of the contract. Our agreement was signed and announced on July 15, 1982.

John McCarter Chosen to Be CEO of Joint Venture

John McCarter was appointed president and CEO of DeKalb-Pfizer Genetics, a joint venture partnership owned 70 percent by DeKalb and 30 percent by Pfizer. Wid Crawford of Pfizer was named executive vice president. Wid had been president of Pfizer-Genetics. John McCarter's earlier responsibilities had ranged from managing corporate development to serving as vice president of our seed business. In that job, he had reported to Harold Noren, our highly respected senior vice president for seed. Assisted by Tom Melton and Kent Schulze, two able seedcorn sales executives, John learned the seed business during the tough years between 1975 and 1981, when Harold Noren retired.

John was, in fact, the man Charlie Roberts and I believed was my logical successor as CEO when Charlie and I retired, which would be sometime in the late 1980s. He was, and is, both a fine man and a very able executive. Our only doubt about John was the feeling among our operating people that his "city" background prevented him from fully understanding and identifying with our farmer customers and dealers.

SOURCE: DeKalb Genetics

The DeKalb-Pfizer Genetics Team
FROM LEFT TO RIGHT - Wid Crawford, John McCarter, T. Roberts, Jr, Rollie Hendrickson, Charlie Roberts, Barry Bloom

Downsizing

The process of merging the two organizations began at once. It was not easy, because both of the parents were overstaffed, DeKalb because of our decline in sales and Pfizer because it had built its staff on the assumption that its sales would soon be growing. Although both partners made every effort to be fair to the employees who were let go, inevitably many were severely disappointed. Downsizing continued throughout the first year of the partnership as our seed sales remained disappointingly flat. Capable, accomplished DeKalb regional sales managers were demoted to jobs they had held ten or fifteen years earlier. Those who were demoted were especially stung if they were replaced by former Pfizer people with less experience in the seedcorn business.

In my opinion, however, the formation of DeKalb-Pfizer Genetics was a saving move for us. Sales of DeKalb-originated hybrids declined significantly after the joint venture was created (I think by as much as 300,000 units) before they turned upward. In the interim, DeKalb-Pfizer T1100, a Pfizer-originated hybrid, was a big factor in leveling off our seedcorn sales decline in the mid-1980s.

In 1990, DeKalb purchased the Pfizer 30 percent interest in the joint venture for $80 million—$30 million in cash and $50 million in zero coupon bonds, as reported in the company's SEC form 10K for 1990. In 1988 the company name had been changed to DeKalb Genetics Corporation. It was the beginning of a new era.

The five-year period between 1980 and 1985 was a gloomy time for DeKalb for these reasons:

- Our important hybrid seedcorn sales dropped by more than 1.2 million units between 1980 and 1983, with 1982 and 1983 showing pre-tax losses of $9.5 million and $9.6 million respectively. These losses were in part attributable to corn acreage reductions brought about by our governments' Conservation Reserve Programs (CRPs). Large seed inventory writeoffs were caused by smaller markets that were the consequence of the CRP, but the 800,000-unit decline in seedcorn sales between 1980 and 1985 was also the consequence of reduced market share. Costs were high, too, because of our merger with Pfizer and subsequent plant closings, early retirements, and downsizing.
- The Heinold Companies, which had turned in annual pre-tax earnings of $15–17 million between 1979 and 1981, were showing signs of weakness as they adjusted to the problems created by negotiated commissions. They did well in their promotion of commodity trading funds, but profits in 1982 were only half what they had been only two years earlier.
- With U.S. oil drilling tapering off, Pride's oil well servicing business was having problems as well. Ray Tolson made a good decision when he canceled orders for $100 million worth of new rigs, but Pride had to write off rigs valued at $3.2 million in 1984, and a much larger writedown in 1985 seemed probable.

On the other hand, our oil business enjoyed profits between 1980 and 1984 that were nearly double those of the prior five years. However, oil prices weakened in 1984, and we expected they would continue to decline.

The Beginning of a Turnaround

Our problems added up to unacceptable return on equity in the first half of the 1980s, and the stock market was telling us we needed to make changes in our business. For all of these reasons, we convened a three-day meeting at the Greenbrier Hotel in West Virginia on July 22, 1985. Table 25-2 shows why we were forced to consider strategic changes in our business.

Attending the Greenbrier meeting were Tom Roberts, Jr., chairman and CEO; Charles C. Roberts, vice chairman of the board; John McCarter, Jr., chief operating officer and president of DK-Pfizer; Bruce P. Bickner, executive vice president; Frank L Bauer, senior vice president; Richard O. Ryan, group vice president; and John Stafford, vice president for finance and treasurer. Paul Judy, a DeKalb director and former president of A. G. Becker, who had served as a consultant for DeKalb, attempted to identify and evaluate moves we might take to recover our momentum. He identified this objective for our meeting:

> DeKalb should plan—and as appropriate, take—such financial strategic steps—including capital reductions, debt incurrence, cash flow allocations, divestitures, corporate reorganization, and operating and financial risks as are reasonable to improve substantially the intermediate and longer-term value of share ownership for the benefit of the longer-term shareholders of the company. The goal is value enhancement by steps sufficiently significant as to justify the interim and ultimate financial, operational, and organizational risks to be incurred.

Table 25-2
Pre-Tax Earnings by Division, 1975–1984
($000)

Year	Animal Products	Heinold Cos.	Seed	Oil and Gas	Pre-Tax Earnings	Post-Tax Return on Equity (%)
1975	(900)	4,600	26,100	16,400	43,100	16
1976	7,800	5,000	29,000	22,000	67,100	18
1977	8,500	5,100	31,600	24,300	69,500	18
1978	700	12,500	27,800	27,700	68,700	13
1979	3,600	16,900	28,600	32,700	81,800	14
1980	5,800	17,600	29,600	50,700	103,700	15
1981	8,700	15,000	26,800	61,500	112,000	10
1982	5,800	6,800	(9,600)	59,400	62,400	5
1983	14,200	11,700	(9,500)	34,300	50,700	4
1984	7,300	9,900	17,300	48,700	83,200	8

SOURCE: SEC form 10K for 1984 Ten-Year Statistical Review, page 66 or AR p. 42.

Charlie and I took Paul's advice seriously and prepared for the Greenbrier meeting by asking Duff & Phelps, a highly regarded management consulting firm, to appraise DeKalb's value and to recommend ways to maximize it. Table 26-2, prepared by Duff & Phelps, valued DeKalb's businesses as they were on April 25, 1985. Duff & Phelps proposed a "staggered divestiture," which recommended that we:

1. Tender 4 million shares of common on April 1, 1985, at $30 per share.
2. Sell HCM and HHM by December 31, 1985, $65 million.
3. Sell our poultry and swine divisions by August 31, 1986, for $25 million.
4. Sell Lindsay by August 31, 1987, for $12 million.
5. Sell Pride by August 31, 1987, for $35 million.
6. Allow DK Financial Services to expire as leases matured.
7. Continue to operate our seed and oil businesses.

If their predictions were realized, the consequence of their staggered divestiture program implemented between 1985 and 1989 would be:

1. An earnings increase from $1.83 to $3.51 per share.
2. A debt decrease from $255.5 million to $122.8 million.
3. An available cash increase from $0.0 to $16.0 million. An increase on NOPAT (net operating profit after tax) from 5.2 percent to 6.7 percent.

Each executive responsible for the businesses that would be eliminated discussed and evaluated the Duff & Phelps recommendations. These good men were highly objective and often concluded that the operations they managed should be either sold or spun off through public offerings to our shareholders, who could then decide for themselves whether to sell or keep their new shares. In the end, we reached agreement that one way or another DeKalb's business must be cut back to the basics, much as Duff & Phelps had suggested.

John Stafford, CFO, showed us that retaining our poultry and swine breeding operations would not be a decisive factor in our decisions.

Frank Bauer, who was responsible for Lindsay's center-pivot and credit operations, presented alternative choices for the future of Lindsay and concluded that a sale of the company and a total rundown of our credit business over a period of seven years was our most practical alternative. Since joining DeKalb in 1977, Frank had worked in corporate development. In 1982 he was made vice president with responsibility for expanding a credit business that Lindsay used to finance sales of its center-pivot irrigation machines. He had been quick to realize that DeKalb's portfolio of unused investment tax credits held in our oil businesses could be exploited by an in-house credit business. Frank was an astute businessman, and his credit business operated profitably until we decided to liquidate it gradually, diverting its funds to more fundamental DeKalb businesses

Rich Ryan, another bright young executive, recommended divesting Heinold Hog Markets separately and suggested potential buyers. He also recommended that the Pride Oil Well Servicing Company be sold or spun off. Both John McCarter, who presided at the meeting, and Bruce Bickner made useful, constructive comments as we evaluated the company's alternatives.

The meeting was simultaneously somewhat depressing as well as decisive and inspirational. The decisions we made there to sell or spin off nearly all of our operations other than genetics and oil would change DeKalb very significantly.

Table 25-3
Comparative Financial Data for DeKalb and Pioneer, 1980–1984

Pioneer

Fiscal Year	Sales ($ mil.)	Pretax Margin (%)	Net Income ($ mil.)	Net Margin (%)	Return on Equity (%)
1980	405.9	27.9	57.2	14.1	26.5
1981	478.0	25.8	63.5	13.3	24.3
1982	557.4	25.0	71.6	12.8	23.2
1983	505.4	15.1	43.7	8.7	12.8
1984	716.4	17.6	69.1	9.7	18.5

DeKalb

Fiscal Year	Sales ($ mil.)	Pretax Margin (%)	Net Income ($ mil.)	Net Margin (%)	Return on Equity (%)
1980	187.1	4.4	5.9	3.2	15
1981	214.5	6.9	14.9	6.9	10
1982	178.1	(.4)	(.4)	(.2)	5
1983	151.6	(13.1)	(20.3)	(13.4)	4
1984	199.1	3.1	2.5	1.3	8

SOURCE: S&P Compustat Service, and DeKalb's SEC form 10K, 1984 results. The ROE column is from 1984 form 10K. There are differences between net income in this table and DeKalb's 1982 and 1983 divisional results, because the 10K reports losses spread more evenly for these years. However, total losses reported for the two years are nearly equal.

TWO KEY EXECUTIVES LEAVE DEKALB

On September 2, 1985, after receiving an increase in salary that he considered inadequate, Art Tiddens tendered his resignation as president of Depco and DPC, our domestic and Canadian oil companies. Charlie and I were sorry to lose him, because he had done a great job of building our important oil businesses.

In March 1986, John McCarter also requested a large salary increase. When I told him that an increase of the size he wanted was not justified by our earnings outlook, he leaned hard on me but did not demand an immediate answer. Charlie agreed with me that John's request was excessive. John was bright, dedicated, hard working, and well educated by Princeton, the London School of Economics, and the Harvard Business School. He had come to DeKalb in March 1973 after serving with distinction as financial adviser to Illinois governor Ogilvie.

During his fifteen years with the company, John had moved steadily up the ladder, serving as manager of corporate development (1973); member of the Board of Directors (1974); and as vice president of seed (1975). In 1981 he was elected DeKalb's chief operating officer, presiding over DeKalb-Pfizer Genetics beginning in July 1982.

I thought the joint venture with Pfizer was not as successful as it should have been and began to doubt the wisdom of our selection of John as its COO. Ed Pratt, Pfizer's CEO had been favorably impressed by him, but he granted that Charlie Roberts and I knew John much better than he did, so he left the final decision on both his compensation and his future to the two of us.

Charlie was even more concerned about John than I was. He was not satisfied with John's handling of our DeKalb-Pfizer joint venture, and he felt John and Bruce Bickner would not function well together as our successors. Charlie thought Bruce's tremendous drive, his no-nonsense approach to problems, and his intelligence made him the best candidate for DeKalb's top job.

I agonized over the decision we had to make and finally agreed with Charlie that we should let John go. It was the most difficult decision I ever made. He returned to the consulting firm he had worked with early in his career, and a few years later was elected President of the prestigious Field Museum of Natural History in Chicago.

The Baton Is Passed to Bruce Bickner

Bruce Bickner was elected president and CEO of DeKalb in June 1986, immediately after John McCarter's departure. I became Chairman of the Board, and Charlie stayed on as Vice Chairman. Bruce, as President and CEO has lived up to his "tough but fair" reputation throughout his business career. After he took up the reins, he managed our U.S. oil business through a huge loss, sold our remaining oil business to Apache, and led the way to a recovery of market share in our seed business.

KEY DEKALB EXECUTIVES

Richard O. Ryan was hired by DeKalb in July 1969 and has served the company with high distinction in many different positions. He served as chief financial officer of the Pride Oil Well Servicing subsidiary until April 1984, when he was elected group vice president of the parent company. He was elected executive vice president and CFO of DeKalb Genetics in 1988 and promoted to president and chief operating officer in January 1990. I have great respect for Rich's business acumen, his knowledge of and dedication to the company, and his gentle but effective way of dealing with people.

Frank L. Bauer joined DeKalb in 1977, coming from McKinsey & Co., a leading management consulting firm. He held several executive positions with the Heinold companies, Lindsay, and the DeKalb Corporation, where he was senior vice president and served as a director of the DeKalb Energy Company from 1985 into the early 1990s. Frank conceived and presided over a very successful operation at DeKalb Financial Services.

Doug Roberts, Charlie's son and my nephew, joined DeKalb in 1974, after graduating from the University of Illinois School of Agriculture. Doug started as a sales trainee and served as district sales manager, first in Indiana and next in our very important northwest Iowa district before moving back to DeKalb, where he held several seed marketing positions, advancing steadily upward. He was appointed vice president of seed marketing in 1994. Doug's recognition of the importance of dealing personally with customers, dealers, corn breeders, and others has made him a tremendously effective marketing leader. He was a key factor in DeKalb's improved competitiveness in the mid-1990s. I think it likely that he will someday lead the company.

Seed Production Leaders

Ed Uhland was one of DeKalb's most solid, likable, and trusted seed production managers. He came to work for DeKalb in 1939 as "inspector" or manager of quality control at Storm Lake, Iowa, where he learned the seed production business from Paul Vance, the most capable plant manager DeKalb ever had. Ed was named assistant plant manager at Shenandoah, Iowa, in 1949. After serving in the Navy air force for more than three years, Ed was appointed plant manager at Marshall, Missouri. I remember being impressed with Ed's ingenuity when, as he harvested the first hybrid sorghum seed ever produced in Missouri, he figured out how to separate the morning-glory seeds from grain sorghum seeds, which were nearly the same size and weight. After Paul Vance's death in 1973, Ed moved to DeKalb as seed production manager. He was appointed manager of international seed operations in 1981 and retired in 1983.

Nate McGuire, an able and dedicated man, came to work for DeKalb right out of the University of Missouri, went through our training program, and was assigned to our seed production operation at

Humboldt, Iowa. He worked his way steadily up from detasseling crew chief to inspector at Marshall, Missouri, to plant superintendent at Tuscola, Illinois, to seed lab manager at DeKalb. After a stretch in the armed services, he worked in advertising at DeKalb before becoming assistant plant manager at Deshler, Ohio. In 1964, he moved to the plant manager job at Marshall, Missouri, before being appointed western regional seed production manager in 1973. He was made vice president for seed operations after Ed Uhland became manager of international seed operations.

Seed Researchers

Dr. Charlie Krull joined DeKalb in 1968. Charlie's first assignment with DeKalb was to develop hybrid wheat adapted to Argentina. Although wheat hybridization failed, the wheat varieties Charlie developed were outstanding and won much-deserved recognition and market share. Charlie became a corn breeder for DeKalb-Italiana, where he served with distinction before becoming vice president for temperate corn research, a position he held from 1978 to 1986, when he was named director of research for DeKalb. He held that position until he left the company in 1993. Charlie is an excellent plant breeder and was invaluable to the company's research efforts in the 1970s and 1980s.

Dr. John Pfund joined DeKalb in 1975 after completing his graduate work at the University of Minnesota. He worked for Del Monte Foods for several years before joining DeKalb as a corn breeder. He became an area director in 1982 and an associate director for the eastern United States in 1990. In 1994 he accepted additional responsibility as director of agronomic services, supervising the activities of all of DeKalb's field agronomists. He was promoted to vice president of research in 1996, reporting to the chairman of the board, Bruce Bickner. He deserves a lot of credit for the development of the hybrids that have been the basis of DeKalb's market share gains in the mid-1990s.

Dr. Dave Smith joined DeKalb in 1973, less than three years after the southern corn leaf blight epidemic swept through the southern and central corn belts. As a graduate student, he worked with Dr. Art Hooker, who was one of our country's leading corn physiologists. Dave set up a network of small corn research plots that allowed him to track the buildup of corn pathogens and permitted him and his colleagues to identify new and potentially dangerous mutant pathogens—and give plant breeders the earliest opportunity to select for resistance in segregating plant populations. Dave was named director of research in 1996. He was named a fellow of the American Phytopathological Society in 1992.

Dr. Forrest Troyer joined DeKalb-Pfizer in 1982 after directing corn research for Pfizer Genetics for five years. Before that, Forrest had led Pioneer's northern and Eastern corn research effort (8 of 14 corn stations), developing several outstanding hybrids. He is in his family's third generation of plant breeders and has degrees from Purdue, Illinois, and Minnesota. Forrest developed a very successful a corn breeding group for Pfizer, as is evident from the fine performance of its leading hybrid in the 1980s, T1100. Forrest is an honored friend and a great corn breeder. He retired from DeKalb in 1993.

Dr. Bill Crum joined DeKalb in 1964 immediately after earning his Ph.D. in genetics at North Carolina State University. From that year through 1976, he rose steadily in stature and ability as a corn breeder and statistician at our research headquarters in DeKalb. Bill was a member of a team that was responsible for integrating pathology, entomology, and physiology into DeKalb's corn breeding programs. His broad knowledge of statistics served him well in the development of improved methods of analyzing research data. Serving as associate director of corn research from 1976 through 1978, his primary emphasis was on nutritional quality, physiology, and entomology. From 1978 to 1986, Bill worked jointly with Dr. Charlie Krull, opening eighteen corn research stations around the world, including facilities in the United States, Italy, Spain, Argentina, and Australia, quadrupling research efforts directed toward line improvement and improved yield trial testing. In 1986 Bill was appointed vice president of DeKalb's International Technical Services. He directs worldwide sunflower research and has expanded DeKalb's crop data system to evaluate product performance in international markets.

Dr. Glen Robison came to work for DeKalb and Dr. Bruce Maunder in sorghum research while earning his bachelor's degree at Texas Tech, which is located in Lubbock, near DeKalb's sorghum research facility. A native of Hereford, Texas, Glen moved to the University of Nebraska, where he earned his Ph.D. In 1966 he established DeKalb's northern research program for sorghum in Nebraska, reporting to Dr. Maunder. In 1984 he moved to DeKalb, Illinois, as director of tropical seed research, covering a wide area of geography ranging from Thailand to Brazil.

Administrators and Sales Personnel

Jerry Armstrong literally grew up with DeKalb. His father, Harry, climbed the ladder with DeKalb in the '30s, '40s, and '50s and was manager of our Warren, Illinois, seedcorn plant while Jerry was growing up. Jerry's first job was the same as mine—he was a waterboy. From that beginning, he moved from Warren to DeKalb (the city), where he went to college and worked as a janitor, moving up every two years in the 1960s from accounting flunky to program analyst to internal auditor to budget director to manager of budget and costs. In 1969 he was made controller of the Genetics Division; in 1978 he became vice president; in 1981 controller of the Seed Division of DeKalb-Pfizer Genetics; in 1986 vice president for finance and CFO; and in 1990 senior vice president and CFO. From 1993 through 1996 he was, successively, vice president and controller of DeKalb Genetics and vice president of Worldwide Supply

Management. Jerry retired on January 17, 1997.

Bill Burrow joined DeKalb as a dealer at Springlake, Texas. In 1957 he joined DeKalb full time as a district manager headquartered in Tulia, Texas. Following a one-year assignment as manager of spring wheat development, Bill moved to Wichita, Kansas, to manage the Central Plains region, covering Kansas and parts of Colorado, Texas, and Missouri. In 1968 Bill was promoted to western area manager, covering all sales west of the Missouri River. In 1977, Bill moved to DeKalb and assumed additional sales responsibilities as area manager covering the southeast region. Bill was a delightful, loyal, and sensitive person. Unfortunately, he was demoted at the time of the DeKalb-Pfizer joint venture and left the company in 1982. He died in 1989.

Leo Damkroger joined DeKalb in 1957 after I interviewed him at the University of Nebraska. Leo worked as a management trainee in the Poultry and Seed Divisions until he moved into sales, his forte. Leo's first district was in Oklahoma starting in 1960. He then managed districts in Pennsylvania, Texas, and Minnesota before moving to DeKalb as sales promotion manager in 1974. Leo served in various staff sales and marketing positions before becoming director of training; he served there until 1995 when he took over a new position as manager of community and employee relations. Leo, in my opinion, was one of the most dedicated employees we ever had.

Dwight Glenn began his career with DeKalb as a sales trainee in Lubbock, Texas, in 1959. A native of Kansas, Dwight got his degree at Kansas State University. He was appointed district manager for the panhandle of Texas, Oklahoma, and southwest Kansas in 1960. In 1961 Dwight moved to Corpus Christi, Texas, to manage the highest-volume district in sorghum sales. In 1964 he moved to DeKalb to take charge of wheat development, a position he held first in DeKalb and then in Wichita before the company sold the wheat division in 1982. He was a very capable and dedicated colleague.

Chuck Lindhart joined DeKalb in 1962 as a sales trainee. He was district manager in Indiana from 1963 to 1969, when he moved to DeKalb to take charge of product planning. In 1970 he was named regional manager for the eastern region headquartered in York, Pennsylvania. Chuck moved back to DeKalb in 1976 as eastern area manager and then manager of seed operations. He was promoted to vice president in 1980 and held that position when he left DeKalb in 1986 to go into the real estate business.

Tom Melton started with DeKalb as a part-time summer employee at the Monmouth production plant. In 1962, after graduating from the University of Illinois, Tom joined DeKalb as a sales trainee in Indiana. He became a district manager in 1963 and then moved to Illinois in 1968. He was promoted to regional sales manager at London, Ohio, in 1972. Tom went back to the home office in 1975 as director of seed planning. He then held a number of marketing and sales roles and was named sales manager in 1977. At the time of the joint venture with Pfizer he was named vice president of marketing. In 1988 he moved into the role of group product director and in 1992 held the position of national accounts manager until retiring in 1995.

Elmer Monson joined DeKalb after his graduation from Iowa State University in 1949, where he and I were classmates. Elmer's first assignment was in the advertising department in DeKalb; he then moved into sales as district manager at Brookings, South Dakota. In 1957, Elmer moved to Redwood Falls as district manager and state manager for Wisconsin in 1962. Elmer was promoted to regional sales manager in 1963 and moved to York, Pennsylvania. In 1968 he moved to DeKalb as manager of market planning. He then transferred to the seed operations department as manager of foundations in 1977. He left the company in 1981.

Kent Schulze started as a summer intern in 1965. A natural leader, he moved rapidly up DeKalb's ladder. He was a district sales manager at Red Oak, Iowa, in 1968. In 1972 he moved to Galesburg, Illinois, as district manager and to London, Ohio, in 1975 as regional sales manager. In 1977, Kent was promoted to eastern area manager and then moved to DeKalb, where he served in various sales and marketing roles. He was promoted to vice president in 1980 and senior vice president in 1985. In 1986, Kent was named president of DeKalb-Pfizer, where he served until leaving in 1990 to become president of Northrup King.

Key Changes, 1980–1995

1980	Roger Rasmusen, vice president, resigns and takes Baxter Labs job. Dr. Bruce Maunder returns to hands-on sorghum research in Lubbock, Texas. Dr. Charlie Krull is made temperate corn research director. Bruce Bickner is made group vice president.
1981	Harold Noren retires; John McCarter carries on. Pride cancels an order for 100 service rigs and saves $50 million.
1982	DeKalb announces a joint venture with Pfizer; McCarter becomes CEO. Soybeans are added to our product line. Tom Melton becomes vice president for seed marketing.
1983	DeKalb buys out Nicor's oil, gains $50 million in tax benefits.
1984	Ralph Klopfenstine is released from Heinold Commodities.
1985	Art Tiddens resigns. Tom Neal replaces him. Important Greenbrier meeting July 22.
1986	John McCarter leaves DeKalb. Bruce Bickner takes over as CEO.

1986	Tom Roberts, Jr., and Charlie Roberts step down as president and vice president, becoming chairman and vice chairman of the board.
	Heinold Commodities is sold to Con-Agra.
1987	Heinold Hog Markets is sold to the employees.
1988	Lindsay Manufacturing is sold to employees in October.
	Bruce Bicker is elected chairman of the board.
	Tom Roberts, Jr., and Charlie Roberts are elected chairman and vice chairman of the Executive Committee.
1989	Pride makes a $20.5 million equity placement.
1990	DeKalb buys out Pfizer's stake in DeKalb Genetics.
	DeKalb "stretches" to buy Royal Exploration Co. and transfers most of its exploration budget to developing the Royal properties.
1991	Exploration of Royal properties fails, DeKalb sells U.S. (Depco) to Louis Dreyfus Gas Holdings for approximately $104 million, and the company takes a loss of $66,653,000 from oil exploration, as reported in its 1993 10K report.
1992	DeKalb takes an additional loss from Royal transactions of $58,695,000, also as reported in its 1993 10K.
	The Thomas H. Roberts, Jr., family, believing DeKalb could not compete over the long term, sells all of its shares to the company.
1993	DeKalb's remaining U.S. oil properties are sold for approximately $5.1 million.
1994	Mike Finnegan, DeKalb's new chief operating officer, dies on September 17.
1995	DeKalb Energy Canada stock is sold by shareholders to Apache for a price close to $25 per share, or a total value of nearly $240 million pre-tax.

Chapter 26

Our International Seed Business Blooms, 1980-1995

This chapter reports on three DeKalb operations through the 1980s to the mid-1990s: DeKalb Argentina, Braskalb (Brazil), an DeKalb Italiana.

DEKALB HYBRIDS ARE WINNERS IN ARGENTINA

Having survived many years of crossing and testing, all of our Argentine product lines are superb. DK4F37, a four-way cross introduced in 1987, quickly became DeKalb's biggest seller, with sales reaching 10,000 metric tons per year in the early 1990s. Then in 1995 we began moving into single-cross hybrids with DK664 and DK752, which Fabio Nider describes as "the best on the market."

Jorge Gherko, DeKalb Argentina President

As enthusiastic as I am about Fabio Nider, I must acknowledge the important contributions of Jorge Gherko, DeKalb Argentina's president, to the success of his company. Jorge was highly recommended by Ramon Agrasar to succeed him as CEO, and he has performed superbly in his job. He is a quiet, hard-working, very intelligent man who understands the economics of both his business and his country.

SOURCE: DeKalb Argentina

Fabio Nider and Jorge Gherko, 1995

SOURCE: DeKalb Argentina

Ramon Agrasar and Fabio Nider, 1995

SOURCE: T. H. Roberts, Jr.

Ramon Agrasar & Orlando Fagioli Retire

Hybrid Sunflowers—A Promising New Idea

As Ramon Agrasar came to know DeKalb, he realized that our most important business goal was to be a leader in the hybridization of seeds. That had been our credo since 1923, when we decided to try to develop hybrid seedcorn, which most agronomists considered a risky project. When we learned that sorghum might be hybridized by pollinating plants with male-sterile cytoplasm with pollen from plants carrying fertility-restoration genes, we moved quickly to become a leader in the development of hybrid sorghum. Similarly, but unsuccessfully, we tried hard to develop hybrid wheat and hybrid cotton.

When Ramon learned that sunflower hybridization might be possible by the same method that made hybrid sorghum possible, he asked us to allow him to try to hybridize sunflowers, which were a significant crop in Argentina. We told him to go ahead with a small program, but to keep us informed.

A Talk with Dr. Anibal Fernandez,
Sunflower Breeder

The next few pages are excerpts from a conversation I had in early 1995 with Dr. Anibal Fernandez, DeKalb Argentina's sunflower breeder, and Ramon Agrasar.

Tom: Ramon, as I recall, your first efforts to hybridize sun flowers were in 1968, about the same time that your friends Juan Carlos San Martin and Dr. Kugler, director of the Pergamino Experiment Station, started a hybrid sunflower breeding program. I think each of you traded ideas and helped each other.

Ramon: Yes, and Anibal joined DeKalb in 1976, when we decided to increase our breeding efforts.

Tom: What is the size of the sunflower seed market?

Anibal: Argentina plants 2 to 3 million hectares annually, mostly in the semi-dry areas west and south of our corn belt. Russia plants about 2.5 million hectares, mostly in their dry and short growing season areas. Ukraine plants more than 1 million hectares, and France plants about 1 million hectares, and their farmers achieve by far the highest sunflower seed yields in the world by using hybrid seed and modern, highly technical farming methods.
China may have more than 1 million hectares, and U.S. plantings in central North and South Dakota have been increasing. However, Russia and the Ukraine, which were the only countries that continued breeding sunflowers for high oil content between 1920 and 1950, greatly increased the oil content in their varietal seed, but didn't plant hybrid seed because it is too costly for their extensive farming methods. At the moment, we are the number two company in France now, and growing. Our newest product, 3790, is growing in demand because of its resistance to a new disease called Formiposis.

Ramon: How many beehives per hectare do you need to get

good pollination in your hybrid seed production fields?

Anibal: We need to use two or three hives per hectare to have good pollination. We like to have the bees hungry when they arrive because the male-sterile female sunflowers are only fertile for one week. I remember one very hot, dry summer when the bees did not want to work. They were in their hives, but they just stayed there, and our seed crop dropped to 500 tons from the prior year's 2,200 tons. After that, we divided our seed production fields into three areas that were many kilometers apart.

Tom: What kinds of sunflowers make the best hybrids when they are crossed?

Anibal: We have been crossing Russian and Argentine seed parents. They produce a high-yielding hybrid having an oil content of about 42 percent, which is acceptable in the marketplace, but farmers get a 2 percent premium for each 1 percent of oil content above 42 percent, so many customers are demanding hybrids with higher oil content. To achieve this, we breed parents with the genetic ability to produce oil.... That means using more Russian high-oil germ plasm in our parents and giving up a little total yield. Just now, DeKalb hybrids predominate in areas wanting high oil content. ICI's Contiflor hybrid is predominant in areas where high yield but lower oil content are in demand. However, we should soon be offering hybrids of the Contiflor type that will considerably out-yield Contiflor.

Tom: How many sunflower breeders does DeKalb now have?

Anibal: Dr. Jose Raith joined us seven years ago after he finished his Ph.D. at Oregon State. He is a very able breeder and is in charge of our Mar del Plata research station. I am responsible for my own breeding work in Buenos Aires Province in addition to being in overall charge of DeKalb's sunflower breeding effort.

Also, Dr. Bill Crum, who is in charge of DeKalb's international research programs, has been very helpful in helping to assemble a large pool of the very best sunflower breeding material in the world. We now have exchange agreements with the Russians, the Ukrainians, the Bulgarians, the Hungarians, the Romanians, and the Turks. In addition, Patrick Wei, who is working with the Chinese, is doing a great job. I believe DeKalb G101 has become a leading hybrid in China.

A Great Team Produces Terrific Results

In the 1980s and early 1990s, DeKalb Argentina's hybrid seedcorn sales rose steadily to a dominant market share, exceeding 40 percent of corn plantings in the early 1990s. Table 26-1 shows the growth in our corn and sunflower plantings and the decline of grain sorghum and Sudax plantings, as better times for the Argentine economy led to intensive farming with modern equipment throughout the pampas. DeKalb hybrid seedcorn in 1994 was the clear industry leader in Argentina, with its market share in excess of 40 percent; Pioneer, our main competitor in Argentina, had 20 percent.

Table 26-1
Argentine Hybrid Seed Sales, 1980–1992
(metric tons)

Fiscal Year	Corn	Sudax and Sorghum	Sunflower	Pre-Tax Earnings ($US)
1980	13,781	6,089	1,194	7,029
1981	15,253	6,694	756	(3,473)
1982	16,688	5,504	1,251	(5,151)
1983	14,250	8,864	2,101	5,983
1984	14,340	7,186	534	6,191
1985	13,686	6,010	1,183	5,813
1986	15,388	3,632	1,683	5,041
1987	13,782	4,606	1,189	662
1988	9,333	3,842	2,261	(1,035)
1989	10,620	3,447	1,985	3,421
1990	8,090	4,492	2,275	(3,314)
1991	9,697	2,847	2,612	2,776
1992	13,315	2,522	2,867	6,060

SOURCE: DeKalb Argentina records.

DEKALB'S SECOND DECADE IN BRAZIL

Amauri DiMarzio Stakes His Future on Hybrid Seedcorn

In 1978, DeKalb's first experimental corn hybrids suited to Brazil were tested on a model farm at Itatiba in the State of Sao Paulo by Amauri Di Marzio, an able, dedicated, brazilian we chose to manage our business in the country. The experimental hybrids he tested were mostly crosses between inbred lines developed by DeKalb at semi-tropical and tropical research stations (in the southeastern U.S. and Mexico) and recommended by Dr. Basil Tsotsis, who was at that time responsible for DeKalb's tropical corn research. Basil had developed and collected good tropical inbred lines, and some of them found their way into new DeKalb hybrids that were well adapted to Brazil..

Another event of long-term importance was the 1978 hiring of Dr. Octavio Solferini to assist Walter Trevisan in the development of hybrids adapted to Brazil. Solferini's employment became very important in 1982, when Trevisan, whose family preferred living in Campinas to the more remote city of Barretos, accepted a corn breeding job with Cargill.

DeKalb Corn Research Program Begins at Barretos, S. P.

In late 1979, Amauri DiMarzio bought a farm outside of Barretos in the State of Sao Paulo 180 miles north of Campinas. He arranged to buy the beautiful 120-hectare Barretos farm through a Brazilian relative for only $1,300 per hectare. This was an important move because (a) it was an excellent farm well suited for selecting hybrids for the growing tropical-subtropical corn growing area; (b) it was located near good public schools, an important consideration for our corn breeders; and (c) it was located close to a good source of irrigation water.

A second research farm was purchased in Passo Fundo in the State of Rio Grande do Sul in 1981. It was a 168-hectare farm representative of Brazil's important semi-tropical southern corn growing area. It cost slightly more per hectare than our tropical corn research station at Barretos and had similar attributes.

DeKalb Introduces Its First Hybrid Adapted to Brazil

DeKalb Brazil released its first Brazilian hybrid (XL560) in 1980. It had performed well in Brazilian tests, and was a four-way cross between a single cross of two inbreds developed by DeKalb in Mexico with another single cross between two inbred lines selected in the southern part of the state of Georgia in the United States. We were still selling it in 1995.

The introduction of XL560 was marred somewhat by our inability to purchase adequate seed drying and cleaning facilities as well as by sloppy detasseling by people who had never detasseled before. But these difficulties were partially overcome the next year with help from Stan Bozdech, an experienced seed processing equipment expert from the United States, and by a decision to purchase an old seed processing plant at Ipua in the State of Sao Paulo area, which allowed us to "get by" in the early 1980s. Much more modern equipment was purchased later.

Our seed production increased slowly from 800 tons in 1980 to 3,600 tons in 1982. We had some production problems related to inadequate seed processing equipment that took us a while to correct. The U.S. parent company was reluctant to invest more U.S. dollars in Brazil's highly inflationary economy, and earnings generated in Brazil were low because indigenous producers wanted to discourage foreign competition. Hybrid seed prices in the early 1980s in Brazil were only half as high as they were in most of the rest of the world.

Rio Grande do Sul Corn Research Plans

Amauri's interest in developing hybrid seedcorn for the semi-tropical, semi-temperate area of southern Brazil was challenged by both the U.S. parent company and by many Brazilians, who pointed out that soybean production occupied most of the productive soil in the area, to the disadvantage of corn. Evidence was developing, however, that soybean diseases were becoming more serious every year because of continuous soybean planting. Some Brazilian agronomists argued that soybeans would soon have to be rotated with corn in order to control the spread of disease. Amauri thought their arguments were sound, and decided to breed hybrids adapted to this highly fertile, wealthy agriculture area. Rapid increases in the practice of alternating corn and soybeans in the area during the early 1990s suggest that his decision to set up research and production of hybrid seedcorn in southern Brazil was very wise.

1984: A Year of Decision for DeKalb and DiMarzio

In March of 1984, a delegation from DeKalb traveled to Brazil to tell Amauri DiMarzio that DeKalb had decided to sell the company's Brazilian operations but to continue supplying the buyer with DeKalb-owned genetic germ plasm. The delegation included John McCarter, president of DeKalb-Pfizer Genetics; Jack Nelson, vice president for animal products; and Larry Nolin, manager of Central and South American seed operations. They told Amauri that their preference was to sell to Amauri DiMarzio or to a group of his best people rather than to a third party.

Amauri asked a group of his key people to join with him in buying the company. He cooperated with the appraiser DeKalb hired and came to the United States with Walter Zacharias, his financial manager, with an offer to buy the company. DeKalb rejected the offer.

Thereafter, Citibank found a prospective Brazilian buyer, but his bid was no higher than Amauri's, and Larry Nolin reported that the buyer planned to liquidate the company immediately in order to collect its Brazilian tax carry-forwards. Because DeKalb wanted the company to continue operating and compensating the U.S. parent company for the use of its germ plasm, Larry Nolin decided that DeKalb should give preference to Amauri and his group.

Both buyers continued to negotiate and agreed to a November 28,

1984, deadline for a final decision from DeKalb. Always optimistic, Amauri prepared a speech and much publicity that would announce his group's purchase of the company at a banquet of DeKalb poultry customers scheduled for the deadline date. He decided with his partners (Walter Zacharias, Tercilio DiMarzio, Roberto Carvalho, and Alfranio Oliveira) to name the new company "Braskalb," and invited the press and many important Brazilian officials as well, hoping that he could make a dramatic announcement at the meeting. Just in case he wasn't the successful bidder, he prepared a completely different speech. The decision he hoped for was delivered to him only a few moments before he was to address the 500 people assembled for the banquet.

For Amauri, it was the fulfillment of his dreams. DeKalb, in turn, received valuable tax benefits immediately, and over the next ten years royalties steadily increased as the seed business grew. In 1994 Amauri reported that Braskalb paid $1.2 million to DeKalb to compensate it for the genetic improvements that are the fundamental source of Braskalb's success.

Braskalb has grown rapidly and successfully in a country undergoing political and economic changes that only local management could respond to quickly and effectively. In my opinion, the success of Braskalb should serve as a model for DeKalb in other countries with high rates of inflation and wildly fluctuating currencies. The key to success, of course, is to find able, honest, energetic entrepreneurs like Amauri DiMarzio, and develop contracts that allow them to prosper personally after compensating DeKalb for the genetic improvements it contributes.

Braskalb's Record So Far

Since its creation on November 28, 1984, Braskalb has been very well managed. In its first ten years, Braskalb reports:

- Gross sales increased to $25 million.
- The number of store dealers increased from 300 to 1,200.
- The number of corn hybrids offered increased from two to twenty.
- Seed sales increased from 2,000 to 12,000 million tons, or 528,000 fifty-pound bags.
- Net profits ranged from less than $1 million to $3 million per year.
- All years were profitable.
- The number of employees increased from 60 to 200.
- The company invested $10 million in seed processing and distribution facilities.
- All financing was been supplied by banks or the government.

Braskalb has been highly successful, but like most successful businesses, its growth did not come easily. It was fueled by Amauri's willingness to borrow heavily at high interest rates to finance the construction of the largest and best-equipped seed processing plants in Brazil, and by his yearly decisions to increase seed production in anticipation that Brazilian farmers would increase their plantings of Braskalb seedcorn. Courage was required to establish a research station and a seed processing plant in the "soybean country" of Rio Grande do Sul when farmers who lived there wanted to plant only soybeans, but Amauri correctly believed that hybrid corn would be used in a crop rotation system with soybeans.

Amauri's most trying times occurred when his company was first organized and its production employees were asked to produce a quality product in inadequate facilities. They made up for their inadequate machinery with long hours of hard work. That hard work, backed up by Amauri's entrepreneurial spirit, is paying off today.

What Is the Future of Braskalb?

Amauri predicts that Braskalb will invest more in corn research for the Cerrado area. This will allow the company to increase its sales at least 50 percent over the next five to ten years. In 1995, this project was already being implemented in Acréuna, Goias, on a new 1,000-hectare farm irrigated with center pivots. The company will also expand plant capacity for ear corn drying to serve an increase in demand for seed production in the state of Goias. Research will be increased to develop new varieties of crops such as soybeans and alfalfa after Brazil issues a plant variety protection law.

Braskalb is also interested in investing in the swine business, using the same model it has used with seed. It has plans to expand its capital, opening it up to allow for growth as well as to allow employees and customers to share in their success. Finally, investments in their people and their customers' well-being will always be priority items for Braskalb.

DEKALB ITALIANA: HARD TIMES

The 1981–1990 decade was as full of serious setbacks as the prior two decades had been full of success for DeKalb Italiana. The biggest problems were as follows:

- Pioneer's became a serious competitor in 1981 with a late-maturing, high-yielding hybrid called Lorena (Pioneer 3183 in the United States). This hybrid hit the market in volume in the mid-1980s, simultaneously with a sharp decline in the cost of natural gas for drying the moisture out of its grain, which was usually high in moisture at harvest time. Lorena yielded well and was a big hit, as Italy's farmers' preference swung to high-yielding, late-maturing, high-moisture (FAO 600 maturity) hybrids, which they could dry with low-cost natural gas. DeKalb Italiana countered with Logos (DK636) in 1989 and Paolo (DK711) in 1990. These were good hybrids, but by the time they hit the market, Pioneer's Lorena, Luana, and Samantha had become solidly entrenched.

- Adding more misery to DeKalb Italiana's problems, XL72a, which had been gaining market acceptance steadily after its introduction into the Italian market in 1979, ran into serious lodging problems during unusually wet harvest seasons in 1988 and 1989.
- An even more significant factor in the company's decline was the death in 1984 of Antonio Marchetto. He had been a strong leader and was greatly missed. When his son, Marco, was not chosen to replace his father, Marco and his sister Isabella filed debilitating lawsuits against the company. These diverted management's attention for several years, during which Sergio Marchetto was being treated for cancer and could not manage effectively. He ultimately retired in 1990. Fortunately, he recovered completely from his illness. His son, Mauritzio, who had trained at DeKalb, stepped into his father's shoes as president and performed well under exceedingly difficult conditions.

SOURCE: DeKalb Italiana

Mauritzio Marchetto, President DeKalb Italiana

Table 26-2 tells the sad story of DeKalb Italiana's hybrid seedcorn sales after 1980. My estimate of royalty payments to the U.S. parent are based on the conservative estimate of $1.00 per 50-lb. bag.

Table 26-2
DeKalb Italiana Seed Corn Sales Record, 1981–1990

Year	Sales (000 metric tons)	Estimated Royalty to DeKalb ($US)
1981	6,057	266,508
1982	5,528	243,232
1983	4,350	191,400
1984	3,840	168,960
1985	3,385	148,940
1986	2,650	116,600
1987	2,210	97,240
1988	2,478	109,032
1989	2,280	100,320
1990	1,493	65,692

SOURCE: DeKalb Italiana.

Peace at Last— and a Competent New Managing Director

Ultimately, DeKalb settled its legal as well as its management issues by buying the interests of both Marchetto families in the company and appointing Mauritzio Marchetto managing director of the new company, which was named DeKalb Italia. Mauritzio has spent his entire working life in the employ of the company, focusing mostly on the marketing side of the business, where he grew steadily in effectiveness as he gained experience. In his youth, he trained for several summers in DeKalb, Illinois.

I had retired from DeKalb at the time of Mauritzio's appointment as managing director of DeKalb Italia, so I played no part in his promotion, but I believe it was a good decision by DeKalb's management. He is hard working, able, and respected by his colleagues.

There appears to be light at the end of the tunnel for DeKalb Italia. Several new and promising hybrids had been produced by DeKalb Italia, so prospects for a turnaround in the business seem to be good.

Chapter 27

DeKalb's Oil Business Runs Dry 1980-1994

The period 1980 through 1995 was one of sharp price fluctuation for the oil industry. Oil prices, which averaged US$10.33 per barrel in Canada in 1979 soared to $24.15 per barrel in 1984, fell off slightly in 1985, and plummeted to $13.63 in 1988 before climbing back to $16.76 in 1992. Gas price swings were even wider.

CANADIAN OPERATIONS

DeKalb's Canadian oil business had by 1985 become DeKalb's most significant oil operation as seen in Table 28-1 on the next page. Bob Johnson and his staff kept very busy, mostly seeking oil or gas in deeper horizons beneath our earlier cardium plays. Very significant gas production was discovered in the glauconite formation in the Leafland area in the early 1980s, the steady pace of field expansion continued at Nevis, and a large gas discovery was made at Sunchild. All information about DeKalb's Canadian oil activities was provided by the DeKalb Energy staff at my request.

Unfortunately, Sunchild was not served by pipelines, so a frustrated Art Tiddens looked into the possibility of developing a carbon black plant (which makes its product by burning natural gas); he decided against the idea when he found out that carbon black was in surplus supply all over the world. Sunchild's 18,131 million cubic feet of gas reserves were the equivalent of 3,037,000 barrels of oil, so our inability to market its product was agonizing. The Sunchild gas finally was marketed in the early 1990s through DeKalb's ownership of a portion of a new pipeline that was built to serve California. The idea of participating in ownership of a new pipeline was Bruce Bickner's, and it was a good one.

Leafland Glauconite—a Key Play in 1980

When Art Tiddens authorized development of the Leafland cardium play in 1963, he recognized that the deeper glauconite gas sands might have more promise than the shallower cardium oil, so he authorized a deep test to the Peskisko, where he encountered twenty feet of gas-bearing glauconitic sand that was not economic at that time (1963). In 1980, after gas prices had risen high enough to make the glauconite gas profitable, Art and Bob decided to develop it. Their success is reported in Chapter 19, which estimates an ultimate gain of $53,837,000 from this "key play."

Bingley

The last of our key plays was discovered at Bingley in 1982 by geologists working under Bob Johnson's leadership. Its success is reported in Chapter 19, which estimates ultimate gains of $112,683,000.

Table 27-1
DeKalb's Oil & Gas Business Summary
DeKalb Energy (Canada), 1980–1994
(U.S.$)

Year	Adjusted Equity[a] (Book) ($000)	Year-End SEC Value (After Tax) ($000)	Adjusted Net Income (After Tax)[b] ($000)	Return on Investm't	Price of Oil (per bbl.)	Price of Gas (Mcf.)
1980	47,713	60,000	11,260	23.6%	12.03	2.01
1981	51,932	65,000	9,219	17.7%	14.46	2.19
1982	57,448	69,200	9,716	16.9%	17.97	2.26
1983	61,119	71,600	10,866	17.8%	22.96	1.90
1984	92,912	104,200	37,969	40.8%	24.15	1.93
1985	100,146	158,100	58,939	58.8%	23.60	1.87
1986	119,165	121,400	(31,881)	(26.8%)	17.18	1.58
1987	135,177	150,000	32,545	24.1%	14.83	1.29
1988	176,260	167,000	26,641	15.1%	13.63	1.31
1989	216,188	191,400	28,994	13.4%	15.64	1.36
1990	232,333	202,300	18,172	7.8%	20.50	1.37
1991	226,612	161,000	(37,233)	(16.4%)	17.68	1.22
1992	194,856	160,500	(12,108)	(6.2%)	16.76	1.16
1993	213,937	202,400	52,906	24.7%	14.45	1.44
1994	213,499	159,600	(35,987)	(16.8%)	13.93	1.53

SOURCE: DeKalb Energy records.
a. Adjusted equity includes dividends declared and paid to the parent company.
b. Adjusted net income includes year-end SEC increase or decrease over the prior year.

Unexplored Zones in Alberta Made Subject to Bidding

On January 1, 1983, Alberta ruled that oil and gas rights below productive horizons would revert to the crown and were available to bidders. This change was, on balance, good for DeKalb Petroleum because it gave us a chance to bid on deep zones, which competitors had been holding by production in shallower zones. The change in regulations gave us a chance, for example, to bid for glauconite zone rights in areas where we had previously been stymied.

As we acquired some key leases, we immediately drilled them. Having learned at Blueberry Mountain how profitable gas plants can be, we decided to participate in the construction of gas plants at both Leafland and Bingley field, because they clearly had enough substantial reserves. The Bingley plant went on-stream in January 1985, and the Leafland plant startup followed one month later. Both plants were very profitable.

DEPCO IN THE UNITED STATES IN THE 1980S

Depco enjoyed the same high oil and gas prices that played such an important part in our Canadian success between 1980 and 1985, except that good drilling prospects were harder to find in the more explored United States. Nevertheless, Art and his staff continued their exploration efforts in the Dakotas, New Mexico, and California, as well as in the remaining unexplored International Oil & Gas properties in Colorado and Wyoming. Some U.S. explorers were finding gas at depths of 20,000 feet or more, and high gas prices justified drilling this deep where seismic data suggested structures were large. Art and his geologists participated in 1983 in drilling the Owl Creek Tribal Unit in Fremont County, Wyoming. The well looked promising but turned out to be a 24,000-foot dry hole that cost in excess of $30 million. Depco had a 10 percent interest.

Art Wins Our Respect One More Time

Art's aggressive acquisition of a very large number of leases in the Williston Basin in the late 1960s, when acreage was cheap, was a bold move, which we at the home office in DeKalb wholeheartedly supported. His efforts to explore the most promising of his Dakota holdings were sound, and results were often encouraging. However, by 1981, Art concluded that our exploration there had been unduly expensive; in too many cases offset wells drilled next to discoveries were dry holes. Nevertheless, North and South Dakota leases were still considered "hot" by many other oil explorers, and oil prices were still high in 1981, so Art decided to sell off most of Depco's leaseholds in North and South Dakota.

Art and his staff prepared "data rooms" and invited interested companies to study our four large blocks of leases and to submit their bids in sealed envelopes. We expected many bids, and planned to accept the highest bid on each block. But when bidding day came we had only one bid on two blocks and two bids on each of the other two! The successful bidders included Texaco, TOTAL (a French exploration company), Transco, and NuCorp. All were fine, experienced explorers. We wished them well, and breathed sighs of relief that the bids had been close to what we had hoped for.

Excessive Aggressiveness Creates a Problem

Bob Kenyon, whose good judgment had served Art very well, resigned in the early 1980s. His loss was a severe one for Art, whose approach to his job was intense and sometimes impulsive; Bob's careful planning had made him a valuable member of the management team. Bob was replaced by Bill Benford, a capable geologist who had been a member of the Depco team for several years. Unfortunately, at least in my opinion, the combination of two strong but impulsive personalities was not a good one for our business.

SOURCE: T.H. Roberts, Jr.

Geologists Benford and Kenyon Discuss a Hot Prospect

The combination of Bill Benford and Art Tiddens created a difficult situation for Charlie and me in 1984, when we found that Depco's U.S. exploration budget had been nearly entirely used up in the first half of the year! This meant that we would have to cut back severely on either Depco's or DeKalb Petroleum's Canadian budget for the remainder of the year in order to keep within the budgets we had agreed to for our oil exploration companies. Bruce Bickner, who was serving as an intermediary between DeKalb's executive office and our oil exploration, sat beside me at the meeting and underlined the key data for me, quietly expressing his dismay.

Charlie Roberts, who presided over our oil operations meetings for the parent company, asked me to comment on reducing Canadian exploration for the remainder of the year, to allow Art to exceed his U.S. budget. I was surprised that he called on me, because many years earlier he and I had agreed to divide our exploration dollars equally between the United States and Canada, and I believed our Canadian opportunities were considerably better than those in the states. Accordingly, I could not accept any proposals to decrease oil exploration in Canada simply because we had overspent our U.S. budget for the year.

A Sad Day for DeKalb's Oil Businesses

A few months later, on September 2, 1985, after several weeks of difficult compensation discussions with Charlie and Bruce, Art Tiddens, the man most responsible for our growth and success in both the United States and Canada, retired early, even though we had offered him a lucrative new contract. We hated losing Art, who was both a close friend and a highly respected associate. We knew he would be hard to replace, and he was.

No one but Art can be sure of his reasons for retiring early from the leadership of DeKalb's oil companies, which he had administered so well for so many years. He may have felt burned out and ready to spend more time enjoying his family and his many other interests while he was still young enough to do so. I am quite sure that he had no use for the young MBAs we had periodically sent to Denver to learn the oil business, and he was not much impressed with either Bruce Bickner or John McCarter, who were being developed to succeed Charlie and me.

With 20-20 hindsight, I am convinced that we should have offered Art a bigger raise. But when it became clear that Art's decision was final, I think we should have replaced him with Bob Johnson, a geologist who had done a great job in Canada, and moved Bob to Denver. However, Charlie Roberts and Bruce Bickner did not feel Bob would be very well received in Denver. I accepted their decision because they were closer to the situation than I was. Bob resigned when he was told he would not be replacing Art. He was replaced by Richard Nash, a capable, well-trained geologist, who was appointed vice president for Canadian exploration and land operations.

Tom Neel, Art's Successor, Joins DeKalb

On October 24, 1985, we hired Tom Neel to replace Art Tiddens as president of both of our oil businesses. Tom was a geologist who had been an executive with Kerr-McGee. He was a very bright man who studied oil plays carefully before proceeding with them. We considered that trait to be desirable, of course, but his circumspect demeanor was in sharp contrast to that of Art, whom we had admired for having a great imagination. Art would usually try out his many creative ideas on his staff, listen to their responses, throw out the bad ideas, and work hard to make the good ones work. Neel was much more prudent and reserved and had some problems with his key people, who thought he overstudied ideas and took forever to make a decision. Nevertheless, reasoned development of fields in both the United States and Canada proceeded satisfactorily under Neel.

As reported in Chapter 28, Charlie Roberts and I decided to step down from our executive positions with DeKalb in May 1986, and the DeKalb board accepted our recommendation that Bruce Bickner be elected president and CEO. I became chairman of the board and Charlie became vice chairman. Changes in the company, most of which had been agreed upon before we stepped down, began to take place rapidly.

OUR OIL BUSINESS GOES PUBLIC ON AUGUST 31, 1988

My father, the company's founder, had considered the company's oil business to be a hedge against a rainy day in the seed business, and I had supported that concept for as long as I was CEO. However, it was abrogated on August 31, 1988, about two years after Bruce Bickner took over, by the offering of DeKalb Energy common stock for public trading. Charlie Roberts supported Bruce's decision because he felt that by listing a "pure" oil company, we would enhance stockholder value. They believed, correctly I think, that analysts and investors would recognize it as an oil company with an impressive record instead of being just an interesting diversification by our hybrid seed business.

The other side of the coin is this question: Did DeKalb give up too much financial capacity that otherwise could have been used to strengthen the seed company's research and its product line? Only the future could answer that question, but the fact that Pioneer, our chief competitor, was spending nearly three times as much on research as DeKalb, was certainly ominous. Part of Pioneer's budget is dedicated to products other than seedcorn and is aimed at some markets that DeKalb has not chosen to enter; nevertheless, there can be little doubt that eliminating access to our oil cash flow made DeKalb's seed business more vulnerable to competitors. In the short term, shareholder value was enhanced by the spinning off and public listing of our oil business, but not so in the long run.

Here is a summary of the transaction from the shareholders' point of view:

- Share value of DeKalb Corporation common before listing three companies in place of one on 8/31/88 was $31.625.
- 12/30/88 shareholder value of the "new" shares exchanged for one share of DeKalb Corporation common:

1 Share of DeKalb Energy Corp. Common:	$19.375
1 Share of Pride Petroleum Services, Inc.:	3.000
Half share of DeKalb Genetics A or B:	12.750
Value of new shares:	$35.125
Net Gain per share after 4 months	
$35.125 less $31.625 equals:	$3.50

By coincidence, shareholders who held on to their new shares for three years would have lost the $3.50 gain shown above. Hence, the "rainy day" value of our oil business to strengthen our seed business was lost forever, and the shareholder value increases that were the primary justification for the separate listings did not amount to much or last very long.

A Fiasco Forces Sale of our U.S. Oil Properties

In 1990 we were all dissatisfied with the market price of DeKalb Energy's shares. A respected investment banking firm advised that DeKalb Energy was too small to attract many investors and recommended that the company acquire an independent oil company (or companies), preferably in south or central Texas, where there had been a flurry of exploration activity. After several of our bids for available companies were rejected, we decided to be more aggressive in our bidding.

We decided to go after the Royal Producing Corporation, a large south Texas independent oil exploration company. When our first offer was rejected, our geologists restudied Royal's properties, and obtained approval from the DeKalb Energy board (of which I was a member) to raise our bid to $130,200,000. We justified this by accepting a report that certain undeveloped properties owned by Royal had considerably more value as oil exploration opportunities than had originally been attributed to them. The board approved the aggressive bid, with some board members expressing concern over its size.

DeKalb's bid was accepted on July 2, 1990. We transferred our interest in certain of the acquired fields in exchange for $5.2 million and an increased interest in one of the fields acquired. Our next step was an all-out drilling program on the Royal properties that used up most of DeKalb Energy's drilling budget, violating our long-standing policy of investing equally each year in the United States and Canada. I questioned the advisability of cutting back our Canadian exploration to speed up Royal exploration, but Bruce argued that the sizable debt we had taken on to buy the properties required their immediate development. He was right about that.

Within the next year, it became clear that the DeKalb Energy Company had paid far too much for Royal. We drilled a lot of dry holes. Worse yet, we had financed our bet with heavy borrowing from banks and were forced to sell virtually all of our U.S. properties to pay off our loans. After several discussions with prospective buyers, we sold almost all of our U.S. properties east of California to Louis Dreyfus Gas Holdings for approximately $104 million and took losses against net earnings of $66,653,000 in 1991 and $58,695,000 in 1992 (as reported in DeKalb's form 10K, 12/31/93). On August 5, 1993, the company sold all of its California wells for $5.1 million.

It was a sad fate for so many good people who had laboriously built our properties. Nearly all of our U.S. employees, except those whose jobs were pumping, were dismissed by the new owner. Our only substantial remaining oil properties were those in Canada, and our oil board was leaning toward selling our Canadian oil business if a good offer came our way.

CANADIAN EXPLORATION—ONE LAST CHANCE

Mike Finnegan, who had served DeKalb in many capacities, was appointed chief operating officer of the DeKalb Energy Corp. (DEC) in early 1994, and our capable Canadian staff performed very well under his direction. Shortly after Mike took charge, we were approached by an American utilities company about acquiring DeKalb Energy at a price in the range of $18 to $25 per share. Mike was very familiar with the wide swings in both product and stock market prices that characterized the Canadian oil industry and advised us to sell if we were offered a price at the high end of that range. We agreed to seriously consider a good offer, influenced significantly by our conviction that our best executives very much needed to focus their attention on our struggling seed business.

Sadly, Mike died of a heart attack suffered on September 17, 1994. His death forced the DEC board to choose between two alternatives: (1) hiring an expensive new chief executive officer and asking him to negotiate a sale of the company at a higher price (while at the same time being willing to stay in the oil exploration business if a higher price was not found), or (2) selling the company to a buyer who would likely retain most of our employees and offer a price acceptable to our shareholders.

I supported the board's decision to seek a suitable buyer at a fair price, partly because I believed that our seedcorn business needed the full attention of our best remaining executives, and partly because I believed it was in my family's financial interest to sell at a price close to $25 per share. Many interested companies were interviewed, and the Apache Corporation's bid was accepted.

THE APACHE DEAL

Apache offered, and DEC accepted, $24.4408 per DEC share in Apache common stock, an attractive price well above other offers and nearly double the market price of DEC shares a year earlier. The share value of Apache on the closing date was $27.8875, so each DEC shareholder received .8764 shares of Apache stock in exchange for each share of DEC common. In total, 9,799,406 shares of DEC common stock were exchanged for 8,588,000 shares of Apache.

The total value of the sale was $239,497,850. This sum purchased everything DEC owned—its entire balance sheet, including all assets and liabilities. The biggest asset, of course, were DEC oil and gas reserves, which the SEC valued at $205,194,000 pre-tax, or $159,600,000 after tax. The SEC valuation system discounts remaining reserves at 10 percent annual rates but makes no allowance for future price increases. It is obviously impossible to know what factors Apache used in its purchase evaluation, but the company very likely valued remaining reserves higher than the after-tax SEC value of $159,600,000. In any event, the value Apache placed on the balance sheet items it purchased in addition to DEC remaining reserves was somewhere between zero and $79,897,850 (the $239,497,850 purchase price less the $159,600,000 after-tax value of remaining reserves). All of the figures in the preceding paragraphs were reported publicly in annual reports, 10K forms, and other publications.

Apache's offer was a very good one for DeKalb Energy shareholders. The negotiating team led by CEO Bruce Bickner had done its work well.

Tables 27-2, 27-3, an 27-4 tell the story of DeKalb's oil businesses from 1980 through April of 1995, when DeKalb's last remaining oil business, the DeKalb Energy Company, was sold to the Apache Corporation. All of the data presented in these tables were provided by DeKalb Energy personnel. I have listed typical oil and gas prices for each year to illustrate the significant influence they had on annual return on investment as well as their effect on the value of DeKalb's oil assets. During periods of low prices for oil and gas, it is necessary to write down asset values to new and lower levels that were quite properly required by the SEC. These are called "ceiling test" writedowns. Losses reported in Canada in 1986 and in the United States in 1986 and 1991 were primarily the consequence of ceiling test writedowns.

Tables 27-2 adds the sales proceeds received in the early 1990s to the cumulative dividends (expressed in $1995) paid to the parent company over the full term of existence of DeKalb's U.S. and Canadian oil operations and compares this fund recovery with the book value of the investment in oil enterprises, to arrive at the net gain realized during the fifty-plus years of its oil and gas exploration efforts.

Table 27-2
DeKalb's U.S. Oil & Gas Operations, 1980–1994
(U.S.$)

Year	Adjusted Equity[a] (Book) ($000)	Year-End SEC Value (After Tax) ($000)	Adjusted Net Income (After Tax)[b] ($000)	Return on Investm't	Price of Oil (per bbl.)	Price of Gas (Mcf.)
1980	91,837	110,000	26,331	28.6%	21.59	1.59
1981	116,902	115,000	26,003	22.2%	31.77	1.96
1982	140,104	119,200	27,342	19.5%	28.52	2.46
1983	161,021	124,900	26,677	16.6%	26.19	2.59
1984	162,765	112,500	23,464	14.4%	25.88	2.68
1985	184,523	69,100	4,033	2.2%	24.09	2.51
1986	174,264	85,300	(62,329)	(35.7%)	12.51	1.94
1987	209,693	77,800	19,314	9.2%	15.40	1.67
1988	229,087	86,100	(7,811)	(3.4%)	12.60	1.69
1989	230,485	186,400	13,178	5.7%	15.90	1.69
1990	230,770	114,300	108,554	47.0%	20.10	1.71
1991	159,297	5,200	(138,753)	(87.1%}	16.50	1.63
1992	100,308		(167,795)	(167.3%)	16.80	1.58
1993	86,239		(5,200)	(6.0%}	15.98	1.44
1994	82,909					

SOURCE: DeKalb Energy records

a. Adjusted equity includes dividends declared and paid to parent company.

b. Adjusted net income includes year-end SEC increase or decrease over prior year.

Table 27-3
Return on Investment to DeKalb Oil Divisions, U.S. and Canada Combined, 1980–1994 (U.S.$)

Year	Adjusted Equity[a] (Book) ($000)	Year-End SEC Value (After Tax) ($000)	Adjusted Net Income (After Tax)b ($000)	Return on Investm't	Price of Oil (per bbl.)	Price of Gas (Mcf.)
1980	139,550	170,000	37,591	26.9%	21.59	2.01
1981	168,834	180,000	35,222	20.9%	31.77	2.19
1982	197,562	188,400	37,058	18.8%	28.52	2.26
1983	222,140	196,500	37,543	16.9%	26.19	1.90
1984	255,677	229,400	61,433	24.0%	25.88	1.93
1985	284,699	270,600	62,972	22.1%	24.09	1.87
1986	293,429	190,500	(94,110)	(32.1%)	12.51	1.58
1987	344,870	235,300	51,859	15.0%	15.40	1.29
1988	405,347	244,800	18,830	4.6%	12.60	1.31
1989	466,673	277,500	42,172	9.4%	15.90	1.36
1990	463,103	388,700	126,726	27.4%	20.10	1.37
1991	386,109	275,300	(175,986)	(45.6%)	16.50	1.22
1992	295,164	165,700	(179,903)	(61.0%)	16.80	1.16
1993	177,957	202,400	47,706	26.8%	15.98	1.44
1994	174,186	159,600	(35,987)	(20.7%)	15.52	1.53

SOURCE: DeKalb Energy records.

a. Adjusted equity include dividends declared and paid to the parent company.

b. Adjusted net income includes year-end SEC increases or decreases over prior year.

Table 27-4
DeKalb Oil Divisions, Summary of Net Gain
(000 1992 U.S.$)

Country	Sale Proceeds.	Cumulative Dividends to U.S Parent	Total Recovery	Book Value before Sale	Net Gain over Book Value
U.S.	109,100	195,343	304,443	(39,313)	265,130
Canada	239,498	82,582	322,080	136,144	185,936
Total	348,598	277,925	626,523	96,831	451,066

SOURCE: DeKalb Energy records

It seems to me that the fine people who were responsible for a net gain over book value of $451,066,000 over the fifty years we spent in the oil business can take pride in their achievement. It could have been better, but it could have been a whole lot worse. Many loyal, talented friends made it possible, and I salute them. My father loved them, and so do I.

APPRECIATED FRIENDS AND COLLEAGUES

Many good and able people contributed to the growth and success of DeKalb's two oil companies, but I have mentioned only a small number of them in the preceding chapters. A few others whose work cannot go unrecognized include those listed below.

Vince Tkachyk, an excellent engineer, rose from the engineering department to president of DeKalb Energy in November of 1992.

Rich Nash, a fine geologist and a good friend, joined DeKalb Energy Canada as vice president of exploration in 1986. Sincerity and dedication to his work have always characterized Rich.

Larry Evans is a terrific engineer who advanced rapidly in the company to become vice president of production in August of 1993. I regret that Apache didn't have a place for him and believe they overlooked a good man.

Bruce Craig is the best marketing man I have ever known in the oil business. He was very much needed when he left Kerr-McGee to join DeKalb Energy as marketing vice president. I expect that Apache will develop the same high regard for his abilities.

Eddy Y. Tse joined DeKalb as manager of taxes and became chief accounting officer on November 11, 1992.

Fred Phillips, a lawyer with the McKimmie Matthews firm in Calgary, which assisted DeKalb in establishing its Canadian oil operations in 1958, became a director and officer of DeKalb's oil and gas subsidiary in Calgary and acted for many years as our chief

Canadian counsel. He was both a good lawyer and a good friend of DeKalb. Fred passed away in 1969.

Jim Millard is both a good lawyer and a good friend who succeeded Fred Phillips as our Calgary attorney with McKimmie-Matthews and served us well for nineteen years as a director and legal counsel.

To all of the others, you know who you are. I respect and value all of you for your abilities, your contributions, your loyalty, and your friendship.

Chapter 28

Back to the Basics
1980-1995

In June of 1992, deeply concerned about the "second-place" objective that DeKalb seemed to be opting for, I appealed to the company's board to seek either a joint venture with another company or a sale of its assets to a competitor like, for example, ICI, a large British pharmaceutical company that was trying, without much success, to increase its hybrid seedcorn market share in the United States; or possibly to Cargill, which had ample resources to buy out DeKalb and to adequately fund seed research. Cargill had periodically expressed interest in buying DeKalb.

When the board rejected my proposal, I offered them the first opportunity to purchase my family's class A (voting) shares. I had been advised that my shares would be worth up to $54 per share if I were able to offer a controlling interest in the company. But Mary and Charlie Roberts and their family held the same proportion of voting shares that my family held (about 37 percent) and did not wish to sell. Accordingly, my family and I sold our stock to DeKalb for $40 per share, consistent with our belief that the company could not compete with Pioneer's research budget. The price we received compared with the then current market price of $36 for class B shares and a public price of $39 per share several months earlier, when my negotiations with Bruce Bickner and Charlie Roberts began. I had agreed to delay taking my case to the board from January to June to avoid rumors that might disrupt our spring seed sales efforts.

A more dramatic view of my decision is told in an article that appeared in Forbes magazine's November 1994 issue. The story appeared just before the company's release of much-improved hybrids produced by conventional breeding. I include it here because it clearly reports DeKalb's more troubled times.

"Gone to Seed," by Marcia Beres
(reprinted with permission)

For over 20 years, Thomas Roberts, Jr., chaired DeKalb Genetics Corp. Founded around 1918 by Roberts' father, DeKalb is the nation's number two producer of corn seed for farmers, after archrival Pioneer Hi-Bred International. But by 1991 Tom Roberts had reached the conclusion that DeKalb was too small to go it alone in developing and marketing new seeds. He told the company's board that DeKalb had to sell out, merge or do a joint venture with another firm.

"This is a research game," explains longtime DeKalb Genetics board member Blair White, "and we hadn't been particularly successful."

The decision was not popular with other Roberts family members. Tom Roberts' brother-in-law, Charles Roberts (the last names are coincidental), led a faction that held 33% of DeKalb's voting stock and felt the firm should remain family controlled and independent. To break the impasse, Tom Roberts agreed in July to sell his 33.8% of the voting stock for $40 a share, nearly 18 million all told. He was paid about a 10% premium to what DeKalb's publicly traded non-voting stock was trading for at the time; that premium generated a stockholder suit that has yet to be resolved.

It turns out that Tom Roberts was dead right: DeKalb Genetics was too small to keep up with Pioneer Hi-Bred. DeKalb (1994 sales, $320 million) now has 9% of the corn seed market, about the same share it held in 1991. By contrast, $1.5 billion (sales) Pioneer has a 45% share, up from 37%. DeKalb's stock was recently $29 per share, well below what Roberts received.

DeKalb's fall is the more remarkable considering the fact that in 1974 DeKalb and Pioneer each had about 23% of the seed corn market. But while Des Moines, Iowa–based Pioneer kept its eye focused on seed, DeKalb diversified, mainly into energy businesses. These businesses were spun off in 1988 as DeKalb Energy, an oil and gas producer, and Pride Petroleum Services, an oil well servicing firm. These two, plus DeKalb Genetics, are now worth less than they were as a package six years ago.

His attention diverted by diversification, Tom Roberts began to miss changes in the seed market. As energy costs climbed, farmers had to spend more money on energy to dry their corn for sale. Pioneer Hi-Bred developed a seed that produced corn that dried better in the field, saving farmers money on their drying operations. Pioneer also came up with hybrids that had higher yields.

DeKalb? It worked on seeds that were more disease-resistant and less likely to suffer from drought. But, with Washington's crop insurance programs that bail out farmers in a drought, farmers are more likely to buy seeds that boost crop yields than ones that offer protection against drought. By 1982 DeKalb's market share had slumped to about 9%, while Pioneer's share was growing strongly, taking much of DeKalb's lost business

That year Tom Roberts formed a research joint venture with the seed unit of drug giant Pfizer. DeKalb owned 70% of the venture. Thanks to Pfizer's genetics, the venture halted

DeKalb's market share drop. But it didn't generate new products to woo farmers who had lost confidence in DeKalb. Its share has remained flat while Pioneer has taken market share from smaller seed outfits, which are units of big drug and chemical firms like Ciba-Geigy.

Tom Roberts, now 70, declined to talk to Forbes about DeKalb. The company's senior managers have clammed up, too. But it's fairly easy to pierce their veil of silence and see how poorly DeKalb is doing.

In 1990 Chief Executive Bruce Bickner said the company should earn near-term 15% and long-term 20% on its shareholders' equity. This year has seen an all-time record for corn crops, yet for fiscal 1994 (ended Aug. 31) DeKalb earned just a 9.3% return on equity, and net earnings ($10.6 million, $2.02 per share) were boosted by inventory accounting changes and one-time pension gains.

Bickner also set an earnings growth goal of 15% to 20%, but earnings have actually declined since 1990 as a result of research outlays. He has said that a debt/capital level of about 30% is reasonable for DeKalb, but the ratio now stands at about 52%. Much of the debt was incurred in 1990, to buy out Pfizer's 30% stake in the seed R&D venture. Meanwhile, Pioneer Hi-Bred continues to outspend DeKalb on research, $105 million to $45 million last year.

The coming year will be no kinder to DeKalb. In November the Agriculture Department announced a 7.5% acreage set-aside for 1995, to boost corn prices. Less corn planted means less seed sold. Tom Roberts' decision to bolt from DeKalb when the bolting was good looks pretty smart these days.

DEKALB SCORES TWO TECHNOLOGICAL BREAKTHROUGHS

Only a few months after the Forbes article appeared, Bruce Bickner, DeKalb's CEO, announced that the company had patented a remarkable biotechnological achievement that would make seed-corn resistant to the European corn borer, a predatory insect thought to have reduced annual corn yields by roughly 5 percent.

Approximately a year later, DeKalb announced another biotech breakthrough: the patenting of corn resistant to Roundup, Monsanto's remarkably successful weed-killer. Until then, Roundup could not be used on corn because it killed both the corn and the weeds.

In March of 1998, Forbes published a followup to its article on my decision to fell my stock. They revised their position on DeKalb's future.

"Too early, Tom" by Bruce Upbin
(reprinted with permission)

Sometimes you can be right and wrong. Three years ago we thought that seed technology firm DeKalb Genetics was too small to go it alone against its bigger archrival Pioneer Hi-Bred (Dec 19, 1994). DeKalb's profits were dropping as it lost market share to Pioneer. The stock went sideways from 1990 to 1994. Its former chairman, Thomas Roberts, Jr., son of the company founder, looked pretty smart selling his 450,000 Class A voting shares for $18 million in 1991.

Wretched timing on Tom Roberts' part, and ours. Almost from the day our story broke, DeKalb's stock has been hotter than a tractor seat in July, up more than 14-fold, adjusted for splits. DeKalb's patents for weed- and pest-resistant crops turned out to be prized assets in the growing field of ag biotech. In 1996 Monsanto paid $160 Million for 40% of the company.

Our timing may have been bad, but we were right in predicting that DeKalb couldn't make it alone. Chemical firms like Du Pont, Novartis and AgrEvo are spending billions of research dollars to engineer the next generation of crops. DeKalb has no such deep pockets. Even Pioneer realized that, selling a 20% stake to Du Pont for $1.7 billion last summer.

In February the rest of the Roberts family, who still control 56% of the voting stock, announced they were putting the company up for sale. The stock nearly doubled, to $62.50. Deal-happy Monsanto has the inside track among the likely bidders. Too bad for Tom Roberts, though. If he'd held on, his stake would have been worth some $170 million.

On September 11, 1996, the Chicago Tribune reported the patenting of DeKalb's second major technological breakthrough in its business section, as follows:

DeKalb Genetics Corp. of DeKalb won a U.S. patent for corn that is resistant to the herbicide glyphosate, the active ingredient in Monsanto Co.'s Roundup herbicide. Use of the genetically altered corn will allow farmers to spray their fields with Roundup to kill weeds without hurting the crop, DeKalb said.

These two important developments could very well mean the next decade will be a great one for DeKalb, giving it the resources necessary to fund expansion of its research efforts sufficiently to give Pioneer real competition over the long pull.

It looks to me as though exactly that has happened. After the announcement of DeKalb's success with the development of corn-borer resistant seedcorn, two very big players in bio-genetics, DuPont and Monsanto, have begun working cooperatively with DeKalb. Monsanto has bought 40% of DeKalb's outstanding shares (but only 10% of the A shares) through a tender offer of $71 per share together with a direct purchase of $30 million worth of newly issued shares. The agreement included three cross-licensing agreements involving biotech intellectual property as well as a research and development/collaboration agreement. Three agreements will go a long way toward leveling the playing field of DeKalb-Pioneer competition in the worldwide hybrid seed industry, and voting control is still firmly in the hands of its officers and the Charles C. Roberts family.

These remarkable developments (resistance to the European corn borer as well as resistance to Roundup) may very well be additive, in my opinion, as the cultivation cost savings and increased yields from being able to use Roundup to control weeds in cornfields seem likely to match the 5 percent yield increases expected from corn having resistance to the European corn borer.

FARMERS QUICKLY ACCEPT BIO-TECH IMPROVEMENT

"Roundup Ready" and "Bt" (corn borer resistant) seedcorns were quickly accepted by farmers, as the next four graphs (all produced by farm managers Martin, Goodrich & Associates) show. The 50 million acres they forecast here to be planted by the year 2001 to biotechnologically improved corn will be approximately two-thirds of U.S. corn acreage.

Table 28-1

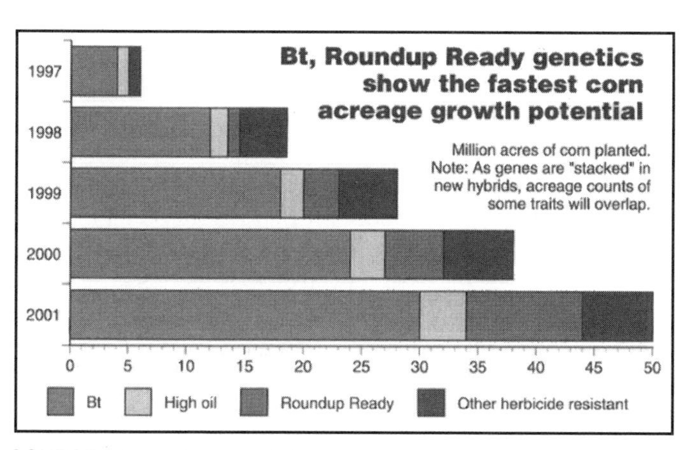

SOURCE: Martin, Goodrich & Associates

Assuming that the annual corn acreage in the U.S. remains close to 80 million acres, the value added by "Bt" (corn borer resistant) seed alone will be $10 per acre, or $800,000,000 per year, and the annual added value of Roundup Ready seedcorn is estimated to be $480,000,000! It seems to me that the scientists and the corporations who created these extra values should be recognized for the immense increases in both increased annual food production and its dollar value their work has made possible. Surely their achievements at least match the achievements of those who have received recognition as great as even the Nobel prize.

How much "added value" will the first six patented bio-technological seedcorns create? Estimates are shown in this graph:

Table 28-2

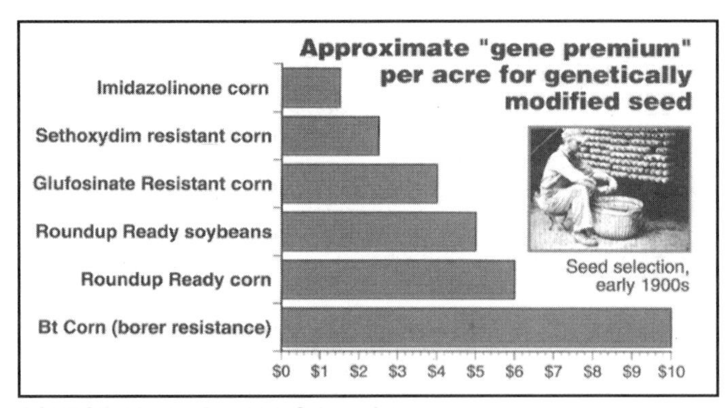

SOURCE: Martin, Goodrich & Associates

INCREASING RESEARCH BUDGETS PAY OFF

Between 1994 and 1998, DeKalb substantially increased its seed research expenditures, as graph 28-3 shows.

The research expense increases reported were certainly a key factor in the market share increases shown in the following graph, but increases in research spending prior to 1991 played a significant role, too.

In 1996, friends in the company told me that several of our newest hybrids were outperforming Pioneer's in major parts of the U.S. cornbelt. For example, in a key southern Minnesota sales district, Don Diehl, the district sales manager, nearly doubled DeKalb sales in his district with three outstanding new DeKalb hybrids that had been introduced for the first time in 1995.

"Official" state yield trials also confirming the new competitiveness of DeKalb's hybrids, and its market share increased steadily in the 1990s, as shown in Table 28-4.

Table 28-3

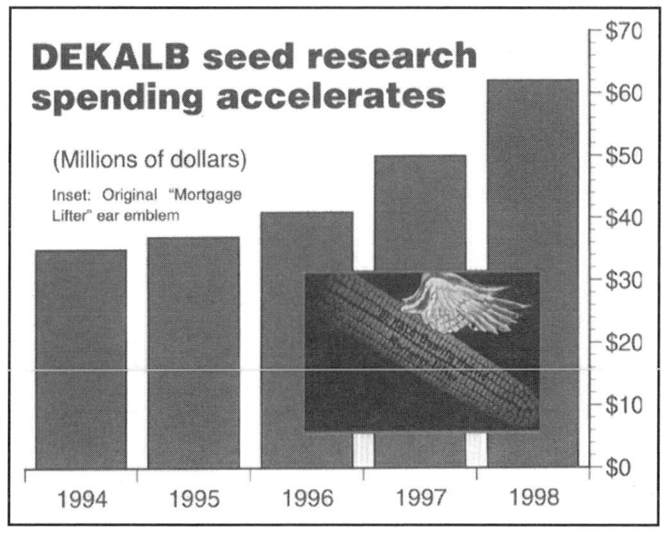

SOURCE:Martin, Goodrich & Associates

Table 28-4

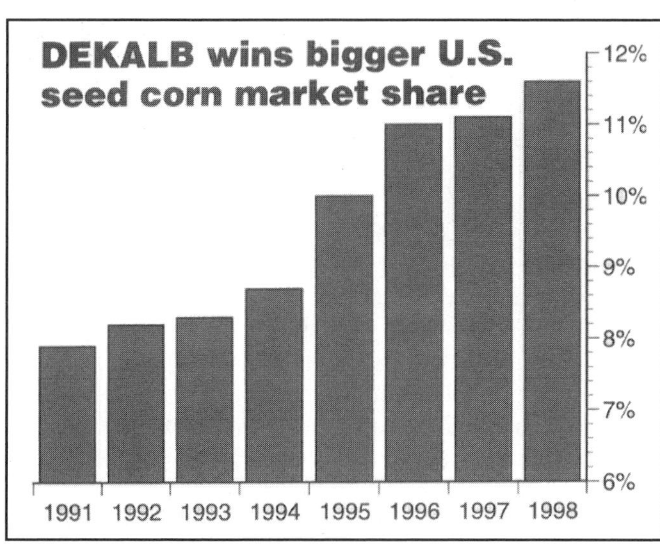

SOURCE:Martin, Goodrich & Associates

In October 1995, I commented as follows in a letter to Bruce Bickner, DeKalb's CEO:

> I realize now that I was wrong in 1991 to believe that DeKalb could not successfully compete with Pioneer with the limited resources then available to our company. At that time I

thought some form of a merger with another company was advisable, but you and the company's board thought differently, and you were right. I am now convinced that under your administration the company has emerged strong, and with a bright future. You have done a fine job.

Tom Roberts, Jr.

A DRAMATIC EPILOG

The value of DeKalb's shares shot up again twice after 1996. The first big increase came when DeKalb announced its willingness to be acquired, as announced in this New York Times article dated February 12, 1998.

"Battle Forecast As a Seed Giant Goes on Block"
by Barnaby J. Feder
(reprinted with permission)

The DeKalb Genetics Corporation, the second-largest seed company in the nation, said today that it was putting itself up for sale, setting the stage for a battle for biotechnology supremacy in agriculture.

Analysts said the most likely buyer would be the Monsanto Company. It is already a major shareholder in DeKalb and has been working with it to genetically transfer such valuable traits as insect and herbicide resistance into important crops like corn and soybeans. Indeed, Monsanto said in a statement today that it was looking forward to bidding for DeKalb.

But many analysts expect any Monsanto bid to face competing bids from other major agrichemical companies, all of which want to develop crops that tolerate their pesticides so that farmers can use them more freely. Developing such tolerance in the laboratory is useless to farmers unless seed companies incorporate such traits in their highest-yielding seed lines.

The Dow Chemical Company, Novartis of Switzerland and Agrevo G.m.b.h., a joint venture of Schering A.G. and Hoechst A.G. of Germany, "could all go after DeKalb," said Bonnie Wittenburg, who follows agribusiness for Dain Bosworth in Minneapolis.

Another potential bidder even larger than those multinational giants is Cargill Inc., the privately held Minneapolis conglomerate that has been expanding its seed business in recent years. Other than Monsanto, potential suitors asked to comment on DeKalb all declined.

Shares of DeKalb jumped 63 percent today, or $20.875, to a record high of $54 in heavy trading on the New York Stock Exchange. Still, analysts said the final sale price could easily top $60 a share, based on the $1.7 billion that E. I. du Pont de Nemours & Company paid last year for a 20 percent stake in Pioneer Hi-Bred International Inc., the seed industry leader. That would value DeKalb at more than $2.2 billion.

DeKalb, which is based in DeKalb, Ill., said the decision to sell reflected the estate planning needs of the Roberts family, which founded the company 80 years ago and controls 56 percent of the A shares that have voting power.

"It was time to diversify," said Bruce P. Bickner, the chairman and chief executive of DeKalb. "They could have sold their voting stock for a premium, but they decided not to leave the other shareholders out to dry."

The family's hand may have been partly forced by the 50 percent tumble in DeKalb's stock from last fall to a low of less than $23 a share early this year. Investors were worried about projected losses this year in DeKalb's swine-breeding business and increased price competition in the seed markets. DeKalb earned $28.8 million on sales of $451.4 million in the fiscal year that ended last Aug. 31.

A sale would highlight the strategic value of DeKalb's seed lines and its experience applying biotechnology to them.

"DeKalb has a long history as a key player and innovator in the seed industry," Hendrik A. Verfaillie, president of Monsanto, noted in his company's statement.

Mr. Bickner said, "We welcome Monsanto's interest, but we also welcome every other bidder," adding that interested acquirers would be given ample time to look at the company. It named Merrill Lynch & Company as its investment banker.

The sale comes at an inconvenient time for Monsanto, which holds 10 percent of the A shares and 45 percent of the non-voting B shares. It had already warned that earnings growth might slow this year and next because of its need to invest more money in developing its agribusiness holdings and in taking several promising drugs at its G. D. Searle subsidiary to market. Monsanto shares fell $1.5625 today, to $51.1875.

Analysts said they would not be surprised if Monsanto, which is based in St. Louis, tried to come up with an early knockout bid.

"Monsanto can't afford to lose DeKalb," said Christine McCracken at Bioscience Securities Inc. in Orinda, Calif.

Others said agriculture was evolving far too rapidly to reach such a conclusion. But one thing is clear, said Carrol Bolin, vice president in charge of Pioneer's joint ventures and regulatory affairs: "The stakes get higher as the consolidation of the industry continues."

The second big increase came when Monsanto acquired DeKalb, as quoted in the NY Times on May 12, 1998.

"Monsanto to Acquire Biotech Seed Firms
(reprinted with permission)

CHICAGO - Monsanto Co. Monday (May 11,1998) announced deals valued at about $4.4 billion that will give it control of DeKalb Genetics Corp. and the Delta & Pine Land Co., two seed companies that had been its partners in creating genetically modified crops.

The DeKalb acquisition had been expected, although not necessarily at the $2.5 billion, or $100 a share price for the 60 percent Monsanto does not already own. The corn and soybean seed producer, which is based in DeKalb, Ill., had announced in February that it would auction itself off to the highest bidder.

But Monsanto, which is based in St. Louis, surprised analysts by simultaneously snapping up Delta & Pine Land, which is based in Scott, Ms., in a stock swap that is valued at about $1.9 billion. Monsanto currently owns 4.7 percent of Delta, which is the world's leading producer of cotton seed.

Analysts said that the two deals reflected Monsanto's willingness in the last three years to invest aggressively to meet growing competition from challengers like E.I. DuPont de Nemours and Novartis of Switzerland in the race to apply biotechnology to agriculture.

Monsanto shares rose $1.9375, to $55.4375.

CLOSING PERSONAL REMARKS

These are the features of my business life I am most proud of:

- I am proud of the way DeKalb treated its employees and of the company's relationship with the community. Our benefit plans were excellent, our personal relations gratifying, and our community is a fine place in which to live, in part because of the DeKalb Ag, which provided both land and financial support to the YMCA, the Kishwaukee Hospital, the Voluntary Action Committee, and the Oakbrook Retirement Center..
- I am proud to have been a part of the vital decision to "bet the farm" on single-cross hybrids.
- I am proud of the success Charlie Roberts and I achieved as partners in running DeKalb. I give a lot of credit to him for both his ability and his patience.

Charlie is a fine man whose advice to me was always sound and well thought through. I believe that Charlie and I have earned the right to be proud of our company and of serving our employees, our shareholders, and our community as my father Tom Roberts, Sr., wanted us to do.

- I am proud of my role in developing DeKalb into seed industry leadership in Argentina, and in expanding our markets into Europe, Latin America, and several countries of Southeast Asia.
- I am proud of my role in developing DeKalb hybrid sorghum.
- I am proud of having insisted that our annual investments in oil and gas exploration be divided equally between our oil businesses in the United States and Canada.
- I am proud of the success we achieved in taking the company public.
- I am proud of my decision to go forward with the Pfizer joint venture.

I close this story of DeKalb from 1912 through 1996 satisfied that the company is back on its feet, growing rapidly, and mounting a real challenge to its competitors. Much of its current success is due to the achievements of its research people and the drive of Bruce Bickner, its chief executive officer. May your hybrids get better and better, and your market penetration be greater and greater!

Financial Results - Part Seven

OPERATING RESULTS, 1980 THROUGH 1995

Table 28-5
DeKalb AgResearch Earnings per Share and Price Range, 1980 through 1987

Year	Earnings/Share ($)	Price Range ($)
1980	3.60	25.80–60.30
1981	3.47	27.80–51.50
1982	1.46	12.30–26.00
1983	1.07	16.10–28.20
1984	2.37	19.80–28.50
1985	1.62	20.80–30.10
1986	(4.30)	14.80–27.30
1987	1.20	17.30–26.90

SOURCE: S&P per share data (8/5/88) on DeKalb Corp., successor to DeKalb AgResearch.

Table 28-6
DeKalb Earnings by Division, 1980–1987
(million U.S.$, pre-tax)

Year	Animal Science	Heinold Co's.	Seed	Energy	Pride Petro	Lindsay, D.F.S.	Corp. Expenses, Writedowns, Taxes, etc.	Net Earn'gs
1980	3.3	17.6	29.6	50.7	4.3	2.5	(79.1)	43.6
1981	1.0	15.0	26.8	61.5	18.0	7.3	(95.2)	34.4
1982	8.0	6.8	(9.6)	59.4	12.0	(2.2)	(55.4)	19.0
1983	3.8	11.7	(9.5)	34.3	(17.6)	10.4	(16.6)	16.5
1984	1.9	8.9	17.3	49.5	(5.3)	7.8	(49.3)	31.3
1985	3.9	4.2	2.8	36.8	(6.0)	2.3	(23.9)	20.1
1986	6.6	2.5*	(13.7)	(41.3)	(31.5}	(0.1)	(26.8)	(50.7)
1987	12.0	1.5*	8.5	12.9	(3.7)	2.7	(19.7)	16.9

SOURCE: DeKalb AgResearch annual report for 1985, p. 10, was the source of data from 1980 through 1985. During that period swine, layers, Lindsay, and DFS were combined into an "Agricultural Products" classification, which is broken down into Animal Sciences (swine & poultry), Lindsay, and DFS. DeKalb Corporation annual report, 1987, p. 9, was the primary source of information for 1986 data. The 1988 DeKalb Genetics 10K was the source of data for 1987. The 1988 DeKalb Energy 10K, p. 18, was the source of 1986. 1987 Energy data. Funds received from discontinued operations are shown in 1986 and 1987 as reported in 1987 DeKalb Corp. 10K, p. 9, as earnings from discontinued operations.
Notes: Heinold Commodities and Heinold Hog Markets were sold in Feb. 1986 and Mar. 1987, respectively.

Table 28-7
The Financial Performance of
DeKalb Energy Co. and DeKalb Genetics Corp., 1988–1996

Year	Earnings ($ millions)				Earnings per Share ($)		Average Stock Price ($)	
	En'gy (pre-tax)	Gen. (pre-tax)	En'gy (after tax)	Gen. (after tax)	En'gy	Gen.	En'gy	Gen.
1988	12.5	14.7	10.5	8.3	.94	1.48	25.31	18.75
1989	14.9	19.0	25.9	12.1	2.48	2.14	26.25	32.75
1990	20.7	25.1	27.1	15.4	2.62	2.72	28.00	37.38
1991	(83.0)	23.7	(62.6)	17.1	(6.51)	2.84	18.50	35.00
1992	(79.0)	13.9	(70.3)	10.3	(7.30)	1.94	13.00	29.00
1993	11.7	(0.6)	11.0	3.1	1.14		14.75	28.25
1994	12.8	14.9	6.8	11.0	0.71	2.11	15.00	30.25
1995	sold	15.1	sold	9.5	sold	1.80	sold	37.63
1996				17.0		3.09		82.50

SOURCE: DK Energy 1994 10K, p. 24, was the source of 1992 through 1994 figures for Energy pre-tax and after-tax earnings, and EPS. The DK Energy 1992 10K, p. 9, was the source of Energy pre-tax and after tax earnings for 1988 through 1991. The 1988 through 1994 prices for Energy shares, which were never split, came from averaging annual highs and lows each year between 1988 and 1994, as projected for that period by Standard & Poor's. DK Genetics 1990 10K, p. 18, reported 1988, 1989, and 1990 earnings, and DK Genetics 1995 10K, p. 11, was the source of earnings for 1991 through 1995. Monthly average stock prices for DK Genetics came from S&P reports for that period. DK Genetics stock price for 1996 was a multiple of more than twice the pre-split average per share market price of $37.63 reported by S&P for 1995. The 1996 average price reported above to have been $82.50 per share was adjusted to a pre-split equivalent after a 3:1 stock split, done to make a valid apples-to-apples comparison of the per share prices reported for the prior years in this table.

The increases in per-share value of DeKalb's shares between 1994 and 1996, as reported here, were both well earned and astounding. The forces behind this huge increase in value were, in my opinion, the announcement of the patenting of DeKalb's two bio-genetic achievements and recognition that DeKalb's conventionally bred hybrids were growing in market share.

Table 28-8
DeKalb Genetics Pre-Tax Earnings by Division, 1988–1995
($ millions)

Year	Swine	North American Seed	International Seed	Poultry	Net Corp. and Interest Expense	Total Pre-Tax Earnings
1988	6.2	11.3	(Included in	0.7	(3.5)	14.7
1989	(0.3)	21.1	N. Amer.	0.7	(2.5)	19.0
1990	4.5	27.0	pre '91)	4.2	(11.6)	25.1
1991	9.3	17.8	7.0	2.5	(10.4)	23.7
1992	4.6	10.1	9.9	0.9	(10.7)	13.9
1993	3.0	5.2	3.3	1.0	(10.8)	(2.6)
1994	5.7	14.7	8.0	(0.3)	(13.2)	15.2
1995	(0.9)	22.3	7.6	sold	(13.9)	15.1
Totals	32.1	129.5	35.8	9.7	(76.6)	130.5

SOURCE: DeKalb Genetics 10K for 1990, p. 20, reports swine, seed, and poultry pre-tax earnings for 1988, 1989, and 1990; and DK Genetics 10K for 1995, p. 11, breaks out N. American Seed, International Seed, and swine for 1991 through 1995.

Notes: The $10.8mm expense figure shown in the 1993 corp. and interest column is the net of corporate expenses less an income tax benefit plus earnings from discontinued operations. May 1995 DeKalb sold its poultry operation to Toshoku, a Japanese trading company, for $12.5 million and retained most of the employees. The price was reported in DeKalb's 10K report for 1995, p. 41

The Tom Roberts Family Story

A family company is usually driven by a single overriding goal. Along the way, the founder, and those who join him, may choose to stay on the road they set out on or explore new routes by diversifying. Usually diversification is successful in direct proportion to its similarity to the original business, and to the abilities of those who drive the company. So it was with the DeKalb Agricultural Association and the three generations of the Roberts family who were involved with the company and whose lives, in turn, have been influenced by it.

My grandfather, Fred Townsend, was one of a group of farmers, teachers, and bankers who in 1912 founded the DeKalb County Soil Improvement Association, an organization that became the DeKalb Agricultural Association, Inc., in 1917.

SOURCE: Al Golden

DeKalb County Soil Improvement Association Founders Left to Right: John Blair, C.D. Schoonmaker, George Hyde, W.G. Eckhardt, Farm Advisor, G.W. Gurler, Aaron Plapp, F.B. Townsend, H.H. Parke, E.E. Hipple, George A. Fox, W.F. Leifheit and Orton Bell

THOMAS HUMPHREY AND ELEANOR TOWNSEND ROBERTS

Tom Roberts, Sr., the man who built the "DeKalb Ag," was born on April 29, 1892. He attended high school in DeKalb, where his yearbook described him as "an agriculturist" and predicted a bright future for him. He spent his first year in college at Northwestern but transferred to Iowa State for his last three years, majoring in agronomy.

After graduation, he worked for two years in his dad's bank in Waterman before deciding to operate a family dairy farm, aiming to work there for the two years of farming necessary to qualify for a job as assistant farm adviser. However, his farming was interrupted in 1917 when he enlisted in the army when war was declared with Germany. After being commissioned a second lieutenant, he was assigned to a cavalry remount unit in Alabama, where he remained until the war was over.

Tom was "mustered out" in late 1918 and returned to dairy farming for six months before making a key decision that would have a profound effect on the growth and development of the DeKalb company: he went to work as Assistant DeKalb County Farm Adviser in June 1919.

His wife, Eleanor, was born in Sycamore, Illinois, on December 9, 1897, where she attended the public schools. She went on to two years at Rockford College (then known as the Rockford Female Seminary), followed by two years at the University of Wisconsin.

SOURCE:T.H. Roberts, Jr.

My mother Eleanor & her father Fred Townsend

As a child, some of Eleanor's happiest times were her daily horseback rides with her father, Fred Townsend, who was mayor of Sycamore and president of The National Bank & Trust Co. I remember my grandfather Fred as a marvelous and entertaining man. On Sundays, he often rode his horse to church after Sunday school to pick up my sister and me. He regularly gave children chocolate candy and a ride in his sulky, an old fashioned two-wheeled cart pulled by his beautiful horse.

Eleanor's saddest experiences were watching Fred struggle with a financial fiasco that cost him his bank presidency. He had invested heavily on margin in Canadian timber and lost nearly everything when timber prices dropped precipitately. When that happened, he started drinking heavily, and Eleanor's mother, "Nano," often asked her to go to Fred's bank after school to walk home with him, in order to keep him from stopping at the local tavern. That experience made an indelible impression on her, leaving her strongly opposed to drinking.

Tom and Eleanor were married on June 12, 1920, in her parents' home. The wedding was held there because Nano didn't believe Tom was a good choice for her daughter and wouldn't allow them to marry in St. Peter's Episcopal Church. This became a long-standing family joke, especially after he came to serve on the church's vestry.

SOURCE: Eleanor Roberts

Eleanor Roberts and son Tom Jr. (your author)

Eleanor was a witty, nurturing woman who was a wonderful mother and an exceptionally loyal corporate wife. She was understandably skeptical of any of her husband's "aggressive" but risky business plans, having seen her father suffer financial ruin. However, she did not attempt to impose her will on her husband, except to encourage him to invest conservatively.

In 1926, when I was two years old, I developed asthma so severe that she felt it necessary to move to a desert climate. Though pregnant with my sister Mary at the time, she and her parents, Fred and

Nano, took me to Riverside, California, in late 1926, hoping my health would improve. It did improve remarkably, either as a result of the climate or because I was under the care of a very good doctor. In 1927, she rejoined my father in DeKalb County, where they lived for the rest of their lives.

SOURCE: Roberts Family

Humphrey Roberts family

As Tom's wife, Eleanor was respectful of the company and never used her position to her advantage. Shortly after Tom died, she went to the corporate office to buy eggs from the Poultry Research Farm, where eggs were available to employees at prices slightly below those in the grocery stores. A clerk who didn't recognize her asked if her husband worked for the company. She replied, "Well, he used to" and was told that she no longer qualified to buy "company eggs." Of course, he was enormously embarrassed later when he found out who she was, but she took the experience with good spirit.

However much she loved the company, she remained serious and soft-spoken as long as she was the chief executive's wife. After my father died, her sense of humor seemed to expand, and she frequently exhibited a loving, dry wit that remained with her until the end of her life. She sent me a card on my fiftieth birthday saying, "Happy Birthday, honey. I can remember perfectly everything that happened 50 years ago, but I can't for the life of me remember what I had for lunch today."

At age 85, Eleanor suffered a stroke and was unable to speak for several days. During this time, she was visited by a lifelong friend, Eva Benson. The nurses had spruced Eleanor up and when Eva arrived, she said, "Oh Eleanor, you look so pretty laying there." My mother's first words in five days were, "It's lying, Eva." She had not only retained her sense of humor, but also her dedication to the correct use of the English language. Eleanor died on Jan 17, 1982, five years after Tom Sr. He died in 1967. His story is told in the first 14 chapters of the book.

SOURCE: Roberts Family

The Tom Roberts Family

MARY ELEANOR AND CHARLIE ROBERTS

My sister, Mary Eleanor Roberts, was born in 1926 in Riverside, California, where my mother, my grandparents, and I had gone to live because of my asthma. About a year later, we moved back to DeKalb County. Mary was always an excellent student and so conscientious that our mother worried about her becoming a bookworm. She decided to pay Mary a dollar for each "B" on her report card and only 50 cents for each "A." (I was paid just the opposite, so I thought she really had a deal.)

In 1947 she met a fellow student named Charlie Roberts (no relation) who was president of the student body at DePauw University. When Charlie first visited Sycamore in 1948, my mother liked him but for some reason thought he was "too smooth" and bet me five dollars that Mary wouldn't marry him. A few years later they were married, and my mother happily paid me the five dollars. After graduating in 1947, Charlie earned an MBA at Northwestern University and was hired by Inland Steel.

About two years later, my father asked me what I thought about his offering Charlie a job with the company. I replied that I thought we needed men like Charlie. My father made the offer, Charlie accepted, and he began in an administrative staff position. During his first two years with the company he made several important changes, including a shift in the way insurance was handled (a change from using local insurance people to using insurance brokers) that saved the company quite a bit of money. Then, to learn more about the seed business, he took a district manager's job in the eastern half of Wisconsin.

Charlie and Mary moved to Okonomowoc, Wisconsin, for two years and then came back to DeKalb. They raised a fine family and Charlie played a major role in the evolution of the company. For many years we enjoyed both a business association and a friendly social relationship. As with many family endeavors, our relationship bore the stress and strain of business changes.

THOMAS HUMPHREY ROBERTS, JR.

As for me, after graduating from Sycamore High School in 1941, I attended the University of Illinois, where I worked hard, primarily because my mother had instilled in me the belief that a good academic record in college could open tremendous opportunities for me.

During my freshman year, when I was seventeen years old, the Japanese attacked Pearl Harbor. The armed services did not draft men out of college for the first year of the war because the training camps were full, but in the fall of 1942 all branches of the armed forces were recruiting at the universities. I signed up for a course in pre-meteorology that was being offered at the University of Chicago in an Army Air Corps program.

On February 7, 1943, I picked up my uniform and got my shots at Camp Grant, an Army post near Rockford, Illinois. Three days later I started a four-quarter course designed to teach me as much about mathematics and physics as I could absorb. The Air Force had 200 men in the pre-meteorology program at the University of Chicago and a similar number at eight other schools.

I finished the program in February of 1944, but the war was so close to being over that the Air Force disbanded its meteorology programs and assigned me to be trained in radio communications. Upon completion of this training, I was commissioned a second lieutenant with a specialty in radio communications at Yale University in November of 1944. Thereafter, I was sent to Boca Raton, Florida, for six months of training in airborne radar, and then to Hawaii, where I was trained to set up radar on the beach in Japan during the coming invasion. This turned out to be unnecessary because the war ended, to everybody's immense relief.

In June of 1946, I returned home and enrolled in agronomy at Iowa State University. Before the war, I had decided not to join DeKalb because there were already many bright young men working for the company and I didn't want to be perceived as "crown prince." However, after the war, the company had diversified into poultry breeding and expected to offer the new poultry product to egg producers in 1949, when I would be graduating. After graduation, I went to work for the new and expanding Poultry Division.

After three years, I felt I should get some experience in the operation that was at the heart of DeKalb—its hybrid seed business. So, in the fall of 1952, I became district manager of the western half of Wisconsin. Soon thereafter I married Margaret Ann Hesse. I stayed in the district manager position for two years before going on to Harvard Business School. In May of 1954, during my first year at Harvard, Tom III was born. At Harvard I selected courses I thought would help me at DeKalb. I loved what I was studying, achieved academic recognition as a Baker Scholar, and was honored to receive the Copeland Award, presented annually to the outstanding marketing student. After graduation, I went back to work at DeKalb, thrilled with an opportunity to be in charge of the development of a new product: hybrid grain sorghum.

My first wife, Maggie, was born and raised in Wichita, Kansas, went to school at the University of Wichita, and became a flight attendant for Braniff, where she was working when I met her. Together we had four children: Tom III, Cathy, Shawn, and Mike, The last three were born in the Sycamore Hospital, which had originally been donated to the city by their great-great grandmother, Eleanor Pierce Townsend. Maggie and I were divorced early in 1974 after nineteen years of marriage. She is an intelligent woman who raised a fine family, but she didn't enjoy her exposure to DeKalb's business.

Later in 1974 I married Nancy Barker Bittinger. Nancy had been raised in Sycamore (where her parents and mine became friends), St. Charles, Rockford, and Rochelle. I met Nancy for the first time in 1946, but we went our separate ways at that time.

Nancy married Mason Bittinger and had four children. When the youngest entered first grade, Nancy went to work as an interviewer and market researcher for the Leo Burnett Advertising Agency in Chicago.

SOURCE: Roberts Family

My wife Nancy

In the early 1970's, Nancy divorced Mason, and I looked her up in 1974, after my divorce from Maggie. Nancy is charming and outgoing and was quickly accepted by both my friends and my DeKalb associates and their wives. She is very supportive of my business life, always available to talk about problems, as well as to entertain DeKalb "Ag" people in our home.

INDEX